Soviet Tanks
and Combat Vehicles 1946 to the Present

1. A Soviet T-72M1, which also had thicker frontal armour than the T-72M. This one has had its side fabric armour skirts removed. This is often done in peacetime, as they are easily damaged or lost during training.

SOVIET TANKS AND COMBAT VEHICLES 1946 TO THE PRESENT

Steven J. Zaloga and James W. Loop

a&ap

ARMS AND ARMOUR PRESS

First published in Great Britain
in 1987 by Arms and Armour Press Limited,
Link House, West Street, Poole, Dorset BH15 1LL.

Distributed in the USA by Sterling Publishing Co. Inc.,
2 Park Avenue, New York, NY 10016.

Distributed in Australia by
Capricorn Link (Australia) Pty. Ltd., P.O. Box 665,
Lane Cove, New South Wales 2066, Australia.

British Library Cataloguing in Publication Data:
Zaloga, Steven J.
Soviet tanks and combat vehicles: 1946 to the present.
1. Organizatsiia Varsharskogo Dogovora – Armed forces – History 2. Armoured Vehicles, Military – Europe, Eastern
I. Title II. Loop, James, W.
623.74′75′091717 UG446.5

ISBN 0-85368-743-9

Jacket illustration: T-54 battle tanks on manoeuvres.

Designed by David Gibbons; edited by Michael Boxall; layout by Anthony A. Evans; typeset by Typesetters (Birmingham) Ltd.; printed and bound in Great Britain by
R. J. Acford, Chichester, Sussex.

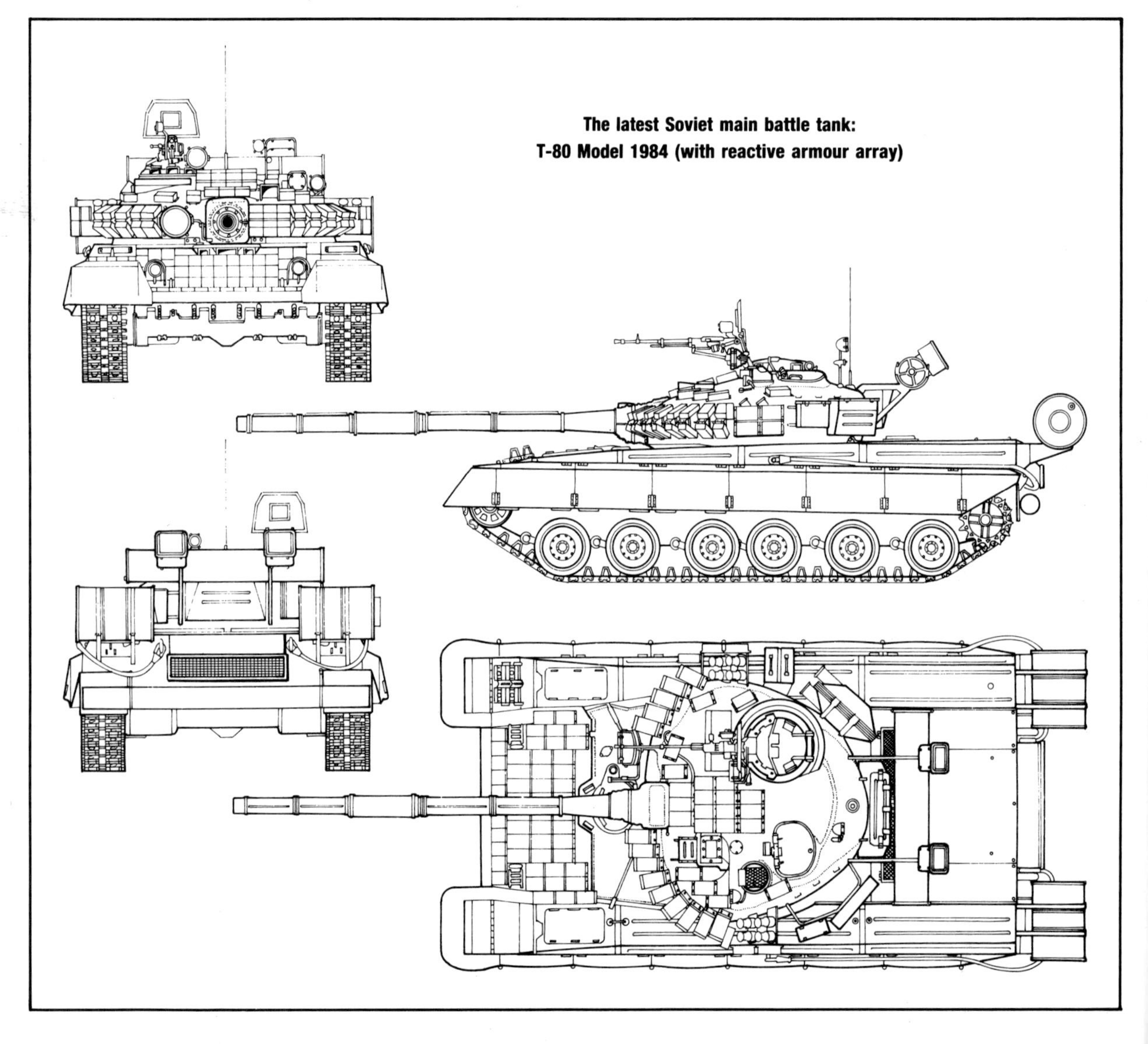

The latest Soviet main battle tank:
T-80 Model 1984 (with reactive armour array)

Contents

Introduction

One of the enduring sources of tension in Europe since the Second World War has been the massive inventory of armoured vehicles of the Warsaw Pact. The Soviet Union has continued to manufacture armoured vehicles at a rate considerably in excess of the rest of the world combined, and currently possesses an inventory about four times as large as that of the United States. This book sets out to examine the growth of the Soviet mechanized forces since the end of the war.

Intended as a companion volume to the earlier *Soviet Tanks and Combat Vehicles of World War Two*, which traced the history of Red Army mechanization from 1917 to 1945, this book concentrates on the build up from 1946 to 1986 and supersedes the author's taxonomic study, *Modern Soviet Armour: Combat Vehicles of the USSR and the Warsaw Pact Today*, published in 1979. This book is longer and more analytic in its examination of particular types of vehicles, and the position of these vehicles within post-war Soviet tactical doctrine and organizations. Although the evolution of Soviet mechanization doctrine is, of necessity, mentioned frequently, the subject is a complicated one and its examination in depth would require a separate volume.

This book contains the first published, unclassified details of the levels of Soviet armoured vehicle production. It should be noted that the Soviet Union does not release any data at all about this, so the production information given here is based primarily on estimates by the United States Defense Intelligence Agency, obtained through Freedom of Information Act requests as well as other declassified Intelligence estimates released to the US Congress.

One of the more confusing aspects of dealing with Soviet military equipment is the issue of nomenclature. The Soviets usually classify equipment designations, and the correct Soviet name or designation is not known until years after the system was introduced into service. In the meantime, many names and designations are applied by Western Intelligence services. To confuse matters further, some Warsaw Pact armies, notably the East Germans, apply their own designations to Soviet weapons. In this book, the aim has been to use the correct Soviet designation, where known, as well as more common Western names. The NATO STANAG system of designations (such as BMP M1981/2) has not been used extensively in this study because of the lack of a comprehensive unclassified list of these designations, as well as the sloppy and confusing nature of the system.

In obtaining the information and photographs presented here, the authors have received assistance from many sources. They would like to thank especially Christopher F. Foss, David C. Isby, Esa Muikku, Kalevi Moilanen, Viktor Suvorov and Just Probst for their help in the preparation of the book. In addition, the authors are indebted to many other friends for their support and aid over the years including George Balin, Joseph S. Bermudez Jr., Thomas R. Blackwood, Kira J. Caiafa, Paul Cardin, Vika Edwards, Karl Gaarsoe, James Goff, Michael R. Green, Philip M. Hinkle, Edward J. Herterich, Bob Lessels, John A. Loop, Robert M. McDonald, Leland Ness, David A. Parham, Ronald T. Pretty, Ricky S. Stauber, J. Tyler Segar, T. P. Schweider, Pierre Touzin, Paul W. Woolf, and Russell P. Vaughan. The authors would like to acknowledge a special debt to the late Colonel Robert J. Icks, the pioneer of research on armoured vehicle technology in the USA, for his generous and continuous support over many years.

The Mechanization of the Ground Forces

The Great Patriotic War of 1941–45 wrought great changes in the Red Army. The post-war Red Army actually had fewer armoured vehicles than it had possessed at the outset of the war; about 16,000 armoured combat vehicles compared to well over 28,000 in June 1941. But the Red Army of 1946 was a battle-hardened and mature force, with a great deal of practical experience in the use of mechanized formations in combat. If, in 1941, there had been many questions about the central role of armoured fighting vehicles in ground combat, by 1946, the questions had been laid to rest. The tank had proved to be the dominant land weapon in the fighting on the Eastern Front, and its role within the Red Army was assured.

During the course of the war, the Red Army reached a peak strength of 593 divisions. Of these, 39 were tank or mechanized corps. (Wartime Soviet tank and mechanized corps were, in fact, divisional-sized formations, not corps in the Western sense). These tanks and mechanized corps represented about 7 per cent of the total Soviet order-of-battle at the end of the war. In 1946, the Red Army began to demobilize. The war had caused appalling manpower losses, and the economy was in a shambles and could not afford to maintain a large standing army. By 1947–48, Soviet line divisions had been reduced to a total of about 175 divisions, some 29 per cent of their peak wartime strength, totalling about 2.8 million troops. Furthermore, a number of these divisions existed at mere cadre strength, with a fairly complete officer cadre, but a greatly reduced troops establishment.

In 1947, the Red Army changed its name to the Soviet Army. This change symbolized the important organizational changes which the Soviet armed forces were beginning to undergo. Even though the Soviet Army as a whole was shrinking because of demobilization, mechanized units grew in number and strength. The wartime tank and mechanized corps were redesignated as tank and mechanized divisions, more befitting their actual strength. By 1948, these had increased in number to about 60 divisions, about two-thirds being mechanized divisions, and the remainder, tank divisions. By the late 1940s, mechanized formations represented about 35 per cent of the line divisions of the Soviet Army, compared to 7 per cent during the war. In 1948, the Soviet Army's two traditional branches, the Ground Forces (*Sukhoputniye Voiska*-SV) and the Air Force (*Voyenno Vozdushniye Sily*-VVS) spawned a third branch, the National Air Defence (*Protivozdushnoy Oborony*-PVO) which was responsible for the greatly expanding strategic air defence forces.

Although the last years of Stalin's reign were marked by a considerable expansion in the size of the Soviet mechanized force, the 1946–53 period was marked by doctrinal lethargy. By 1950–51, Soviet forces had been doubled in size to about 5.7 million men because of the Cold War tension between the Soviet Union and the United States and the outbreak of the Korean War. But Stalin imposed very strict limits on doctrinal modernization, going so far as to discourage studies of the lessons of the 'Great Patriotic War'. Stalin's doctrinal thoughts were summarized by his banal concept of the 'permanent factors of war'. The stultifying effects of Stalin's notions retarded Ground Forces studies on the impact of nuclear weapons on a future battlefield, and slowed the examination of the future role of mechanized infantry on the battlefield.

Stalin's death in 1953 unshackled Soviet military thinkers, and lead to considerable ferment in the Ground Forces. The tactical lessons of the war were examined in depth, and Stalin's viewpoints were gradually superseded by the concepts of professional military officers. In the forefront of these debates was the wartime tank commander, General Pavel A. Rotmistrov, who taught at the General Staff Academy and in 1958 commanded the Armoured Force Academy.

Soviet studies of the wartime experiences of their tank forces inevitably confronted the issue of the tactical superiority of German forces throughout most of the war. The Wehrmacht's Panzer forces on the Eastern Front were almost consistently outnumbered by Soviet tanks and yet managed to exact disproportionate kill ratios against Soviet armoured vehicles. In the grim days of 1942, the Red Army was losing 6–8 armoured vehicles for every German tank lost. Even as late as the first months of 1944, the Wehrmacht was scoring 4 Soviet armoured vehicles for every German armoured vehicle lost. What was particularly troubling was that these unbalanced attrition rates often occurred when the qualitative balance between German and Soviet tank units was fairly even. Soviet tank designs were much closer in quality to the Germans' than, for example, the US-British v. German balance. Yet US and British units did not suffer these disproportionate loss rates.

The imbalance in battlefield attrition of tanks was not confined to armoured vehicles, but was evident in other areas such as aircraft. At a strategic level, it was evident from historical studies that Soviet divisions did not equal German divisions in combat power, and that Soviet operational successes were dependent upon disproportionate advantages in the numbers of troops, units and equipment.

This was hardly a novel experience in Russian military history. For several hundred years, Russian forces have frequently suffered at the hands of numerically inferior West European armed forces. Although the Red Army had believed that it had broken this cycle of qualitative inferiority with the West by its massive arms build-up of the 1930s, the experiences of 1941–45 made it clear that the possession of greater quantities of technically equivalent weapons alone cannot ensure battlefield success.

The Soviet Army could not openly admit its qualitative shortcomings with Western armies. Criticism of the army or critical comparison of Russian institutions versus West European systems has not been characteristic of Russian society whether Tsarist or Soviet. Public acknowledgement of the qualitative shortcomings of the Soviet army was particularly unacceptable since this would call into question the political and social roots of the Red Army's inadequacies. These unpalatable lessons from the war were masqueraded instead in the more-palatable notions of 'superiority norms'. Soviet post-war military studies focused on quantitative operational requirements in offensive operations, and consciously ignored the qualitative issues that lay at the root of the disproportionately high numerical requirements. The qualitative issues were further hidden by the usual numbing ritual repetition of the moral and technical superiority of the Soviet soldier to his non-Soviet counterpart. Yet a consciousness of qualitative inferiority with Western European or American military forces became very manifest in Soviet war planning and in its Ground Forces' order of battle.

Throughout the post-war period, Soviet Ground Force line divisions have greatly outnumbered the divisions available to NATO or to the People's Republic of China. While the large order of battle is undoubtedly a result in part of Soviet concerns over the need to maintain a force capable of engaging in a two-front war against both China and NATO, the bloated balance of force directed towards NATO is rooted in the 'superiority norm' mentality that camouflages this traditional Russian sense of inferiority when dealing with Western adversaries. The issue of qualitative balance of forces between the USSR and NATO remains a sensitive political issue within the political and military hierarchy of the USSR to this day. The Soviet Army of the post-war period is undoubtedly closer qualitatively to West European forces as compared to the 1941 balance between the Soviet Union and Germany. But the embarrassing performance of Soviet allies in the Middle East, using Soviet equipment, training and tactics against Israeli forces using Western (primarily American) equipment, has probably reinforced this pattern of thought among Soviet military and political leaders.

The 'superiority norm' mentality was probably a major factor in the Soviet decision in the mid-1950s to stabilize the Ground Forces order of battle at about 175 divisions. It should be noted that although the Ground Forces during this period had a nominal strength of about 175 line divisions, these divisions were not all maintained at the same readiness level. Soviet line divisions have traditionally been maintained at three readiness levels, formerly called Categories A, B and V, but today more commonly called Categories 1, 2 and 3. Category 1 divisions are at wartime readiness level, having 75–110 per cent of its troops and equipment. A Category 2 division, deployable in 10–30 days, has about 50–75 per cent of its troops and about 90 per cent of its equipment. A Category 3 division, deployable in 60 days, has 10–35 per cent of its troops and 35–50 per cent of its equipment, mostly in storage. Generally speaking, about a third of all Soviet divisions fall into each of the three category levels. Soviet forces facing NATO in Central Europe or the western Soviet military districts are almost entirely at Category 1, while units facing China are usually about 15 per cent Category 1 and 35 per cent Category 2.

Besides shaping the size of the Ground Forces, the lessons of the war also began changing the tactical and operational doctrine of the Ground Forces. The Red Army had been very backward in infantry mechanization. The German, American and British Armies had divided their armoured vehicle production almost evenly between tanks, armoured infantry vehicles and armoured artillery vehicles. The Red Army completely ignored production of armoured infantry vehicles throughout the war. This was in part due to doctrinal shortcomings stemming from the paralysis in Soviet tactical thinking in the wake of the bloody purges of the army's officers during the late 1930s. A greater factor was the simple inability of the Soviet vehicle industry to devote any of its resources to armoured infantry vehicle production because of its difficulties in barely keeping the more critical inventory of tanks ahead of battlefield attrition.

In the early 1950s, the Ground Forces finally began to experiment with infantry mechanization with the advent of its first generation of armoured infantry vehicles such as the BTR-152 and the later BTR-50. This took place nearly a decade after most other European armies.

The Nuclear Battlefield

Besides absorbing the lessons of the war, the Ground Forces also began examining the effects of nuclear weapons on the tactical battlefield. Soviet tacticians quickly appreciated that nuclear weapons had revolutionary implications. A single nuclear bomb could destroy an entire division if it were caught massed in the Second World War fashion. The operational implications of nuclear weapons led to changes in the basic concepts of modern land warfare. Slow-moving armies, based around infantry divisions would be vulnerable to annihilation by relatively small numbers of nuclear bombs. Furthermore, even those rifle divisions which escaped nuclear attack would be unable to fight in a nuclear contaminated environment. The Ground Forces began to develop suitable operational doctrines for a tactical nuclear war. Central to these plans were the gradual conversion of the outdated rifle divisions to mechanized divisions, which the Russians called motor rifle divisions. A fully mechanized army, consisting of tank and motor rifle divisions, was mobile enough to remain widely dispersed before offensive operations, making it less vulnerable to nuclear attack. The divisions could move quickly to mass for an attack. The use of tanks and armoured infantry vehicles would permit an army to fight on a nuclear contaminated battlefield, since the vehicles offered a measure of radiation shielding.

These doctrinal changes during the period 1955–57 had effects on both the organization of the Soviet Army and its equipment requirements. In 1957–58, the Ground Forces gradually began to disband the mechanized and rifle divisions, reforming them as motor rifle divisions. With the disbandment of the cavalry divisions in 1955–56, this left the Ground Forces with only two standard divisional organizations, the tank division and the motor rifle division. (Airborne divisions became part of the Ground Forces in 1956, but reverted to a semi-autonomous status under the Defense Ministry in 1964.) This major reorganization of the Ground Force divisions took about seven years, lasting until 1964. Although the rifle divisions had been nominally converted to motor rifle divisions, in 1964 very few divisions had anywhere near the total number of armoured troop vehicles required. Indeed, even at present, many Soviet motor rifle divisions are not fully equipped with armoured infantry vehicles, simply because of the sheer numbers required by so large an army as the Soviet Ground Forces.

The debate over the implications of nuclear weapons on the battlefield proved to be one of the most controversial issues in the relations between the Communist Party leadership under Nikita Khrushchev and the leadership of the Soviet Armed Forces. In the wake of the war, the Soviet Armed Forces were dominated by the Soviet Army, especially the Ground Forces. The Soviet Navy had played a minimal role. The Air Force was subordinate to the Soviet Army and heavily focused on tactical air support of the Ground Forces, rather than independent strategic missions. The artillery branch of the Ground Forces had managed the new strategic missile programme of the 1950s, which had resulted in the first practical Soviet ICBM, the R-7 (SS-6 Sapwood) in 1957. In 1959, Khrushchev decided to remove control over strategic weapons from the Ground Forces to a new service, the Strategic Missile Force (*Raketniye Voiska Strategicheskovo Naznacheniya*-RVSN). This marked the beginning of a major effort by Khrushchev and his supporters within the Communist Party to shift the emphasis of the Soviet Armed Forces from conventional forces to the new strategic missile forces.

While there was little debate within the Soviet defence community over the desirability to reach strategic weapons parity with the USA, the pace and trade-offs of such a policy were widely disputed. Development of a strategic missile force was an enormously costly undertaking for a nation still reeling from the economic devastation of the war. The Soviet Ground Forces had not dispensed with horse transport until 1955, and within the space of four years was already talking of centring its power on intercontinental ballistic missiles with nuclear warheads. Khrushchev began by making relatively easy cuts, such as slicing back proposed Soviet warship construction, but the big drain on the Soviet military budget was the hitherto sancrosanct Ground Forces. During 1955–57, according to various estimates, the Soviet Army was obliged to cut back its numbers by about 1.8–2.1 million men.

The Ground Forces had another serious problem. They received most of the men called up under the large conscription programme, but by the early 1960s, as a consequence of the enormous losses sustained during the war, there was a significant decline in the numbers of young men available for conscription, and in any case they were desperately needed within the civilian economy.

Khrushchev hoped to solve both problems by trimming the Ground Forces even farther. This would ameliorate the labour shortage, and cut Ground Forces expenses in favour of modernization of the strategic missile forces. In 1960, Khrushchev fired the first salvo in this political struggle over the Soviet Armed Forces, in a speech referring to the Strategic Missile Force as the primary service of the Soviet Armed Forces and the basis of modern warfare capabilities. Furthermore, the Soviet Armed Forces would be trimmed by another 1.2 million men. This included a quarter of a million officers, mainly from the Ground Forces. Criticism of the programme by senior Army leaders such as the commander of Warsaw Pact Forces, Marshal Koniev, and the Chief of the General Staff, Marshal Sokolovskiy, lead to their removal from their posts.

While not dramatically affecting the order of battle of the Ground Forces, Khrushchev's troop cuts did have important effects. The disbandment of 63 divisions and independent brigades did not substantially alter the order of battle because the divisions affected were supporting divisions such as anti-aircraft artillery divisions, and these were not removed from service but were reformed as brigades. However, the programme forced the Ground Forces to trim the size of divisional tables of organization and equipment in the tank and motor rifle divisions. The decline in armoured vehicle production since 1956 reached its lowest ebb in 1963 as funds were diverted to support strategic weapons development and production. The heyday of the Soviet Ground Forces had passed, and there was no small amount of resentment within the military over Khrushchev's actions.

In the wake of the Cuban missile crisis and other failures by the Khrushchev regime, Khrushchev was finally ousted from power in 1965. The anti-Khrushchev forces in the Communist Party were clearly supported by much of the leadership of the Soviet Army which was upset by Khrushchev's reliance on strategic weapons for national defence at the expense of the more traditional services. It is not clear whether there were any explicit political deals between the insurgent Communist Party leaders and the Army leadership, but the Party leadership quickly appreciated the danger in exacerbating relations with the tradition-bound Ground Forces.

The Brezhnev Build-Up

In the wake of Khrushchev's ouster, the Ground Forces experienced significant growth through the next decade, particularly with regard to equipment modernization. Ironically, this was not accomplished so much by reversion to pre-Khrushchev funding patterns in the defence budget so much as by the general increase made possible by the steady growth of the national economy. The defence budget continued to absorb a significant fraction of the national product (about 15 per cent), and so grew as the economy grew. Indeed, while the Strategic Missile Forces' budget declined in relative terms from 10 per cent of the budget in 1967 to 5 per cent of the budget in 1973, the Ground Forces' budget remained almost constant, going from 21 per cent of the defence budget in 1967 to 22 per cent in 1973.

During the latter half of the 1960s and early 1970s, the Ground Forces' annual budget continued to increase at a steady rate, permitting a significant increase in armoured vehicle production, and fostering a continued growth in Ground Forces' vehicle inventories. In about 1965, the Ground Forces began to embark on one of the most controversial aspects of the modernization of its mechanized formations: the adoption of an infantry fighting vehicle, the BMP. The BMP was the result of the recognition that the second generation of armoured infantry vehicles, like the BTR-60PB and BTR-50PK, were not entirely suitable for use on the nuclear battlefield. Although these vehicles could offer a measure of protection from radiation hazards, they were designed primarily to transport troops. Once an objective was reached, the troops had to disembark to carry out their mission on foot. This was not practicable in a contaminated environment. The Ground Forces proposed development of an infantry transporter that would be more than just a battlefield taxi; it would have to permit the infantry squad to fight from within the protective shell of the vehicle. It was also decided to give this new vehicle a measure of anti-tank capability with a novel gun/missile armament system.

The debate over the BMP was prompted by the high cost inherent in such a vehicle and

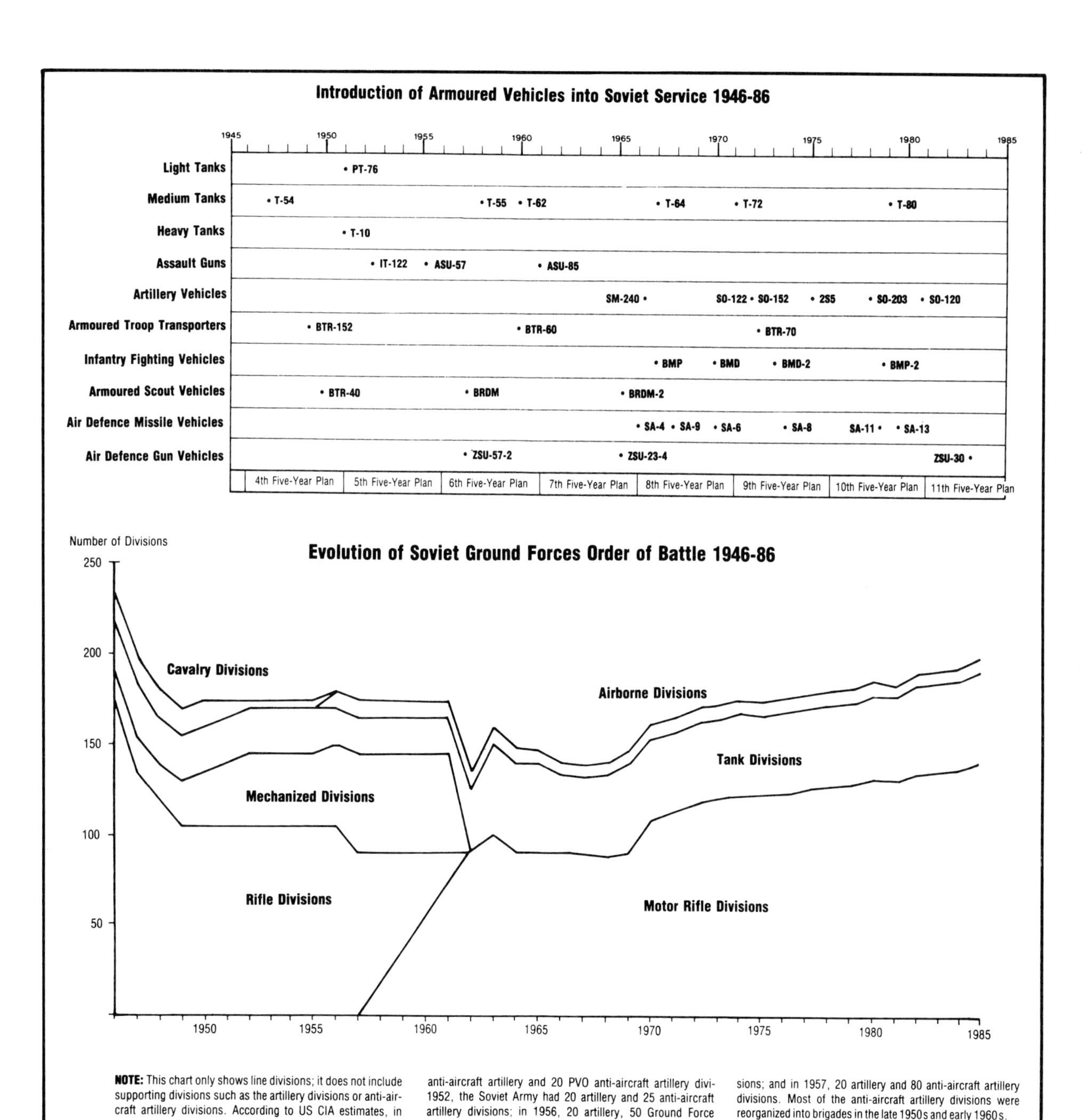

NOTE: This chart only shows line divisions; it does not include supporting divisions such as the artillery divisions or anti-aircraft artillery divisions. According to US CIA estimates, in 1952, the Soviet Army had 20 artillery and 25 anti-aircraft artillery divisions; in 1956, 20 artillery, 50 Ground Force anti-aircraft artillery and 20 PVO anti-aircraft artillery divisions; and in 1957, 20 artillery and 80 anti-aircraft artillery divisions. Most of the anti-aircraft artillery divisions were reorganized into brigades in the late 1950s and early 1960s.

questions about its combat utility. While earlier armoured infantry vehicles like the BTR-60 cost about one-seventh the price of a contemporary tank like the T-55, the BMP probably cost about as much as a T-55, and about half as much as the newer T-64. This marked a drastic change in funding priorities within the Ground Forces which had traditionally favoured tank requirements over infantry requirements. Adoption of large numbers of the BMP, and its cheaper wheeled counterpart, the BTR-60, was probably a significant factor in the gradual reduction in size of Soviet tank production in the late 1960s and 1970s. There was also some concern that the BMP was better suited to the nuclear battlefield than to a conventional battlefield.

Despite the controversy, the leadership of the Ground Forces eventually supported the general shift in favour of infantry mechanization at the expense of tank modernization in the 1970s. Tank inventories continued to be modernized and expanded throughout the decade, but not as rapidly as armoured infantry vehicle inventories. This is an important reflection of the Ground Forces' forceful commitment to combined arms doctrine in the 1970s.

2. The small size of Soviet tanks is very clearly shown in this comparison of a T-54 and an American M60A1. The American tank is nearly twice as heavy as its smaller Soviet counterpart. (Ron Foulks)

The 1970s also marked the significant modernization of two other arms of the combined arms team: artillery and air defence. In the late 1960s, the Soviet Ground Forces had begun acquiring the ZSU-23-4 Shilka air defence gun system which was intended to replace the earlier ZSU-57-2. The Shilka represented a significant increase in mechanized air defence capability due to the use of radar fire control. ZSU-23-4 was complemented by a trio of new mechanized air defence missile vehicles: the ZRK Krug (SA-4 Ganef), ZRK Kub (SA-6 Gainful) and ZRK Strela 1 (SA-9 Gaskin). The Krug system began appearing in about 1964, but its development was troubled and it was not seen in large numbers until the 1970s. It provides high-altitude air defence coverage at army level. The first mobile air defence missile system at divisional level was the Strela 1 (SA-9 Gaskin), a low-altitude system mounted on the wheeled BRDM-2 chassis which began to appear in the late 1960s. A more sophisticated medium-altitude system, the Kub (SA-6 Gainful), entered service in about 1970. In the late 1960s, the divisions also began to receive the man-portable Strela 2 (SA-7 Grail). In the mid-1970s, the Kub (SA-6 Gainful) began to be supplemented by an even more sophisticated system, the ZRK Romb (SA-8 Gecko). The Romb was the first Soviet air defence missile system to have the acquisition and tracking radars mounted on the launch vehicle itself rather than on a separate vehicle.

Although not as costly an effort as the modernization of Ground Forces' air defence, the mechanization of the artillery branch took a significant bite out of the army budget in the 1970s. The artillery branch has always been one of the more conservative arms of the service, but in the 1950s, much of the best talent of the artillery branch was distracted from the mundane tasks of artillery modernization to the more pressing concerns of strategic weapons development which was managed by the artillery branch. The split off of the Strategic Missile Force from the Ground Forces drew away many of the artillery forces' finest officers, but permitted the artillery branch to turn its attention back to more traditional concerns.

The army had adopted assault guns since the war, but these were employed mainly as direct fire weapons by the tank force, not in the more traditional indirect fire artillery role. In this respect, the Soviet Army was far behind most other European armies. In 1972, the first SO-122 Gvozdika and SO-152 Akatsiya self-propelled howitzers began to enter Ground Forces service. These new self-propelled howitzers were adopted in response to a variety of factors. Soviet doctrine insisted on the ability of its forces to conduct operations in chemical warfare and nuclear conditions, and conventional towed artillery is ill-suited to these conditions. On the other hand, the improvements in artillery fire control and counter-battery techniques in the NATO armies make towed artillery very vulnerable. Self-propelled artillery is mobile enough to avoid counter-battery fire and protected enough to permit operation in a variety of hostile conditions.

Besides the mechanization of the Ground Forces, in the 1970s, the Soviet Army also undertook the mechanization of the VDV (*Vozdushno Desantnaya Voiska*-Air Assault Force). The VDV is a semi-autonomous branch of the Soviet Army under direct Ministry of Defence control. In 1973, the VDV air assault divisions began to receive the BMD airborne assault vehicle. The BMD is a direct counterpart of the Ground Forces' BMP, but is smaller to permit easier carrying by aircraft and to permit its dropping by parachute. The BMD was adopted for many of the same reasons as the BMP.

The adoption of a comprehensive range of new armoured vehicles in the 1970s marked the culmination of nearly four decades of Soviet military doctrine. In many respects, these programmes can be seen as the final realization of the advanced concepts proposed by such Soviet military thinkers as V. K. Triandafillov and Marshal Mikhail Tukhachevskiy in the 1930s. The implementation of these ideas was greatly prolonged by the corrosive effects of Josef Stalin's malignant attention to Army affairs, particularly the purges of the late 1930s, and his maladroit interferences in Soviet Army doctrine in the late 1940s. Yet even with Stalin's control gone, it still took another two decades before some branches of the Ground Forces began to be significantly mechanized. The experiences of the Khrushchev years forced the Soviet Army to recognize that strategic power now lay in the hands of the Strategic Missile Force, and that the primary role of the Ground Forces' of previous decades was no longer tenable. Still, the relative economic prosperity of the Brezhnev years, and the *modus vivendi* reached between the Communist Party and the armed forces, permitted the Ground Forces to grow and flourish throughout the 1970s.

Soviet Divisional Equipment 1946-86

		Armour						Infantry AFVs			Other Vehicles							Artillery														Air Defence				
	Troops	Scout Tank	Medium Tank	Heavy Tank	ISU Assault Gun	SU-85/SU-100 Assault Gun	SU-76	BTR-152 APC	BTR-60/70 APC	BMP-1/BMP-2 IFV	BA-64 Scout AFV	BTR-40, BRDM, BRDM-2 Scout AFV	BRDM AT Missile AFV	BRDM-RKh CBR Scout AFV	Armored Command Vehicle	Armoured Recovery Vehicle	Truck/Lorry	SO-122 (2S1) SP Howitzer	SO-152 (2S3) SP Howitzer	ACRV-1, -2, -3	Artillery Radar Vehicle	FROG-7, SS-21 Rocket Vehicle	152mm Towed Howitzer	122mm Towed Howitzer	Multiple Rocket Launcher Vehicle	76mm/85mm Field Gun	Anti-tank Gun/ AT Recoilless Rifle	Manportable Anti-tank Missile Launcher	160mm Mortar	120mm Mortar	82mm Mortar	ZSU-23-4 Air Defence Gun Vehicle	SA-6/SA-11/SA-8 Air Defence Missile Vehicle	SA-9/ SA-13 Air Defence Missile Vehicle	SA-7/SA-14 Manportable Air Defence Missile	Towed Air Defence Gun
1949 Tank Division	10,300		205	44	21			8			30					13	1360							12	12	12	28			42	52					22
1956 Tank Division	13,000	15	324	44	21			195				67				19	1771							48	12	12	52		12	6	40					54
1959 Tank Division	12,500	25	377	46	33			221				40				25	2020							48	12		42		12	6	18					12
1964 Tank Division	8,859	18	313	30					227			40				38	1435					2		36	14		24	15		6	18					30
1977 Tank Division	9,429	19	325						96	147		40	9	29	95	25	2000	18		8	2	4		36	18		6	6		18		16	20	16	36	
1985 Tank Division	11,470		328						23	240		28	9	29	95	27	2284	72	18	40	9	4		36	18					36		16	20	16	93	
1949 Mechanized Division	12,844		183	21	44			38			39					13	1521							24	8	36	32			54	82					22
1956 Mechanized Division	15,000	20	224	44	54			300				102				17	1861							48	12	12	99		12	18	64					54
1949 Rifle Division	11,013		52			16	18				9	65					1290							36		24	48		12	18	81					18
1956 Rifle Division	13,000		52			16	18	190									1268							36		24	99		8	18	85					36
1959 Motor Rifle Division	8,711	25	223	46	54			318				108				19	2027							48	18	12	72		12	18	64					54
1964 Motor Rifle Division	10,841	15	186	10					319			88				26	1533					2	18	18	14		84	57	12	18	54					30
1977 Motor Rifle Division	11,922	19	215						194	117		71	27	29	75	24	2100					4	18	54	18		36	18		54		16		16	112	24
1985 Motor Rifle Division	12,695		220						247	132		28	36	29	111	23	2413	36	18	24	9	4		72	18		24	24		54		16	20	16	120	

NOTE: This table shows the nominal equipment holdings of a Category 1 division of the period according to US Army estimates.

Soviet Armoured Vehicle Production

The image of great hordes of Soviet tanks massed on the eastern frontiers of Europe has been one of the enduring anxieties plaguing NATO defence planners since the 1950s. The Soviet Union has continued to build tanks and armoured vehicles at a rate far in excess of that of any other state, and indeed, Soviet production since the war has exceeded the rest of the world combined. Many explanations have been put forward to account for the prodigious rate of Soviet armoured vehicle production, ranging from alarmist warnings that such production represents evidence of Soviet plans to invade West Europe, through apologist excuses that such production represents normal Soviet defensive preparations in the wake of foreign depradations against Russia over the past century.

The high levels of Soviet armoured vehicle production can be traced to a variety of factors. To begin with, the large Soviet order of battle described in the earlier chapter is a major factor in driving Soviet production. The Soviet desire to maintain a very large standing army inevitably demands commensurate attempts to arm and equip these forces. The Ground Forces have not succeeded in fully equipping their divisions to complete levels due to the sheer numbers of vehicles required. This discrepancy between actual Soviet vehicle inventory and the requirements of the relevant tables of organization and equipment (TO&E) is an important rationale by which the Ground Forces can solicit approval for continued high levels of armoured vehicle production from the Soviet Politburo. The two charts here provide some historical examples of this factor. These charts show US estimates of Soviet tank and light armoured vehicle inventories from 1965–85. By taking TO&Es for Soviet motor rifle and tank divisions of the period, multiplied by the number of divisions, an estimated Soviet tank and light armoured vehicle requirement was created. It should be noted that this estimated requirement does not include non-divisional equipment requirements such as independent tank regiments attached to armies. Nevertheless, these charts provide some indication of one important stimulus in Soviet armoured vehicle production. As is evident from the charts, by the 1970s, the Soviet Army had succeeded in reaching inventory requirements in tanks. However, the Ground Forces have not succeeded in fulfilling full light armoured vehicle requirements in this period. This is partly due to the increasing number of light armoured vehicles demanded by expansion in the organization and equipment of Soviet divisions. The result of these shortfalls is that many Soviet divisions, notably the Category 3 divisions, have significant shortages of light armoured vehicles compared to Category 1 divisions. For example, many Cate-

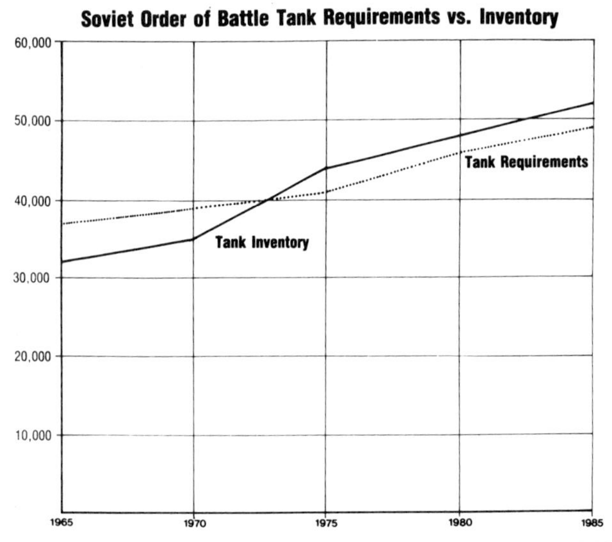

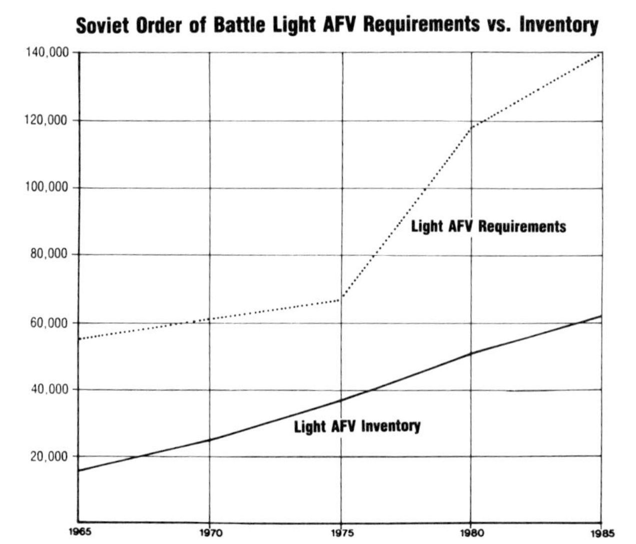

gory 3 divisions would use towed instead of self-propelled howitzers. Likewise, many Category 3 divisions would be obliged to use trucks in lieu of armoured troop carriers.

Another important stimulus in Soviet armoured vehicle production is the Soviet conception of battlefield attrition of weapons. During the Second World War, Soviet industry produced more than 102,000 armoured vehicles; a further 20,000 were added by Lend-Lease. Despite this prodigious output, the inventory of Red Army tanks crept up very slowly after the staggering defeats of 1941. Attrition was so severe that it took Soviet industry nearly four years to enlarge the autumn 1941 holdings of about 4,000 armoured vehicles to the 16,000 vehicle level of 1945.

These experiences, an essential element of the 'superiority norm' mentality described in the previous chapter, have also served as a stimulus in Soviet armoured vehicle production. The Soviet Army expects that battlefield losses in modern war would be extremely high, as is evidenced by their own experiences in the Second World War, and hence there is a requirement to have a large stockpile of *matériel*.

Acquisition of sufficient armoured vehicles to fill out the large Soviet order of battle has resulted in significant differences between Soviet and NATO armoured vehicle production practises. The Soviet Ground Forces cannot possibly afford to equip all of their units with the latest, or with the best equipment. Even with production levels running at 10,000 armoured vehicles annually, it takes the Ground Forces nearly twenty years to completely re-equip with a new generation of equipment. Inevitably, a large percentage of the Soviet units are equipped with dated equipment. Furthermore, the enormous equipment demands of the large order of battle preclude the Soviets from adopting premium equipment for all of its units. If they wish to maintain 175 (or more) divisions, the Ground Forces cannot equip all infantry units with the BMP, or all tank units with the T-64. Instead, they have been obliged to rely on a high–low production mix to satisfy equipment requirements.

A typical high–low mix programme can be seen in the mechanization of the motor rifle regiments in the late 1960s and 1970s. The Ground Forces procured both the wheeled BTR-60 and the tracked BMP infantry vehicles simultaneously. The BTR-60 was a much cheaper vehicle than the BMP, probably costing about a third as much. Furthermore, the life cycle cost of a wheeled vehicle like the BTR-60 is considerably less than that of a tracked vehicle. The cost per mile of a tracked vehicle versus a wheeled vehicle in terms of repair costs, new track, etc., is about three times as high. The BTR-60s cost advantages outweighed its serious performance shortcomings compared to the BMP. Being wheeled, it is far less mobile than the BMP, especially in snow; it is much less well armed and it is less well armoured. These shortcomings had to be accepted in order to fill out the equipment requirements of the new motor rifle divisions. The other alternative, to produce only BMP, would have forced the Ground Forces to reduce the number of motor rifle divisions. This option has not been adjudged as acceptable as the alternative of the high–low equipment mix. In contrast, most European armies, and the US Army, usually adopt only a single type of armoured infantry vehicle at one time, and usually of a high-quality level.

The same high–low pattern can be seen in other equipment areas, such as tanks. The Ground Forces have almost consistently procured a mix of high-cost, premium tanks as well as lower-cost tanks at the same time. For example, in the late 1940s, the Ground Forces were acquiring both the old T-34-85, and the new T-54; in the 1950s, the heavy T-10 and the cheaper T-54; in the 1960s, the cheaper T-55, the medium-priced T-62 and the high-cost T-64; and at the present, the high cost T-80 and the cheaper T-72.

The size and expense of Soviet vehicle acquisition programmes also affects the design characteristics of armoured vehicles, as well as management of their life cycle costs. Soviet tanks are not designed to be smaller than Western tanks simply because they make smaller targets. They are smaller since smaller size means less weight. Less weight means that a smaller engine can be used, and both factors bring down the basic cost of the tank. These features degrade performance since a smaller tank carries less ammunition, does not foster crew effectiveness, and forces design compromises such as external storage of fuel. But this degradation in quality is viewed as being acceptable in view of cost savings. Very little detailed information on Soviet tank costs are available, but from the prices charged to Soviet export clients, some estimates can be made. In 1970, a T-55 cost about $115,000; a T-62 tank cost about $175,000 and a US M60A1 tank cost about $250,000. Current US estimates indicate that a T-72 tank costs about $1,000,000, or half the cost of an American M1 tank.

In order to keep the initial purchase costs of such an enormous armoured vehicle park low, the basic durability of most Soviet armoured vehicles is lower than comparable NATO designs. Soviet tank engines of the 1960s and early 1970s had a life of only about 500–1200 running hours. Comparable US engines have at least four times the life. Soviet tank gun barrels, even the smooth-bore designs like the U-5TS on the T-62, have a bore life of only 120 rounds, compared to about 400 rounds on the M68A1 gun of the M60A1 tank (which is rifled to boot). The mean time between failures of a Soviet tank of the 1960s, such as the T-62, has been estimated at about 100–125 miles compared to about 200 miles for a comparable US tank. Less durable armoured vehicles are cheaper to manufacture, but their lower durability obliges the Ground Forces to restrict their employment in peacetime training for fear of wearing them out.

A Soviet tank crew on average fires only twelve rounds of ammunition annually to avoid wearing out the barrel. This permits the gun tube on an average tank to last ten years. In contrast, US tank crews fire an average of 100 rounds annually, allowing a barrel to last about four years. The US Army feels that this level of live-round training is necessary for adequate crew proficiency; the Soviets could not possibly afford this level of training in terms of ammunition costs and barrel wear. An average Soviet tank is restricted to about 250 miles of running annually; a US tank averages 1,000 miles. At this rate of use, both a Soviet and US tank will last for about 20 years of peacetime use, but in the process, the more durable US tank will permit four times the level of peacetime training.

Soviet Weapons Export

When examining the massive scale of Soviet weapons production, a factor which is frequently overlooked is the heavy level of Soviet arms export to the Third World since the beginning of the 1970s. During the period from 1972 to 1983, the USSR exported 15,275 tanks and 18,285 light armoured vehicles to countries outside the Warsaw Pact (mainly the Middle East and India) according to US sources. This export is the equivalent of 44 per cent of total Soviet tank production during the period, and 24 per cent of the production of light armoured vehicles.

Although these exports represent a significant fraction of Soviet production, it should be noted that the Soviets do not actually export such a large fraction of their new production. Rather, about 56 per cent of the tanks exported during this period were new production vehicles, and about 75 per cent of the light armoured vehicles. The remainder of the exported vehicles were taken out of Soviet Army stockpiles. Generally, favoured clients who pay in hard currency (such as India or Iraq) receive new production equipment, while countries on the arms dole such as Nicaragua or Angola, receive older equipment taken out of reserves.

The signficant role of weapons export in Soviet weapons production is a relatively new phenomenon. Before the war, Soviet arms export was very limited. Modest numbers of armoured vehicles went to Spain during the Civil War (482 armoured vehicles) and to the Nationalist Chinese in 1938 (87 tanks, and some armoured cars). There were small exports to Turkey (127 armoured vehicles) and to Afghanistan. After the Second World War, Russia was mainly concerned with building up the forces of neighbouring allies, notably the armies of the Warsaw Pact, the People's Republic of China and North Korea. Soviet arms export outside these countries began in earnest in 1955–56 with the first shipments of tanks and other equipment to Egypt. However, much of these initial exports actually consisted of the export of Czechoslovak-manufactured armoured vehicles; the entire 1956 shipments of T-34-85 tanks and SU-100 assault guns to Egypt were of Czechoslovak manufacture. In the early 1960s, this pattern began to change. The USSR began selling Soviet-manufactured armoured vehicles to new clients in the Middle East, notably Syria, Iraq and Egypt, and began actively to market weapons in other areas, such as Indonesia. The Middle East Wars of 1956, 1967, and 1973 were a major stimuli to arms purchases from the Soviet Union.

The devotion of a considerable proportion of Soviet military industrial capacity to arms export is prompted by a variety of factors. To some extent, arms aid, and arms sales, are one aspect of larger Soviet political aims to expand Soviet influence in the world. Soviet economic aid programmes of the Khrushchev era such as a

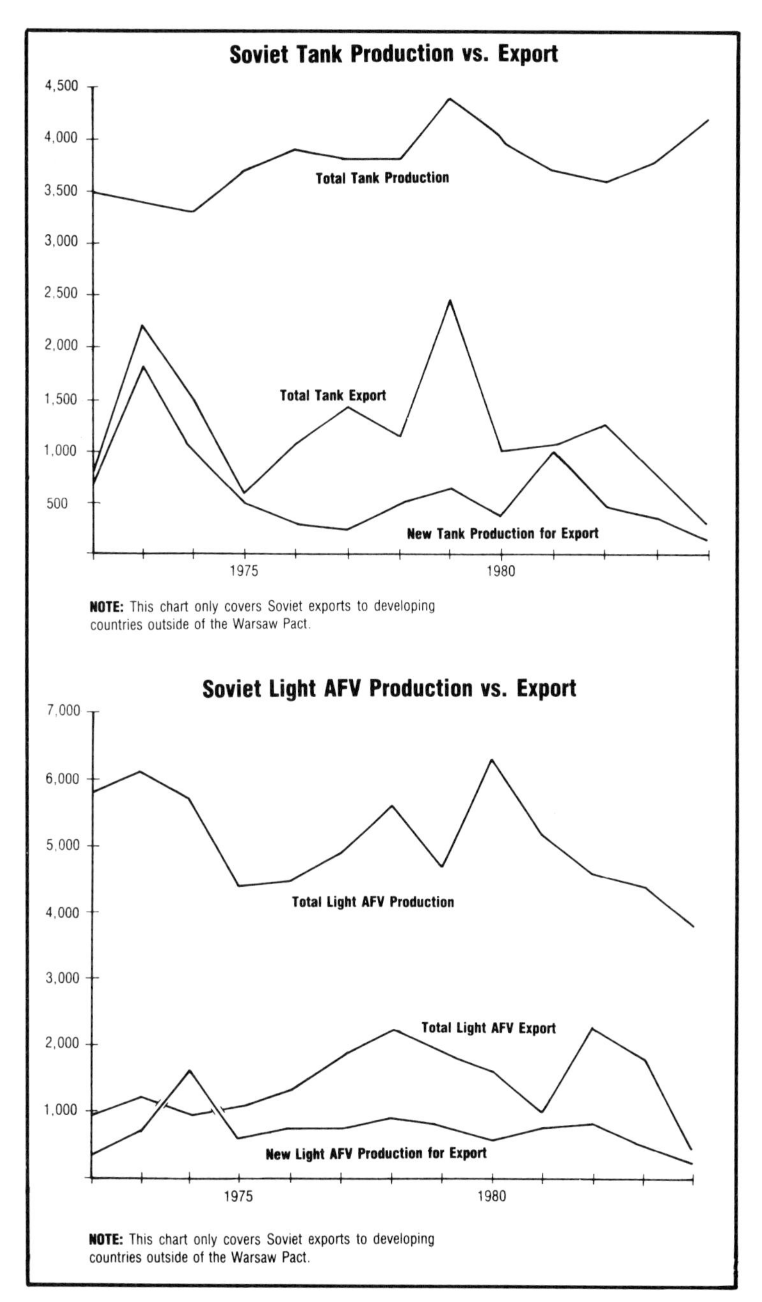

number of showpiece steel mills, dam projects and road development schemes were not entirely successful. Many Third World countries have shown a decided preference for European or American assistance in these areas. In contrast, Soviet influence through military assistance has continued to expand. Soviet weapons are generally cheaper than comparable Western weapons; Soviet credit terms are generally very favourable; Soviet technical assistance and training is very inexpensive and the USSR is not as squeamish as some Western countries such as the USA or the FRG in selling arms to combatant nations (for example, the Iran-Iraq fighting). Soviet prices are frequently tailored to the client. In the 1960s, when Egypt and the USSR were on very friendly terms, the Soviets charged the Egyptian Army half the list cost for tanks, with very favourable credit and payment terms. In the early 1970s, when relations were more strained, the Soviets charged full list price for more modern tanks such as the T-62, and insisted on cash payment. When the Jordanians purchased SA-8 Gecko and ZSU-23-4 air defence vehicles from the Soviets in the early 1980s, they were charged four times the cost charged to more favoured clients such as Libya and Iraq.

Low prices for Soviet weapons should not be interpreted as suggesting Soviet magnanimity in its arms aid policy. Soviet weapons exports are beneficial to the Soviet arms industry as well since they support Soviet industrial efforts to maintain large weapons facilities to provide war production surge capability. This surge capability would probably be maintained even if there were no weapons export, but at a cost to the Soviet military economy. Soviet arms sales are a major source of hard currency to the Soviet economy. For example, Soviet arms sales currently account for about 25 per cent of total Soviet hard currency export earnings (compared to the USA where arms exports account for only about 5 per cent of export earnings).

Increased Soviet arms export now shapes Soviet armoured vehicle production. The Soviets seldom offer their most modern vehicles for sale, and are usually obliged to maintain production of older types to accommodate export clients. For example, the USSR continued to produce the T-55 tank throughout 1979, almost exclusively for export, even though more modern types such as the T-62 and T-64 had been removed from production even earlier.

WARSAW PACT ARMOURED VEHICLE EXPORT TO DEVELOPING COUNTRIES

	1969–71	1972	1973	1974	1975	1976	1977	1978	1979	1980	1981	1982	1983
Tanks (USSR)*	2685	770	2220	1500	590	1075	1430	1150	2435	990	1060	1260	890
Tanks (NSWP)	n/a	280	525	215	645	695	435	560	530	340	325	310	n/a
Other AFV (USSR)	1479	955	1225	955	1090	1340	1855	2250	1915	1635	1005	2260	1450
Other AFV (NSWP)	n/a	300	30	125	250	95	110	20	0	35	0	130	n/a

Source: US Arms Control & Disarmament Agency
*NSWP=Non-Soviet Warsaw Pact

The Soviet Armoured Vehicle Industry

From 1941 to 1945, Soviet armoured vehicle production was directed by The People's Commissariat for the Tank Industry (NKTP) headed by V. A. Malyshev. On 15 October 1945, as part of the general industrial reorganization following the war, this became the People's Commissariat of Transport Machine Building (NKTMP). The NKTMP began the gradual process of reorienting the tank industry from war-time to peacetime production. The largest war-time tank plant, the Ural Tank Plant No. 183 (I. V. Stalin) in Nizhni Tagil, reverted to its peacetime name as the Ural Railway Car Plant No. 183 (Kaganovich). During the war this plant had produced some 35,000 armoured vehicles, about a third of total Soviet production. In the final months of 1945, two of its three assembly lines reverted to railway production, the third line being retained for the production of tanks. The massive Tankograd complex in Chelyabinsk, consisting of three plants, had produced more than 18,000 tanks and assault guns during the war. The Kirovskiy Works in Chelyabinsk, also known as Heavy Tank Plant No. 100 (Stalin), continued to produce the heavy IS-3 tank. The associated Chelyabinsk Tractor Factory stopped producing T-34 tanks in the spring of 1944 and reverted to tractor production. The engine and accessories plant, No. 255, was not used for tank production. In 1946, the combine reverted to its pre-war name as the Chelyabinsk Tractor Factory No. 178 (I. V. Stalin), better known by its acronym ChTZ. The Krasnoye Sormovo Factory No. 112 (Zhdanov) in Gorkiy produced 12,000 tanks during the war. One of its tank assembly lines was shut down early in 1946 and by 1947 the remainder had reverted to locomotive, submarine, and river craft production. The Heavy Machinery Plant No. 185 (Kirov), which was one of the largest pre-war tank plants, had been evacuated at the time of the encirclement of Leningrad. It was re-established in the closing days of the war. By 1947, it had been brought back on line, manufacturing ISU-152K assault guns. Before the war, Kharkov also had been a major centre of tank production, housing the Koshkin design bureau which had developed the T-34 tank. Both the Diesel Engine Plant No. 75 and the Kharkov Tractor Factory No. 183 had been evacuated during the war. In 1944, the Kharkov Locomotive Plant (KhPZ) No. 75 (V. A. Malyshev) was re-established on the site of the old Factory No. 183 where production of the T-44 and later the T-54 was begun. The Uralskiy Heavy Machine Building Factory No. 9 (Ordzhonikidze), better known by its nickname Uralmash or its acronym (UZTM), stopped producing T-34-85 tanks in September 1945, and phased out SU-100 production in May 1946. SU-100 production resumed in Sverdlovsk in July 1948. The Factory No. 174 (Voroshilov) in Omsk continued to produce T-34-85 tanks during the immediate post-war period. The Gorkiy Automobile Factory (Molotov), better known by its acronym (GAZ) produced SU-76 assault guns until the end of May 1945, when production reverted to automobiles.

In March 1946, the NKTMP became the Ministry of Transport Machine Building. During the 1946–48 period, most of the wartime tank plants began reversion to pre-war manu-

SOVIET ARMOURED VEHICLE PRODUCTION 1960–83

	1960	1961	1962	1963	1964	1965	1966	1967	1968	1969	1970	1971	1972	1973	1974	1975	1976	1977	1978	1979	1980	1981	1982	1983
Heavy Tanks	400	200	200	0	0	0	0	0	0	0	0	0	0	0	0	0	0	0	0	0	0	0	0	0
Medium Tanks	2500	2600	3500	3400	3800	4000	4500	5200	4500	4800	4500	3800	3300	3100	2800	2900	3100	3000	3000	3500	3100	2000	2500	2700
Infantry Fighting Vehicles	0	0	0	0	0	0	0	100	200	800	1000	1500	2000	2100	2300	2400	2500	2500	2800	2600	3200	3200	3300	3400
Armoured Personnel Carriers	800	800	900	800	1000	1200	1200	1300	1400	1600	1900	2300	2600	3000	2400	1000	1000	1300	1700	1900	1900	1000	500	200
Armoured Recce Vehicles	800	1000	1000	1000	1000	1500	1500	1500	1500	1500	1500	1400	1200	1000	1000	1000	1000	1100	1100	1200	1200	1000	800	800
Self-Propelled Howitzers	0	0	0	0	0	0	0	0	0	0	0	0	150	250	500	800	800	800	800	900	1100	1100	1100	1100
Assault Guns	500	500	100	100	100	100	50	50	0	0	0	0	0	0	0	0	0	0	0	0	0	0	0	0
Self-propelled Air Defence Guns	1000	700	100	100	100	100	100	100	200	300	300	350	350	350	350	350	300	300	300	300	300	300	200	100

*Source: US Defense Intelligence Agency

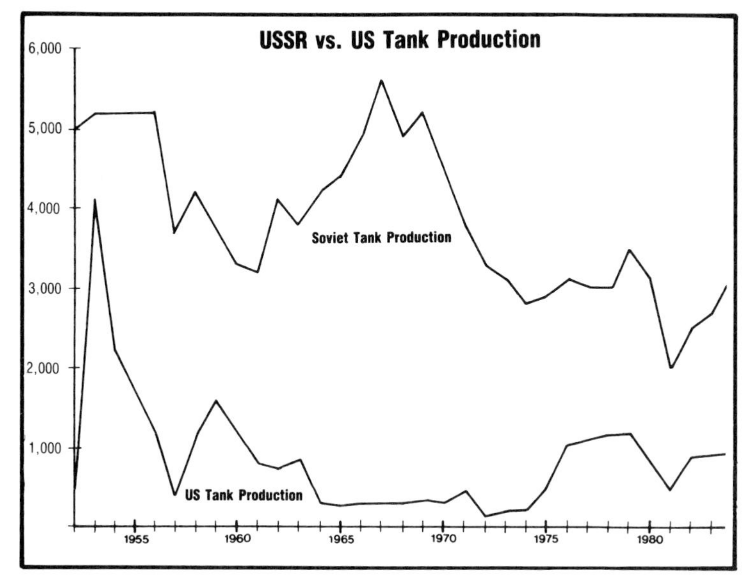

facture. The pressures of wartime had forced the near total abandonment of railway production and substantial curtailment of automotive production, a renewal of which was desperately needed for post-war reconstruction. In 1945, automotive production reached a wartime high of 74,657 trucks and cars. It was not until 1949 that production reached pre-war levels with the production of 275,992 vehicles that year.

Tank and armoured vehicle production increased sharply by 1949 as a consequence of increase in Cold War tensions and the decision by the Soviet Army to begin mechanizing its rifle divisions with new armoured transporters such as the BTR-40 and BTR-152. Following the death of Stalin and Khrushchev's rise to power, armoured vehicle production again fell. While this was in part attributable to the reduction in tensions after the Korean War, its economic roots can be traced to the Soviet Army's enormous investment in strategic weapons development during this period. The development and fielding of thermonuclear weapons, intercontinental bombers such as the Tu-95, the first generation of strategic air defence systems such as the SA-1 and SA-2 air defence missiles, and work on early intercontinental ballistic missiles, all placed a serious drain on the military economy which was felt most severely by the Navy and the Ground Forces. In 1953–54, the Transport Machine Building Industry was again reorganized, becoming the Transport and Heavy Machine Building Industry (TiTMP), a name which it has retained to this day.

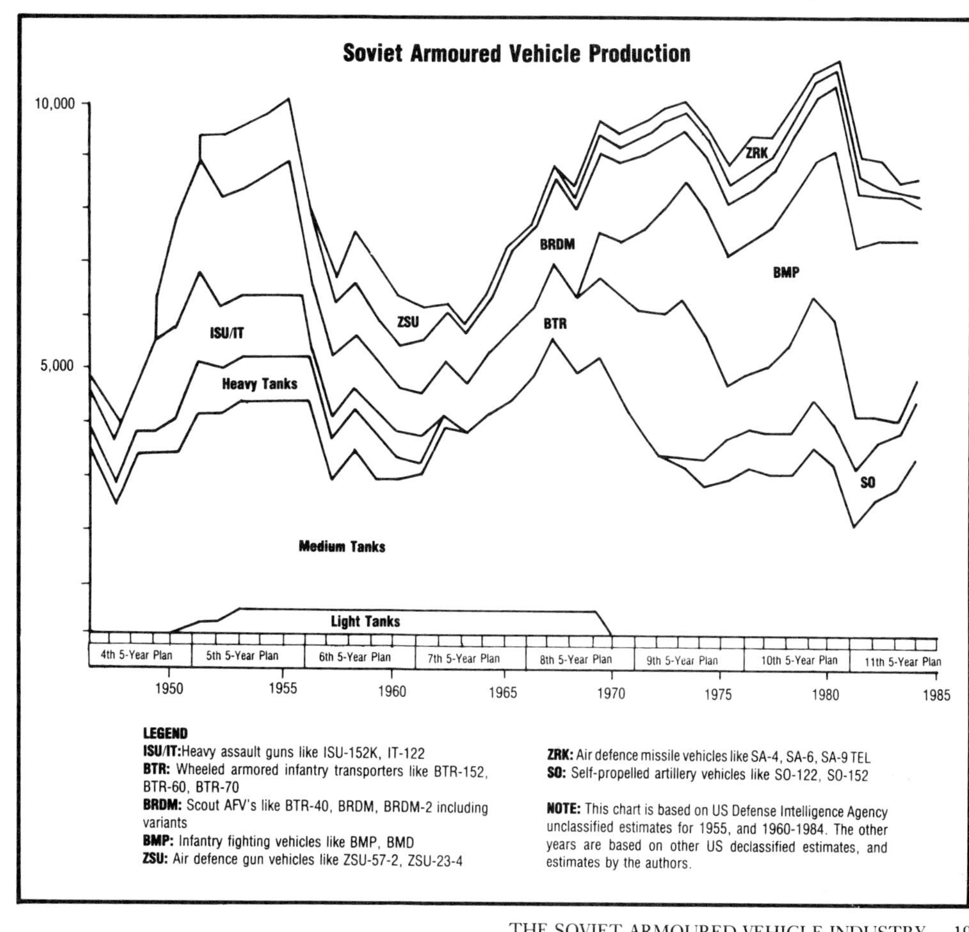

The confusing welter of names for the different organizations in charge of armoured vehicle production highlights the complexity of the Soviet military economy which is nominally divided between industrial ministries devoted to military production and industrial ministries devoted to the civilian economy. However, as much as 40 per cent of the output from the plants controlled by the defence industrial ministries goes to the civilian market, and about 60 per cent of the civil industrial ministries participate to some extent in defence output. Armoured vehicle construction is nominally under the civil industrial ministries.

In the late 1960s, following Khrushchev's fall from power, there was another surge in armoured vehicle production, characterized by a diversification in vehicle categories. Unlike the war-time period when production was almost exclusively concentrated on tracked tanks and assault guns, armoured vehicle production now encompassed tanks, wheeled and tracked armoured transporters, and lightly armoured transporters used for air defence missile systems and other specialized roles. By the 1970s, as a result of this increasing specialization, three civil industrial ministries were responsible for armoured vehicle production. The Transport and Heavy Machine Building Industry (TiTMP) is responsible for the production of tanks and assault guns. The Automotive Industry (AP) is responsible for the production of wheeled armoured troop carriers. The Tractor and Agricultural Machine Building Industry (TiSMP) is responsible for the production of other tracked vehicles including infantry fighting vehicles, self-propelled artillery and other specialized off-road vehicles.

These ministries are responsible for the management of the factories which produce armoured vehicles, and the costs for this production are presumably incorporated into their budgets under the general economic budget. The assumption of military production costs by ostensibly 'civilian' ministries is one of the reasons that the official 'defence' budget is so small.

Detailed information about current Soviet armoured vehicle production facilities is very limited. Unclassified US sources would seem to indicate that by 1965, the number of tank assembly plants dropped to only two. During the post-Khrushchev tank-building surge, a third plant was reassigned to tank production, peaking at four plants in 1977. By 1980, this had been reduced to three plants. From 1980 to 1984, the three plants were the Kharkov Malyshev Diesel Locomotive Plant No. 75, the Omsk Locomotive Repair Plant No. 174/13 (OTZ: *Omskiy Tankoviy Zavod*), and the Ural Railway Car Plant (UVSZ) No. 183 (F. E. Dzherzhinskiy) in Nizhni Tagil. In 1984, the Chelyabinsk Tractor Plant No. 178 (V. I. Lenin) returned to tank production after a hiatus of about four years. Of these four plants, the role of the Nizhni Tagil plant is clearly the dominant one. For example, in 1980, the US DIA estimated that Nizhni Tagil produced 2,500 of the 3,000 tanks manufactured in the USSR that year (83 per cent). Besides the main assembly plants, a number of other facilities are involved in supporting the tank production programme. For example, the Perm Machine Building Plant No. 172 (V. I. Lenin) produces tank guns (as well as other forms of artillery, including howitzers for self-propelled artillery). Other major war-time tank plants like Krasnoye Sormovo in Gorkiy, while not producing tanks, are probably involved in the production of other armoured vehicles such as self-propelled artillery. The Uralmash complex in Sverdlovsk is also a likely self-propelled artillery plant in view of its current production of towed artillery, and its considerable wartime experience with tanks and assault guns.

Details of other armoured vehicle production facilities are sparse. From unclassified DIA testimony before the US Congress, it would appear that there were about six plants connected with light armoured vehicle production in 1965, rising to eight by 1970 and ten–eleven in 1977. The current total is not known. However, from *emigré* testimony and certain US sources, it is possible to list a number of facilities probably involved in current armoured vehicle production. The list is divided into three groups on the basis of the relevant civilian ministries responsible for managing these plants. These groups

SOVIET ARMOURED VEHICLE PRODUCTION PLANTS

Transport and Heavy Machine Building Industry (TiTMP)
(Tanks and Self-propelled Artillery)
Ural Railway Car Plant No. 183, Nizhni Tagil
Omsk Locomotive Repair Plant No. 174/13
Kharkov Malyshev Tractor Plant No. 75
Chelyabinsk Tractor Plant No. 178 (V. I. Lenin)
Krasnoye Sormovo Heavy Machine Plant No. 112, Gorkiy
Ural Heavy Machine Plant No. 9 (Orzhonikidze), Sverdlovsk

Automotive Industry (AP)
(Wheeled Armoured Vehicles)
Gorkiy Vehicle Plant (GAZ)
Ulyanovsk Vehicle Plant (UAZ)
Kurgan Bus Plant (KAvZ)
Zaporozhye Vehicle Plant (ZAZ)
Chelyabinsk Special Vehicle Plant (ChMZAP)
Volgograd Vehicle Plant (VAZ)

Tractor and Agricultural Machine Industry (TiSMP)
(Tracked Light Armoured Vehicles)
Izhevsk Motor Vehicle Plant (IZh)
Volgograd Tractor Plant (VTZ)
Kurgan Wheeled Tractor Plant (D. M. Karbishev) (KZKT)
Kirov Tractor Plant, Leningrad

correspond roughly to tank and self-propelled gun production, wheeled armoured vehicle production and tracked light armoured vehicle production.

Armoured Vehicle Production Planning

Although the automotive industries are managerially responsible for vehicle production, planning of armoured vehicle production is in the hands of the Ministry of Defence. The Soviet General Staff solicits requirements from the different branches of the services and incorporates them into the production requirements of three economic plans. The Long-Range Plan is an offshoot of the General Staff's Strategic Plan and examines general requirements likely to be manifest over the next 15–20 years. This plan tends to effect long-term development of new technologies or new categories of weapons rather than established categories such as armoured vehicles. The 5-Year Plan is the military portion of the general Soviet 5-Year Plan which is the principal element in Soviet central economic planning. This plan includes all proposed armoured vehicle production during the period. The 1-Year Plan is a short-term plan that can be used to redirect industry into areas not foreseen in the original 5-Year Plan. The responsibility for preparing the 5-Year Plan falls to the General Staff's Department for Planning, Organization and Technology, under a Deputy Chief of the General Staff.

Once the General Staff has prepared its 5-Year Plan, it is then handled by the Central Planning Commission, better known by its acronym, GOSPLAN. GOSPLAN has a direct military counterpart of its Administrative Directorate, known as the Military Directorate (currently headed by Vice Premier of the USSR, L. V. Smirnov). The Military Directorate of GOSPLAN must integrate the Ground Force's requirements for armoured vehicles within the general 5-Year Plan of the Soviet Union. Once this integration takes place, the responsibility for ironing out the responsibilities of the industrial ministries in armoured vehicle production, as well as smoothing any conflicts between civilian automotive production requirements and military requirements, is the work of the Military Industrial Commission (VPK). This standing commission is not a permanent organization, but brings together high state officials responsible for carrying out the industrial production plans reached by GOSPLAN. The commission has at least three permanent members: the head of the Military Directorate of GOSPLAN, the head of the General Staff's Department for Organization, Planning and Technology and the Minister of the Defence Industries. Depending on the matters that must be dealt with, additional members come from the Military Departments of the Communist Party Central Committee, the Chief of the Military Department of the Ministry of International Trade (on matters of weapons export), and members of various elements of the Defence Ministry or armed forces.

Armoured Vehicle Development

The development of armoured vehicles for the Soviet Ground Forces is a complex process managed by the Defence Ministry and carried out by the industrial ministries. Any decision to adopt a new type of vehicle for the Ground Forces is a major Party and governmental concern since the Ground Forces are so large. For example, a decision to replace a vehicle like the BMP with a new generation of armoured infantry fighting vehicles is a major governmental and economic action since it will probably eventually involve the production of up to 30,000 vehicles over the course of fifteen years at the cost of several billion roubles.

The design process consists both of conceptual operational studies by the Defence Ministry and advanced technological research by research institutes. For example, the Main Administration for Armoured Forces, in conjunction with the General Staff, will examine future operational requirements for new tanks. At the same time, research institutes like the Technical Institute for Armoured Technology (NIIBT) at the Kubinka Armoured Proving Grounds, will be working on novel technological approaches to future armoured vehicle design such as new armour or track technology. Another important research organization is the NII-VTM (Military Transport Machine Building Research Institute) in Gorelovo outside Leningrad, which is responsible for the development of automotive technology for both tracked and wheeled military vehicles. A commission, consisting of staff from the Ground Forces, the General Staff, and the relevant Administrative and Technical Agencies of the Defence Ministry will meet to prepare a requirement which will eventually be formalized by the technical agency as a Tactical-Technical Assignment (TTZ). In the case of armoured vehicles, there are several relevant agencies. The Main Armour Directorate, currently under Colonel-General Yuri Potapov, is responsible for tanks, assault guns, and probably armoured infantry transporters. The Central Auto-Tractor

▲3

▲4

▲5

▲6

3. Aleksandr Aleksandrovich Morozov (1904–79), head of the main tank design bureau from 1940 until his death in 1979.
4. Nikolai Leonidovich Dukhov (1904–64), head of Soviet post-war heavy tank design projects.
5. Zhozef Yakovlevich Kotin (1908–79), wartime head of the Soviet heavy tank design bureau, head of post-war efforts to adapt tank chassis for ballistic missile launchers.
6. Nikolai Aleksandrovich Astrov (1906–1986), wartime head of the light tank and assault gun bureau, post-war head of design bureau responsible for light armoured vehicles including ASU-85 assault gun, ZSU-23-4 air defence gun vehicle and Kub air defence missile vehicles.

Directorate, currently under Colonel-General I. V. Balabai, is responsible for tracked and wheeled combat vehicles used for specialized roles such as missile launch vehicles and air defence missile vehicles. The Main Rocket and Artillery Directorate is responsible for vehicles such as self-propelled guns and Katyushas.

Once advanced development is completed, the project is assessed for its merit. If deemed acceptable, a Technical Tactical Requirement (TTT) is formulated. The Tactical Technical Requirement document must win the approval of higher elements of the Defence Ministry, including the General Staff, and at that point is incorporated into the 1-Year or 5-Year Plan by GOSPLAN and the VPK. Having won the approval of the military and political hierarchy, the TTT is passed down to the design bureau (KB). Design bureaux have no direct counterpart in European or American defence economies. They are not simply design teams, since they often control weapons plants as well as design weapons. In many respects, they are closer in organization and role to a corporation or company.

A design bureau is headed by a General Designer after whom the bureau is normally named. Under the General Designer are Chief Designers (*glavniy konstruktor*) who may head design teams or be in charge of development of particular sub-components such as engines, suspension, armour configuration, etc. According to US sources, there are seven design bureaux associated with tank, armoured vehicle and artillery development in the Soviet Union today. Not all of these can be positively identified from open sources. The main medium tank design bureau is the Morozov KB, located at the Kharkov Tank Plant (Malyshev). The former head designer of the bureau, A. A. Morozov (who died in 1979), headed the T-34 design bureau in Nizhni Tagil during the war. This bureau was responsible for the development of the T-44, T-54, T-55 and T-62. The bureau was transferred back to Kharkov in 1958. The war-time TsKB-2 heavy tank design bureau, also known as the Kotin KB, was headed by Zh.Ya.Kotin. Kotin was the deputy to the war-time head of the tank industry, and after the war, transferred back to the Kirov Plant in Leningrad. He is associated with some post-war design work including the adaptation of tank chassis as ballistic missile launchers, probably including the early Frog and Scud launchers. Although his bureau is often associated with the development of the PT-76 light tank, it was in fact an independent design team headed by one of his subordinates, Shashmurin, that designed this tank. Due to Kotin's responsibilities with higher administrative functions, one of his chief designers, N. L. Dukhov, gradually came to replace Kotin in much of the design work at Chelyabinsk. Dukhov headed the design teams responsible for the IS-3, IS-4 and T-10 tanks. Finally, in 1954, Dukhov was named General Designer of his own design bureau, probably under the Main Armour Directorate, and responsible for heavy tank designs. The Dukhov KB may have been responsible for the T-64 tank. Dukhov died in 1964, and it is not known if his design team remained intact. The head of the war-time light tank design bureau, N. I. Astrov, continued to head a bureau concerned with light armoured vehicles. Astrov's team was responsible for a variety of specialized armoured vehicles including the ZSU-25-2 and ZSU-37 air defence gun vehicles; ASU-76 and ASU-57 airmobile assault guns, and the light armoured vehicle family including the ASU-85, ZSU-23-4, and SA-6 Gainful launcher and radar vehicles.

The decision by the Ground Forces to begin to mechanize the rifle divisions in the late 1940s

7▲

8▲

9▲

10▲

7. Fedor Fedorovich Petrov (1902–78), head of post-war Central Artillery Design Bureau, premier post-war tank gun design bureau.
8. Vladimir Pavlovich Barmin (1909–), head of design bureau responsible for the development of multiple rocket-launchers (Katyushas).
9. Boris Ivanovich Shavyrin (1902–65), head of artillery design bureau responsible for mortars (including M-240), recoilless rifles (B-10, B-11), and early guided anti-tank missiles.
10. Vasiliy Yemelyanovich Makarov (1903–75), head of a smallarms design team most famous for pistol design, later assigned to the development of guided anti-tank missiles.

led to the addition of another design bureau for wheeled armoured transporters. These design efforts were initially headed by B. M. Fitterman at the ZiS Factory in Moscow, but eventually the design bureau at the Gorkiy Automobile Factory under General Designer V. A. Dedkov took over the dominant role in this field. Dedkov had been a member of the Astrov design bureau during the war, among his accomplishments being the design of the T-70 light tank turret. The actual design work on such vehicles as the BTR-40, BTR-152, BTR-60 and the BRDM was undertaken by Chief Designer V. K. Rubtsov of this bureau. The Dedkov KB has another design team at Gorkiy, headed by V. Rogozhin, responsible for light tracked vehicles such as the GT-S series.

A name long associated with Soviet artillery and tank gun development is F. F. Petrov (who died in 1978). Petrov headed the Main Artillery Design Bureau (GAKB) at Kaliningrad (in the Moscow suburbs) and at its branch in Perm at the Permskiy Mashinostroitelniy Zvod (V. I. Lenin) No. 172 (PMsZ). Petrov designed the main guns used in the T-54, T-55, T-62, T-64 and T-72 tanks, as well as many artillery pieces used in self-propelled vehicles such as the 122mm howitzer on the SO-122 and the 152mm howitzer on the SO-152.

The development of truck-launched unguided rocket systems, better known as Katyushas, was the responsibility of the V. P. Barmin KB at the Kompressor Factory in Moscow. This bureau is believed to have designed most post-war Katyusha including the ubiquitous BM-21.

Soviet design bureaux generally have certain plants assigned to them. Often, the design bureau is co-located at one of its plants, but the bureau may design vehicles that are manufactured elsewhere. The design bureaux are not the sole organizations involved in armoured vehicle development. The bureaux are supported by research institutes (NII) which are of both the 'civilian' and 'military' type. Civilian institutes associated with armoured vehicle development would include organizations such as the State Scientific Research Institute of Auto Transport (NIIAT), which is involved in the development of automotive components, power trains and engines relevant to armoured vehicle design. Other civil research institutes provide technical support in areas such as metallurgy (armour configurations), electronics (vehicle communications and sensors), electro-optics (night vision devices, laser rangefinders) and industrial production methodology. Besides the civil institutes, the bureaux are often supported by military research institutes. These are often located at military academies, but independent institutes engaged in basic research of particular military interest also exist. For example, the Armoured Force has one higher engineering academy (in Kiev) and six higher command academies. Three of the higher command academies are located in cities with significant armoured vehicle production (Omsk, Chelyabinsk and Kharkov), and the Kiev school is located near the largest Soviet tank rebuild facility. Engineering students pursuing their doctorates with a speciality in armoured vehicle design are frequently assigned to design an armoured vehicle as a final requirement for their degree.

Soviet Armoured Vehicle Design Practices

Soviet armoured vehicle design follows much the same course as weapons development elsewhere. Nevertheless, the process has some features which distinguish it from American and British practice.

The concept of a new armoured vehicle can be prompted by the work of a design bureau (KB), or a research institute (NII) on the basis of a major technical advance (such as new armour, powerplant or armament developments), or on the basis of a tactical requirement determined by a branch of the Ground Forces or General Staff. In the case of tanks and most armoured vehicles, the requirement is then more formally drawn up by the Main Armour Directorate, which is issued as a Tactical-Technical Assignment (TTZ). At this stage it would appear that the new system receives its first designation. At least two types of designation are applied at this stage: a name and a project number. Certain project numbers, literally 'factory product' (*zavodskoe izdeliye*) numbers, may be issued by the Main Armour Directorate at the time of the TTT, as they appear to follow a fairly common pattern. Some examples of these projects number have been '*zavodskoe izdeliye 140*' (BTR-152), '*141*' (BTR-40), '*49*' and '*62B*' (BTR-60), '*40A*' (BRDM), '*41*' (BRDM-2), '*765*' (BMP), '*137*' (T-54), and '*155*' (T-55). It would appear that the design bureaux themselves give their projects their own designations, for example, B-40 (T-54) and B-45 (T-55) were used by the Morozov KB. Some names associated with armoured vehicle programmes include *Korshun* (BMP), *Yubileniye* (T-62), *Akatsiya* (SO-152) and *Gvozdika* (SO-122). The TTZ is followed by a requirements document (TTT) when development work transits from scientific exploratory work (NIR) to the experimental design stage (OKR).

The Soviet Ground Forces do not appear to use competitions widely between design bureaux at this stage. There have been exceptions. For example, in the case of the PT-76 tank, it is known that at least four design teams drew up initial designs, of which one was selected for further development. It is not known if any other than the winning design progressed beyond paper design studies. It would appear that competition within a design bureau is a more common practise. There have been numerous known cases of this approach, for example, the many efforts of the Kotin design bureau's prolific teams. Nevertheless, it is hard to make a definitive judgement of this issue owing to a lack of detailed information on post-1960 programmes.

Once a design has been accepted from the TTZ stage, whether through a competitive effort by bureaux or teams, more definitive choices are made regarding new sub-systems, or the selection of existing sub-systems at the TTT/OKR stage. There are usually some novel sub-systems in any new design, such as a new main gun, a new engine, or a new fire control system. These elements are frequently prepared by bureaux outside the armoured vehicle bureau, such as Petrov's GAKB which has designed most tank guns since 1945. Nevertheless, Soviet design bureaux are not encouraged to introduce new sub-systems unless they are required. Instead, are encouraged to employ as many sub-components as possible from standard catalogues of sub-components already in production. To some extent, the selection of sub-components is already determined in the TTT. For example, it would appear that in the case of designs like the BTR-60 or MT-LB, the engine selection had already been made in the TTT, and such a decision was not at the discretion of the design teams. The reason for applying these limitations is that it helps to cut costs on the programme, simplifies logistical support of the vehicle once it is in service, and speeds the design process. There are real limits on the industrial resources available to the Ground Forces, and by conserving resources on such less demanding sub-systems as headlights, hatch covers, periscopes, suspension assemblies and the like, the military economy is better able to support new technology initiatives such as the introduction of laser rangefinders, metallurgical improvements in barrel production, new suspension designs, etc.

This tendency to employ common sub-components has often been misunderstood outside the Soviet Union. For example, it has been widely assumed that the ZSU-23-4, ASU-85, SA-6 launch vehicle and MT-LB are all derivatives of the PT-76 tank. This is clearly not the case, as the PT-76 was designed by the Kotin bureau (Shashmurin's team), while the ZSU-23-4, ASU-85 and SA-6 are all products of Astrov's bureau. They use different powerplants, different transmissions, different suspension elements, etc., and have very little in common technically.

With the sub-systems developed or selected, technical documentation is prepared for the construction of prototypes. Tests of the prototype are conducted and the system undergoes further refinement. Most design bureaux have small test tracks available, such as the Kharkov Poligon used by the Morozov bureau at Kharkov. At this stage, the system is subjected to state trials which are usually conducted away from the development site; in the case of tanks, most probably at the NIIBT facility in Kubinka. This stage is not directly comparable to Western practise; for example, the type classification stage in US armoured vehicle development. The state trials merely confirm that the vehicle design approaches the requirements of the TTT and is mature enough to permit initial series production. In the USA, series production would be delayed until a later stage (after operational trials) before series production would be authorized.

With the state trials complete, the design bureau is involved in preparing the vehicle for series production. At this stage, the vehicle seems to receive an industrial index number. Since vehicles are produced in nominally 'civilian' industries, a cover designation is applied to hide the true service designation. Some examples of this style of number include 2S1 (SO-122), and 2P27 (3M6 Shmel ATGM on BRDM). These industrial index numbers are also applied to vehicle sub-components. For example, the U-5T 115mm gun on the T-62 has the industrial index number of 2A20. The industrial index system seems to identify the ministry (first number), class of weapon (second number) and sequence of issue (third number). Once a significant number of initial series production vehicles are completed, they are issued to select Ground Forces units for operational trials. These units are often special officer candidate battalions or regiments. For example, the T-64A initially was issued to the 100th Guards Tank Training Regiment formed from officers of the Kharkov Guards Higher Tank Command School, which was not far from the Kharkov Locomotive Factory (Malyshev) where the production facility was located. During this stage, the tankers train with the new vehicle in the presence of engineers from the design bureau in order to locate any particular faults with the design. These faults may be inherent design flaws or may simply be production problems. With these troubles identified, the engineers transmit recommendations to the design bureau, which modifies the design or production techniques to ameliorate the problems. This belated testing programme frequently leads to the existence of initial series production vehicles which differ in a number of details from the definitive series production vehicles. It is only at this stage that the vehicle is accepted by the Ground Forces for operational service. The vehicle receives its normal service designation at this stage (e.g., T-55, BMP, etc.), even though such a designation may as yet be classified and accessible only to officers.

Development of most vehicles continues beyond the acceptance for operational service. Improvements are developed and gradually introduced into the production. These improvements are also often incorporated into earlier production vehicles at the time of their rebuilding. For example, early production T-54 were later refitted with infra-red night fighting equipment during their rebuilding. This rebuilding usually takes place after 500 hours of engine running time, by which time the tank requires a complete overhaul. Beyond such detail changes, evolutionary development of a more substantive nature also takes place. For example, the T-55 was a direct outgrowth of the T-54 series, and incorporated a wide range of improvements including nuclear protection, a turret basket, more ammunition, etc. Only when this evolutionary development has been exhausted will a new design be undertaken.

Warsaw Pact Armoured Vehicle Production

Soviet armoured vehicle production is supported by armoured vehicle production in several countries of the Warsaw Pact. For example, from 1980 to 1984, non-Soviet Warsaw Pact countries manufactured 2,800 tanks, amounting to 21 per cent of total Soviet production. The two principal armoured vehicle manufacturing countries outside the USSR are Czechoslovakia and Poland, with much smaller programmes existing in Hungary and Romania. East Germany and Bulgaria are not involved in armoured vehicle production. Although detailed unclassified data is not available, it would appear that the non-Soviet Warsaw Pact is approaching self-sufficiency in armoured vehicles. Most Warsaw Pact countries import a certain quantity of Soviet manufactured armoured vehicles when they first appear, but supply usually shifts to Czechoslovakia or Poland once production has been initiated in those countries. Besides supplying other non-Soviet Warsaw Pact members, Czechoslovakia and Poland export armoured vehicles to developing countries as well as to the Soviet Union. For example, Czechoslovakia shipped virtually its entire production run of T-62 either to export clients or to the Soviet Union, and exports about 70 per cent of its BMP production to the USSR. Poland exported almost its entire production of the ATS-59 and ATS-59G, as well as much of its MT-LB production to the USSR. Although the Military-Industrial Commission of the COMECON nominally guides the weapons export policy of the non-Soviet Pact countries, actually the Soviet Union's export agencies dominate any weapons export programmes from Pact countries. Indeed, the heavy demands for equipment in the wake of the 1967 and 1973 wars was a major factor in the Soviet Union's encouragement to Czechoslovakia to build up its armoured vehicle industry.

Czechoslovakia

Czechoslovakia is undoubtedly the largest manufacturer of armoured vehicles outside the USSR in the Warsaw Pact. Czechoslovakia had a vigorous and independent armoured vehicle industry prior to the Second World War that was heavily involved in tank export. During the war occupied Czech factories continued to manufacture armoured vehicles for the German war effort, including the Czech-designed Pzkpw 38(t) series, and the related Hetzer tank destroyer. In the brief interval between the end of the war and the imposition of Communist rule, the Czechoslovak tank industry began reconstruction with an aim towards supplying both the Czechoslovak Army and export clients. The Hetzer was built in the ST-I tank destroyer and ST-III training vehicle versions for the Czechoslovak Army, and as the G-13 for export (to Switzerland). The AH light tank was exported to Ethiopia. Plans were under way to manufacture a modernized version of the German SdKfz 251 series for both domestic use and export. This eventually appeared in 1958 as the OT-810. Both Skoda and CKD were contracted by the Czechoslovak government competitively to develop a new medium tank, the VTU, and CKD undertook the development of a new heavy tank. These efforts were largely squashed when the Communists came to power. Czechoslovakia was gradually integrated into the Soviet military-industrial sphere. Due to the extent of Czechoslovak heavy industries, the Soviet Union decided to foster Czechoslovak armoured vehicle production.

In 1951, CKD in Prague began production of the Soviet T-34-85 tank. Production lasted until 1958 and amounted to about 3,000 tanks. Production of the related SU-100 assault gun began in 1952, and is believed to have totalled about 1,400 vehicles. A smaller number of armoured recovery vehicles based on the T-34 were also manufactured, designated VT-34. In 1956, the Soviet Union reached agreement with Egypt over the supply of tanks and other equipment. This initially included about 200 Czechoslovak T-34-85 and 100 SU-100. This marked the first use of Czechoslovakia as a major arms exporter to Soviet clients, a pattern which has continued to this day. It would appear that the Martin Machine Building Works gradually supplanted CKD as the principal Czech tank manufacturer. CKD remains the principal transmission manufacturer, Skoda the engine manufacturer, Vikovice the armour manufacturer, and Martin, the final assembly works.

In 1958, production shifted from the T-34-85 to the T-54A which was produced for both the Czechoslovak People's Army (CSLA) as well as Soviet export clients and other members of the Warsaw Pact. In order to begin the gradual process of mechanizing CSLA motor rifle divisions, production was finally begun of the long-delayed OT-810 armoured half-track. This project corresponded to the Soviet BTR-152, and was short-lived, lasting only until 1962 by which time about 1,700 vehicles had been manufactured. During this period, Tatra also developed a wheeled armoured scout car, the Tatra 805, and a wheeled armoured troop transporter, based on the Praga V3S truck. Neither was accepted for production.

In place of the OT-810, the CSLA had decided to manufacture a derivative of the Soviet BTR-50 tracked troop carrier, the OT-62 TOPAS. TOPAS production ran from 1961 to about 1971 by which time about 3,000 had been manufactured. The TOPAS was adopted by the CSLA, was exported to several Warsaw Pact countries (notably Poland), and to several Soviet client states including India, Syria and Egypt.

In mechanizing their motor rifle divisions, the Czechs ran into the same cost problems with tracked infantry vehicles as had the Soviets. Czechoslovakia and Poland reached agreement in 1959 to develop a wheeled armoured troop carrier in lieu of the Soviet BTR-60. This emerged in 1961 as the OT-64 SKOT. Basic design work was undertaken by Tatra in Czechoslovakia, with the Poles responsible for vehicle armament systems. Tatra manufactures the chassis and engine, with FSC/Lublin in Poland providing the armoured body and armament system. A total of about 7,000 SKOT were built by Poland and Czechoslovakia until the mid-1970s when production appears to have ended. The SKOT was exported to a number of Soviet clients including India.

Czechoslovakia shifted to T-55 production from 1964 to 1973, producing a total of about 6,500 T-54 and T-55 from 1958 to 1973. In 1973, production of the T-62 was undertaken, lasting until about 1978. Total production was about 1,000 tanks, nearly all of which were exported. In about 1978, production of the T-72M began and continued until 1985. Czechoslovakia began production of the Soviet BMP in

ARMOURED VEHICLE PRODUCTION IN THE NON-SOVIET WARSAW PACT

	1976	1977	1978	1979	1980	1981	1982	1983	1984
Tanks	800	800	800	800	700	520	600	550	450
Other AFV	1800	1900	1800	1800	1300	1300	1400	1300	1200
SP Artillery	0	0	0	10	50	50	150	200	300
SP Air Defence Guns	100	100	100	100	100	50	50	0	0

Source: US Department of Defense

1971 (as the BVP). On average, about 70 per cent of this production has been exported to the USSR.

In recent years, Czechoslovakia has continued to develop certain types of armoured vehicle of its own design, including the vz.77 Dana 152mm self-propelled howitzer which has been manufactured for the CSLA and for export (to such countries as Libya).

Poland

Poland is the second largest manufacturer of armoured vehicles in the Warsaw Pact after Czechoslovakia. Before the war Poland had a very modest armoured vehicle industry, but most of the industries taken over by the Germans during the war were removed by the Soviet Union as reparations in the immediate post-war years. In 1950, a new factory was set up in Labedy, the Labedy Design and Experimental Facility (ZKD), which began production of T-34-85 tanks in 1951. This continued until 1956–57 when production shifted to the T-54A. According to US estimates, total T-34-85 production was about 1,600 vehicles and was aimed almost entirely at the Polish People's Army (LWP). T-54A production at ZKD lasted until 1960 when production of the improved T-55 began. As in Czechoslovakia, the Polish T-54A incorporated a number of technical improvements over the original Soviet design. T-54 production in Poland probably amounted to about 3,000 vehicles, and production of the T-55 and T-55A, which probably lasted until 1972, amounted to another 5,000 vehicles. In about 1977–78 ZKD shifted to production of the T-72M which continued throughout 1985. Polish-built tanks are the mainstay of the East German and Hungarian armies as well as the LWP.

Besides the basic tank versions of the T-54 and T-55, the Polish Military Institute for Automotive and Armoured Technology (WITPiS), the Polish equivalent of the Soviet NIIBT, developed a number of specialized variants including the WZT-2 armoured recovery vehicle, the BLG-60M bridge-layer, the PW-LWD and IWT combat engineer vehicles and others. ZKD or other Polish facilities also manufactured the ATS-59 and ATS-59G artillery tractors at this time for export to the Soviet Union.

In the armoured troop carrier field, Poland joined a development effort with Czechoslovakia in 1959 to build the OT-64 SKOT wheeled infantry transporter. Poland manufactures the armoured body and armament of this vehicle, with final assembly believed to take place at the FSC/Lublin truck plant. In about 1973–74, Poland began producing the SO-122 (2S1) 122mm self-propelled howitzer, and probably the related MT-LB armoured transporter.

Hungary

Hungary had a small armoured vehicle production capacity during the war, mainly manufacturing licensed variants of Czechoslovak (Turan) and Swedish (Toldi/Nimrod) tanks, and indigenous armoured cars like the Csaba. After the war, Hungarian armoured vehicle development withered. In the early 1960s, the Hungarians began development of an indigenous light armoured transporter somewhat akin to the Soviet BRDM-1, the D-442 FUG. This entered production in 1963, and was built for Hungarian as well as Polish, Bulgarian, German and Czechoslovak forces. A total of about 3,000 were manufactured before production shifted to the improved PSzH-IV in 1969–70. The production of the turreted PSzH-IV continued until the late 1970s, by which time about 3,500 had been built for domestic and export use. The Hungarian armoured scout vehicles are generally preferred by the Warsaw Pact countries to their Soviet counterpart, the BRDM-2, because of their higher quality and use of a diesel engine. Hungarian production is so small, however, that many Warsaw Pact armies are obliged to acquire BRDM-2 as well as FUG and PSzH-IV.

Romania

Romania had a very modest armoured vehicle industry during the war, consisting mainly of automotive plants like the Brasov Works involved in armoured vehicle modification programmes. In 1970, Romania began licensed production of the Soviet BTR-60PB in modified form as the TAB-72. Production of these vehicles continued throughout the late 1970s, when they were supplanted by a licensed copy of the BTR-70, the TAB-77. The TAB-72 has been exported to the Middle East, but Romania's armoured vehicle factories are so modest that extensive export is outside their capabilities. The TAB-77 is built in both an eight-wheeled troop transporter version, and a shortened four-wheeled scout version, the TAB-C. In the late 1970s, the Romanians began attempts to manufacture their own tank, based on the T-54/55. The original versions of this vehicle, believed to be based on rebuilt T-55A, paraded in Bucharest in 1979. They are believed to be designated M-77. Some were exported to Egypt in 1984, but the manufacturing quality was reported to be so poor that they were returned.

WARSAW PACT ARMOURED VEHICLES IN SERVICE 1986*

	T-34-85	T-54/T-55	T-62	T-72	BTR-152	BTR-50	OT-62	BTR-60	OT-64	BMP	BTR-70	PT-76	BRDM-1	BRDM-2	FUG	PSzH-IV	SO-122	ZSU-23-4	ZSU-57-2	SA-4
Afghanistan	x	500	100		x							30								
Albania	70	15			x	x														
Algeria	100	300	350	100	250	200		200		700			50	150			x	x	x	
Angola	78	150	82	x	x	x		x				50	x	175				100	40	
Austria	*																			
Benin		4										10		12						
Botswana								30												
Bulgaria	*	1800	100		200	150		800					x	200	50			35	60	
C. African Rep.		4		4									10	22						
Congo	10	17		25	20		24					3	10	15				8		
Cuba	100	400	160	x	100			100		60		60	50	75				36	25	
Czechoslovakia	*	3100		150			2500		2500	700			*		500	300	150	100		25
Djibouti								10				x		10						
Egypt	100	850	750		x	x	x	x	x	200			x	225				100	100	
Ethiopia	x	500		40								80		200						
Finland	*	75		50		60		60		85			50						12	
Germany (DDR)	*	2300		100	200	200		600		600	100	10	*	400	x	250	100	100	*	25
Guinea	15	25			40							50		25						
Guinea-Bissau	14	30			x	x		x				20		20						
Hungary	*	1500		80	100	300		300	1500			12			1500	1500	100	50	30	
India		950		70	x	x			x	50		100						100		
Indonesia						25						90	30							
Iran		x	x			300		300		x		75						x	80	
Iraq	100	700	1600	200	x	x		x		200				x				x	x	
Israel	100	440	150		x	x		x				100		x						
Jordan												x						16		
Korea (North)	250	1500	200		x	x		x				x		x						
Kuwait																				
Laos												10								
Libya	50	2000	750			300		300	100	300				250			x	250		
Madagascar												x		30						
Mali	27	25			10			30				x		20						
Mongolia	*	100						100												
Morocco		27							30					x						
Mozambique	x	150	x		x			x		x		42	50	100				25		
Nicaragua		190			x	20		50				28		39						
Nigeria		80																30		
Peru		250																40		
Poland	*	3200		400	*		750		2500	500		300	*	1500		200	300	250	*	
Romania	*	1300		30	200	400		900					x	300				60	60	
Somalia	50		30		100	50		50						50				20		
South Africa	15	10										5								
Sri Lanka					10															
Sudan	20	130			50	50			60					40						
Syria	200	800	500	600	x	x		x	x	500		100	x	x				x	x	
Tanzania		x			30															
Togo	7	2																		
Uganda		10							35											
Vietnam	x	250										150							x	
Yugoslavia	*	900		50	x	x		x				100	x					x	x	
Zaïre					250	15														
Zambia		70										50	x	50						
Zimbabwe	6	15																		

*This chart attempts to show the extent of Soviet and Warsaw Pact armoured vehicle exports. The figures are based on published estimates of the inventory of Soviet and Warsaw Pact armoured vehicles in various armies in late 1985–early 1986. In the case of armies which used particular types of armoured vehicles but have retired them, this is indicated by an asterisk (*). In the case of equipment reportedly in service, but for which no accurate numerical data is available, an x has been used.

SA-6	SA-8	SA-9	SA-13
10	10	20	
6	30	30	
30		x	
12		50	
180		150	100
75			
120	40	95	
6		32	
80	8	50	
30	20	50	
25	x		
	20		
	x	x	
340	90		x
280		225	
50			
		5	
50	20	150	x
20			
		x	
x			

Main Battle Tanks

At the end of the Second World War, the Soviet Army was in the process of re-equipping its tank force with a new generation of vehicles. The legendary T-34 was reaching the end of its developmental potential, and a new medium tank, the T-44, had seen limited service with the 2nd Ukrainian Front in the closing days of the war. The heavy IS-2 tank was being supplanted by the improved IS-3 *Shchuka* (Pike). Light tank production had ceased in 1944, but work was beginning on a new light scout tank, the K-90. As a consequence of the advent of the German Tiger and Panther tanks in 1943, Soviet tank development focused on gun and armour improvements. In the final year of the war, there was a gradual shift in emphasis towards heavier and better-armed vehicles, with heavy tanks representing a larger fraction of overall Soviet tank production than had been the case during the first years of the war.

Medium Tank Development

Development of the T-44 was completed by the Morozov KB (design bureau) in the summer of 1944, and production work was shifted to a small design team under N. V. Barykov at the re-established Kharkov Locomotive Plant No. 75. A small number, probably about 250, were produced in time to see limited fighting during the final months of the war. The principal difference between the T-44 and the T-34–85 was in the hull. The tanks had very similar turrets and used the same 85mm gun. The T-44 had an improved

11. The legendary T-34 ▶ remained in widespread use after the Second World War, and many were exported to Soviet clients, like these T-34-85 on parade with the Somalian Army in the 1970s.

12. A T-34-85 of the Angolan Army, supplied by the Soviet Union in the 1970s.
13. During the 1950s, the T-34-85 was manufactured in Poland. This is a Polish T-34-85M1 retrofitted with deep wading gear and other improvements.
14. Czechoslovakia was the largest manufacturer of the T-34-85 outside the USSR, and was the major supplier of the Egyptian Army in 1956. Here, a Czechoslovak-manufactured T-34-85 is seen abandoned in the Sinai Desert after the 1956 war with Israel.
15. Yugoslavia considered manufacturing a locally modified version of the T-34-85, but it progressed only to prototype stage (seen here) and did not enter wide-scale production.
16. Many T-34-85s in Soviet stockpiles were modernized as the T-34-85M, like this Angolan tank knocked out by South African forces. The T-34-85M had T-54A wheels used to replace the earlier worn-out types, as well as internal improvements.

▲12

▲13 ▼14

15▲ 16▼

▲17 ▼18

17. An early production model of the T-44 with the original T-34 track. The production of the T-44 was short-lived, ending quickly in favour of the T-54.
18. The T-44M had a number of improvements, including a new, wider track. This tank, still in service in the 1970s, is fitted with an STU snowplough dozer blade. (Sovfoto)

19. A T-44 fitted with the PT-3 mineclearing roller system.

19▲

version of the T-34-85's V-2 engine, but was fitted with a new (and troublesome) transmission. The two main advantages offered by the T-44 were the improved torsion bar suspension, and the improved hull design which was simpler to manufacture and offered better ballistic protection than that of the archaic T-34.

The main tactical disadvantage of the T-44 was that its 85mm gun was becoming increasingly inadequate. Although it could penetrate the armour of the German Panther tank at close ranges (500m), it was not adequate to deal with the Royal Tiger heavy tank. The Soviets had received a single American M-26 Pershing tank through Lend Lease, and its armour was thick enough to be proof against the T-44's gun in frontal engagements. Although the German Panther, American Pershing and British Centurion tanks were heavy tanks by Soviet standards, it had become evident to Soviet tank designers that these 45-ton tanks would become the medium tank class of the post-war generation.

To defeat tanks like these, Morozov's design bureau had a perfectly adequate gun, the D-10 100mm gun designed by Petrov's GAKB for the SU-100 tank destroyer. This was the obvious choice since 100mm ammunition was now in production for both the SU-100 assault gun and the BS-3 100mm field gun. Attempts were made by Barykov's team to adapt the 100mm gun to the T-44 as the T-44-100. There was also an attempt to upgun the T-34 with the same weapon as the T-34-100. Although both designs proved acceptable, Morozov's bureau in the meantime had developed a more successful alternative. By December 1944 they had completed initial design work on *Obiekt 137*, also known as the B-40. This design envisaged using an improved version of the T-44 hull with a wholly new turret, more thickly armoured than the turret on the T-44, and designed from the outset to carry the D-10 100mm gun. On 20 May 1945, the final drawings of the vehicle were transferred to the factory for prototype construction. The initial state trials were successful, leading to initial trials production in the winter of 1945–46. This new tank was designated the T-54.

The T-54 Tank

The T-54 did not completely supplant the T-34-85 in production at this stage. There had been problems with various aspects of the T-44 and T-54, mainly concerning the powertrain and transmission and so the T-34-85 remained in production until 1950. Numerically the T-34-85 was the most important tank produced from 1945 to 1950, with total production after the war probably reaching 15,000 tanks (in addition to the 29,000 produced during the war). In 1951, T-34-85 production was initiated in Czechoslovakia, and in 1953 in Poland. The Czechs are believed to have produced about 3,000 T-34-85, many for export, and the Poles about half that number. Yugoslavia considered manufacturing a locally modified version, but this programme came to naught except for a few prototype vehicles.

▲20

20. The first versions of the T-54 Model 1946 had a wide gun mantlet, very evident in this view.

21. The first production models of the T-54 Model 1949 had a round underhang around the turret, unlike the later, and more common types.

22. Interesting rear view of a T-54 Model 1949, showing the changed contours of the turret side. This tank is boarding a GSP tracked ferry.

23. The T-54 Model 1951 used a new, pig-snout mantlet, but still had a distinctive rear turret overhang. This tank is on a GSP tracked ferry. It has obviously been rebuilt, as it has both the OPVT deep wading equipment and the improved starfish wheels.

Operational trials of the initial T-54 were reasonably successful, and in 1948, Morozov and his bureau (including A. Kolesnikov, V. Matyukhin, P. Vasiliev and N. Kucherenko) received a state prize for their performance on this tank design effort. Morozov's team was not entirely satisfied with the design, and prior to the start of initial series production, improvements were developed. A larger turret race was adopted the better to absorb the 100mm gun's recoil, and new, wider tracks were added for better mobility on soft soil. This second model of the T-54 entered production in 1949. The ballistic shape of the T-54 Model 1949 turret was far from ideal since it provided a shot-trap at the base and the casting was overly complex, so a new turret was designed and entered production in 1951. The turret on the T-54 Model 1951 also substituted a pig-snout mantlet for the wide mantlet used on the T-54 Models 1946 and 1949.

By 1951, the T-54 had completely replaced the T-34-85 and the T-44 on the assembly lines and had become the standard medium tank of the Ground Forces. The definitive version of the T-54 appeared in 1953, with further turret improvements, notably the deletion of the rear turret overhang, giving the turret a nearly hemispherical appearance. The turret on the T-54 Model 1953 proved to be the final configuration for this series.

The new turret was an early off-shoot of a programme to modernize the T-54. In 1954, this improved type appeared as the T-54A which closely resembled the T-54 Model 1953 but introduced a number of innovative features. A new gun, the D-10TG, was introduced, with power replacing manual elevation, as well as one-axis gun stabilization. The driver was provided with infra-red night driving equipment including an infra-red driving light and a metascope/periscope for night use. The T-54A also was the first Soviet tank to be regularly configured for the OPVT deep wading equipment which, after suitable preparation, permitted it to cross rivers under water.

The OPVT system consisted of vehicle sealing equipment and a snorkel tube. Although part of the sealing system is already fitted to the vehicle, attaching the snorkel and adding the additional sealing takes about 1.2 hours to complete. The OPVT system allows a tank to ford rivers to a maximum depth of 5 metres, a maximum width of 700 metres and a maximum river flow speed of 1.5m/sec. The tank can fire its main gun about 30 seconds after having left the river, but it takes 10–15 minutes to completely remove the sealing

▼21

22▲ 23▼

equipment from the tank. The tank is steered under water using the GPK-48 gyro-compass. The crew usually wear a special escape breathing apparatus. If a tank is stranded in mid-stream, the tank interior is gradually flooded, and once filled, the hatches are opened, and the crew escapes. Deep wading is a very dangerous process since river bottoms are irregular, and the tank has a certain measure of buoyancy which degrades traction and steering. Deep wading operations are usually prepared by special river reconnaissance teams, and often a tank recovery vehicle is sent across first to help tow out stranded tanks. Nevertheless, this feature allows Soviet tank units to cross river obstacles, unaided by engineer bridging equipment. The OPVT system was retrofitted to many older tanks including the T-34-85, and has been a standard feature of Soviet tanks since the T-54A.

Externally, the T-54A was nearly identical with the T-54 Model 1953. The new five-spoke 'starfish' wheel was gradually introduced to replace the 'skeleton' wheel previously in use. The original T-54A had a small muzzle counterweight at the end of the D-10TG gun tube, but this soon gave way to a fume extractor because of the inadequacy of the turret ventilation system to clear out gun fumes.

In 1955, the T-54A was followed by the T-54B whose main feature was the incorporation of the D-10T2S gun with 2-axis stabilization and power turret traverse, as well as a new, active infra-red night fighting system. The electric power traverse supplemented the normal manual

▲24 ▼25

24. A T-54 Model 1951 in service with the Syrian Army in 1970, showing the distinctive rear turret overhang of this version.
25. The T-54 Model 1953 introduced the definitive turret shape to the T-54 series, without rear overhang, and with the narrow, pig-snout mantlet. This tank of the Afghan Army has been rebuilt as is evident from the later starfish wheels.

turret traverse and enabled the turret to be completely rotated in less than 30 seconds. The new stabilization system, based around the STP-2, was of a fairly primitive nature and did not offer real fire-on-the-move capability. Rather, it kept the main gun pointing with a rough accuracy so that once the tank halted for firing, only minor aiming adjustments would be needed. The earlier T-54A had been fitted with an infra-red night driving system, consisting of an FG-100 infra-red headlight and a driver's TVN-2 night periscope. The T-54B added a full infra-red night fighting system. An L-2 Luna infra-red searchlight was positioned alongside the main gun tube, with a smaller OU-3GK searchlight for the tank commander. All of the main tank sights were modified to permit use of night-time IR sights. Although the German Army had pioneered the use of infra-red night fighting equipment in 1945, the Soviet Army was the first army to adopt it as a standard item on its tanks. The US Army did not begin regularly to equip its tanks with such systems until 1959. It should be noted that T-54 development varied somewhat outside the Soviet Union. For example, the Poles and Czechoslovaks added hydraulic clutch assistance on their T-54A before the Soviets did so on their T-55, and the Poles added further external turret stowage in the form of two boxes. The Poles designated their equivalent of the Soviet T-54B as T-54AM.

In the late 1950s, the Soviet Ground Forces embarked on a major tank modernization programme. As older versions of the T-54 tank were

26▲

26. The T-54A introduced gun stabilization to the T-54 series. This is one of the initial T-54A, fitted with a small muzzle counterweight rather than the later fume-extractor. It has been rebuilt with the Luna infra-red night vision equipment, and so would be designated T-54A(M). (Sovfoto)

27▼

27. An early production T-54A fitted with the wide tube used when practising deep wading. The tactical deep wading snorkel is much narrower and is not wide enough to allow the crew to escape if the tank stalls underwater as can be done with this training tube.

28. The definitive Polish-built version of the T-54A with the starfish wheels. The Polish LWP used the national white eagle insignia as seen here until the mid 1960s when it switched to the red and white checkerboard diamond, similar to that used by the Air Force.

29. The definitive production model of the T-54A had a muzzle bore evacuator added at the end of the gun tube. This tank is interesting in that it has the original skeleton wheels, but has been rebuilt as a T-54A(M) with the infra-red night-fighting equipment. (Sovfoto)

▲28 ▼29

gradually returned for their 500 running-hour rebuilding, some of the new features were added including the new wheels, infra-red night firing equipment, OPVT deep wading fittings, and other features. NATO usually designates these vehicles as T-54(M) and T-54A(M). It is very difficult to identify the various versions of the T-54 on the basis of external appearance. For example, a T-54 Model 1953, rebuilt with a new gun tube, IR equipment and new wheels, is virtually indistinguishable from a T-54B. US Army sources claim that the final version of the T-54, which they call T-54(X), had a flush loader's hatch as on the later T-55, but this variant may in fact have been a misidentified T-55.

The T-54A was first seen close-up by Western Intelligence in 1956 when a Soviet tank was driven into the grounds of the British Embassy in Budapest during the Hungarian Uprising. The thickness of the armour on the T-54A was something of a shock to NATO and prompted the adoption of the new British L7 105mm gun on later US, UK and FRG tanks. Compared to NATO tanks of the period, the T-54A was impressive in many respects. It was much smaller than such NATO tanks as the US M48 Patton or the British Centurion, but was comparably armoured. Its 100mm gun was similar in performance to the 90mm gun on the US M48, though actual anti-armour penetration was more dependent on the type of ammunition fired than on the gun itself. Smaller size meant lighter weight, and lower overall cost; it also meant that more T-54 were produced than all other NATO tanks of the period combined. The T-54A had mobility comparable to that of the M48 Patton tank, although the ride was a bit harder. Soviet tanks of the period were more apt to have infra-red night fighting equipment than NATO tanks, and more thought had been given to river-crossing requirements with the provision of OPVT equipment. Soviet choice of a mature diesel engine also gave the T-54A excellent range without refuelling, so that they were not plagued by the range restraints that restricted NATO gasoline-powered tanks like the M48 Patton and Centurion.

On the debit side, the T-54A had mediocre fire controls by NATO standards. It was a good tank in close terrain where engagements would take place at ranges of less than 1,000m. At greater ranges, it was outclassed by NATO tanks which could take advantage of better fire controls and optics, better gunlaying and gun stabilization equipment. The Soviets had opted for a tank fire

30. A Polish T-54A, with the original skeleton wheels and the improved D-10TG gun with bore evacuator.

30▼

31. An East German T-54A, probably of Czechoslovak or Polish production. Both the Czechoslovak and Polish factories later added one or two external stowage bins to the left turret side and rear.
32. The T-54(M) is a T-54, re-manufactured with the Luna infra-red night vision equipment, like these vehicles here. They still have the original D-10T gun without muzzle counterweight or bore evacuator. (Sovfoto)
33. Inside a T-54, looking towards the left side of the turret. The commander station is under the hatch, and the gunner sits in front of him, on the right of the picture. The gun breech is at the far right. (S. Zaloga)

▲31

control system optimized for shorter range engagements. This was not simply a matter of cost. Soviet studies of Central European terrain as well as actual combat experience in 1944–45 had shown that much of the terrain was fine grained, and that long-range engagements were likely to be the exception, rather than the rule. For example, a later West German study of the inter-German border region found that only 6 per cent of the terrain offered sighting ranges over 2.5km; only 10 per cent over 2km; 17 per cent over 1.5km and 45 per cent over 0.5km. In fact, more than 55 per cent of the terrain surveyed had sighting ranges under 500m. For this reason, the Soviets favoured simpler stadia rangefinders instead of the coincidence rangefinders used on US tanks of the period. Although stadia rangefinders were less accurate at longer ranges, they offered comparable accuracy at 1,000m when used with APDS ammunition, compared to US tanks using coincidence rangefinders, but firing HEAT ammunition. At the time, the US Army and the German Bundeswehr preferred to use HEAT ammunition because of its very high armour penetration. However, while APDS rounds have a very flat ballistic arc at ranges of 1,000m, and are therefore not very dependent on accurate rangefinding, HEAT rounds have a pronounced ballistic arc which require good rangefinding for proper elevation correction. The Soviets did use HEAT ammunition, but favoured APDS for tank fighting even if its armour penetration characteristics were inferior to HEAT during this period.

In close-range tank mêlées, the T-54A suffered from a very cramped interior which meant less ammunition carried, poorer layout of ready ammunition, and slower and more difficult reloading. The T-54A was not as maintainable as NATO tanks. NATO tanks of the period were designed to facilitate even extensive repairs at as low a level as practicable.

The T-54 was in production in the Soviet Union from 1946 to 1958, during which time a total of about 35,000 tanks is believed to have been produced. In 1957–58, T-54 production was initiated at one plant in Czechoslovakia and one in Poland, and at two plants in China. Total Czech production is believed to have been about 2,500 tanks, and total Polish production about 3,000 tanks. The Chinese manufactured the T-54A as the Type 59, and modified it later as the Type 69. Production continues, and is believed to have reached 16,000 tanks by 1985.

In the late 1950s, Soviet tactical doctrine was in a state of flux, with growing emphasis being placed on the need to prepare for fighting on the

32▲ 33▼

▲34 ▼35

34. Although the T-55 closely resembled the T-54, it had been substantially re-manufactured. The most distinctive external identifying feature of the T-55 is the absence of the large mushroom turret vent dome in front of the loader's hatch. (Sovfoto)
35. Another clear view of a T-55, probably a T-55(M) with the loader's hatch fitted for a 12.7mm DShK anti-aircraft machine-gun (not fitted here).
36. From the left side of the tank, the T-55 is very difficult to distinguish from a T-54A(M) or T-54B.

nuclear battlefield. The first manifestation of this doctrinal evolution in tank design came with the new T-55 tank which was adopted in 1958. The T-55 closely resembled the T-54B externally. The only noticeable external changes were the deletion of the large vent dome cover in front of the loader's hatch on the turret, and the new, flush loader's hatch. Internally, many changes had been adopted including an improved engine and transmission, a partial turret basket floor, improved oil filtration, a new engine-starting system, an automatic fire extinguisher system, a bilge pump to support the OPVT deep wading system and greater ammunition stowage. A central element in the new design was a PAZ nuclear contamination detection and filtration system and an improved system to seal the tank from contaminated outside air.

The PAZ system was based around an RBZ/1M gamma ray detector system. This system, once triggered by a nuclear blast or nuclear contamination, turned off the engine to alert the crew and turned on an overpressure system to keep out airborne radioactive contaminants. The mild overpressure of 0.0015kp/cubic cm obviated the need for complicated sealing equipment. The PAZ system became a standard feature on all subsequent Soviet tanks, though the later systems were often more elaborate. The PAZ system included an explosive squib system to automatically close louvres and vent covers. Later PAZ systems also incorporated PBZ chemical protection features.

Further anti-nuclear improvements were added on the T-55A which appeared in about 1960. The T-55A finally dispensed with the fixed, hull-mounted machine-gun. One of the major internal additions was the use of plasticized lead sheeting for anti-radiation protection. External evidence of this were the driver's enlarged hatch, and enlarged combings over the commander's and loader's hatches. Originally, the T-55 and T-55A did not carry the 12.7mm DShK anti-aircraft machine-gun on the turret (which had been typical of the T-54), but later in the 1960s, the T-55 reverted to the use of a 12.7mm DShK machine-gun over the loader's hatch in response to the growing role of anti-tank helicopters in NATO doctrine. The US Army designates refitted vehicles as T-55(M) and T-55A(M), though some may have had the machine-gun added during production.

Besides the basic version of the T-55, a special command version, the T-55K, was also produced. The T-55K is fitted with two radios (an R-112 and R-113), an additional AB-1P/30 generator for the radios, and a special 10-metre aerial carried in a tube at the hull rear. To accommodate the added equipment, the T-55K had the hull SGMT machine-gun deleted, and six fewer rounds of ammunition are carried. This vehicle is used by battalion and other tank formation commanders. The Poles build their own version of the T-55 command vehicle, called the T-55AD. This differs from the Soviet type in that it is fitted with a slight rear turret

36▼

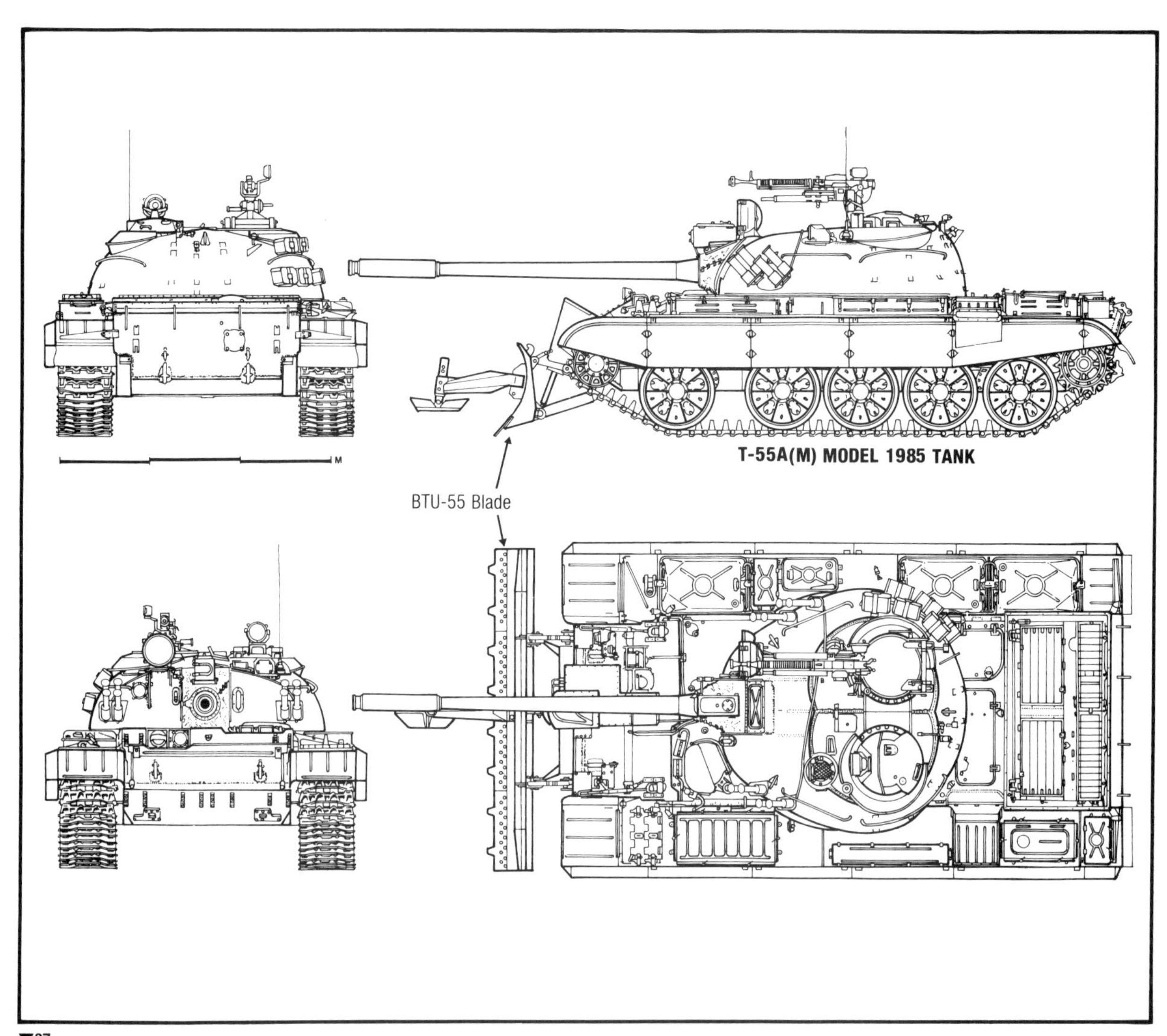

▼37

37. A pair of T-54A. In the background is an armoured recovery unit equipped with a BTS-2 and ISU-T recovery vehicles.
38. Inside a T-55, with the loader, in the right side of the turret, loading a round of 100mm ammunition.
39. Reloading the ammunition stowage racks of a T-55A. The very thick lead/plastic anti-radiation lining of the loader's hatch is very evident.

38▲ 39▼

40. The T-54A had anti-radiation linings added. Externally, it is distinguished by the loader's larger hatch, commander's hatch combing, and driver's hatch changes. These T-55A belong to the Romanian ASR.
41. This Polish-manufactured T-55A clearly shows the large combing added around the commander's hatch on the left side of the turret, as well as the driver's thickened hatch.
42. This T-55A was later rebuilt as a T-55A(M) with a 12.7mm DShK anti-aircraft machine-gun added. The size of the modified hatch arrangement is clearly apparent.

▲40

▲41 ▼42

bulge to accommodate the added communications equipment.

A combat engineer tank version of the T-55 was also developed, the TO-55. Externally the TO-55 is similar to the normal T-55 tank, but in place of the coaxial machine-gun, an ATO-200 flamethrower is fitted. This version can be distinguished by the large pig-snout mantlet over the ATO-200 barrel. The ATO-200 flamethrower uses a unique revolver system fitted with twelve charges to ignite the flammable liquid. A total of 460 litres of fuel is carried, with 35 litres used in each burst. The ATO-200 can fire at a rate of seven bursts a minute, and has a maximum range of 200 metres. The TO-55 is fitted with the same D-10 guns as a normal tank, but carries considerably fewer rounds of ammunition. The distribution of the TO-55 is not known, but it probably equips special combat engineer tank regiments, rather than being used in normal tank regiments.

Quite surprisingly, T-55 production continued up to 1979, though at a reduced rate from production levels of the 1960s as newer medium tanks entered production. This later production was undertaken almost entirely for export, and in the 1970s, a T-55 variant appeared which seems to be this export variant. This model has a 12.7mm DShK over the loader's hatch, externally stowed DShK machine-gune containers, an OPVT snorkel tube stowed on the right turret side, and no interior anti-radiation lining. It has been widely exported to the Middle East. Total Soviet production of the T-55 probably totalled about 27,500 tanks. Czechoslovak and Polish production is believed to have been about 10,000 tanks combined. This brought total T-54 and T-55 production to about 95,000 vehicles, making this series the most widely produced tank type ever. Besides the basic tank versions, the T-54 and T-55 formed the basis for air defence gun vehicles such as the ZSU-57-2, armoured recovery vehicles such as the BTS-1, BTS-2, BTS-3 and BTS-4, and assault guns such as the IT-122. These derivatives are covered in following chapters.

43. This rebuilt T-55 in Peru has many of the features of the final production batches, such as the high collar combing around the loader's hatch and the OPVT snorkel tube stowed on the right turret side. (US DoD)

43▼

▲44

▲45 ▼46

44. Some T-55A and other tanks of the series were later modernized by the addition of a laser rangefinder in an armoured box over the main gun tube. The tank shown here is a late production T-55A with the loader's simple hatch, external DShK ammunition stowage and turret OPVT stowage. (Sovfoto)
45. The TO-55 was a combat engineer tank, which substituted an ATO-200 flamethrower for the coaxial machine-gun normally mounted to the right of the main gun. The pig-snout mantlet of the flamethrower can be seen here, under the main searchlight. (Sovfoto)
46. In the 1960s the Polish Army experimented with this form of appliqué armour to counter the growing number of anti-tank rockets and missiles appearing on the battlefield. The screening around the turret is supposed to offer stand-off protection from shaped-charge warheads, as is the added armour on the tank's bow.

47▲ 48▼

47. In the late 1970s, the Romanian ASR began modernizing its T-55 as the M-77, seen here on parade with a new suspension, and reconfigured side armour over the roadwheels.
48. These Soviet T-55A(M) in Afghanistan have been fitted with added skirts and smoke mortar attachments. Some T-55 in Afghanistan have also been fitted with added turret armour, like the type shown here on the plan of the T-62E.

Heavy Tank Development

At the end of the war, Soviet heavy tank production and design was concentrated at the sprawling Tankograd plants in Chelyabinsk. The design bureau there, TsKB-2, was nominally headed by Zh.Ya.Kotin, but Kotin's responsibilities as Vice Deputy to Vyachislav A. Malyshev, head of the Commissariat for Tank Industry, reduced his role. As a result, his Chief Designer, Nikolai L. Dukhov, tended to play a more important role. By 1945, the IS-2 heavy tank, designed by a team led by Shashmurin and Sichev, was being supplanted on the production line by the IS-3, designed by another team headed by Dukhov and Balzhy. The IS-3 saw very limited service in the last weeks of the war, including a brief appearance during the battle for Berlin. Soviet Intelligence had learned of German attempts at 100-ton superheavy tanks like the E-100 and Maus, and so the TsKB-2 team had been assigned to develop two counterparts, codenamed *Shchuka* (pike) and *Zverboi* (animal hunter). The Shchuka was an enlarged IS-3 with heavier armour and the turret mounted to the rear. The Zverboi was a heavily redesigned ISU-152 heavy assault gun. Very little is known about these projects. References also exist to a superheavy tank designated the VL-1 (Vladimir Lenin-1). The VL-1 may have been the Shchuka or a competitive design. For counter-Intelligence purposes, the IS-3 was also called the Shchuka to divert attention away from the superheavy tank projects. Neither of these superheavies entered series production. At the same time, a team headed by Troyanov was assigned to develop a derivative of the IS-3 with a larger engine. This emerged in 1945 as the IS-4, but only about 250 were produced.

With the IS-3, and the slightly improved IS-3M in production, the TsKB-2 turned its attention to new heavy tank projects. The IS-5 was a paper study, never committed to prototype form. The IS-6 project, undertaken by a team headed by Dukhov and Shashmurin, was a continuation of the wartime IS-1E programme which investigated new suspension configurations for heavy tanks. The first radically new design was the IS-7, undertaken by Shashmurin in fulfillment of requirements for his engineering doctorate. The IS-7 incorporated several very radical innovations. The gun was fitted in a rigid mount, and for elevation the turret was mounted on internal trunnions. This oscillating turret preceded similar US and French attempts although their designs tended to employ external trunnions. The IS-7 was too radical, and was not accepted for production.

In about 1948, Dukhov's team began work on the IS-8 which was intended as an evolutionary development of the IS-3 and IS-4. An improved 122mm gun was added, developed by Petrov's GAKB in Perm, and a new, more powerful engine was fitted. The new engine configuration required lengthening the hull as had been done on the IS-4 design. The IS-8 entered production in 1950, probably in Chelyabinsk, and possibly in Osmk as well. In 1953, after the death of Stalin, it was felt prudent to rename the tank, and it became the T-10. In 1954, Dukhov was finally named General Designer of his own bureau. The first product of the bureau was the modified T-10M tank which incorporated an improved gun with a new muzzle brake, and fire control improvements. The T-10M remained in production until 1962. According to various US estimates, total post-war heavy tank production amounted to about 9,000 vehicles. About 1,000 of these were probably IS-3M and IS-4, the remainder being T-10 and T-10M.

In the post-war Soviet Army, heavy tanks were normally deployed in independent tank regiments (21 tanks) or independent heavy tank brigades (65 tanks). These units were placed under corps or army control and could be allotted to provide long-range fire support for tank divisions. During the 1947 reorganization, a special heavy armoured regiment was added to the tank and mechanized divisions, containing 44–46 heavy tanks and 21 of the related ISU-122 or ISU-152 assault guns. This extra formation reflected Soviet recognition of the fact that the standard Soviet tank regiments, still primarily equipped with the T-34-85, could not deal with the newer British or American tanks such as the M-26 Pershing or the Centurion. During the 1958–9 reorganization, this regiment in the tank divisions was replaced by a homogeneous heavy tank regiment equipped with 100 T-10 heavy tanks. Under this configuration, a tank division had two medium tank regiments and one heavy tank regiment. The Ground Forces also began to experiment with heavy tank divisions having two heavy tank regiments and one medium tank regiment. The 13th and 25th Heavy Tank Divisions served with the Group of Soviet Forces-Germany (GSFG) in the 1950s. This was the heyday of Soviet heavy tanks. In the late 1950s and early 1960s, heavy tanks represented about a fifth of total Soviet tank strength. In 1969, however, the heavy tank divisions had one of their heavy tank regiments replaced by a medium tank regiment, and in 1970, the process was begun to remove the heavy tank from the divisions. They were gradually shifted into independent heavy tank regiments for corps or

49. Artist's impression of the planned Shchuka super heavy tank which was under consideration during the period 1945–47.
50. After the war, many IS-2m were modernized as IS-2M like this vehicle in the Kiev Army Museum which shows the added hull stowage bins and other features of this version.
51. The wartime IS-3 continued to see service with the Soviet Ground Forces into the 1960s, when it was replaced by the T-10.

49▲

50▲ 51▼

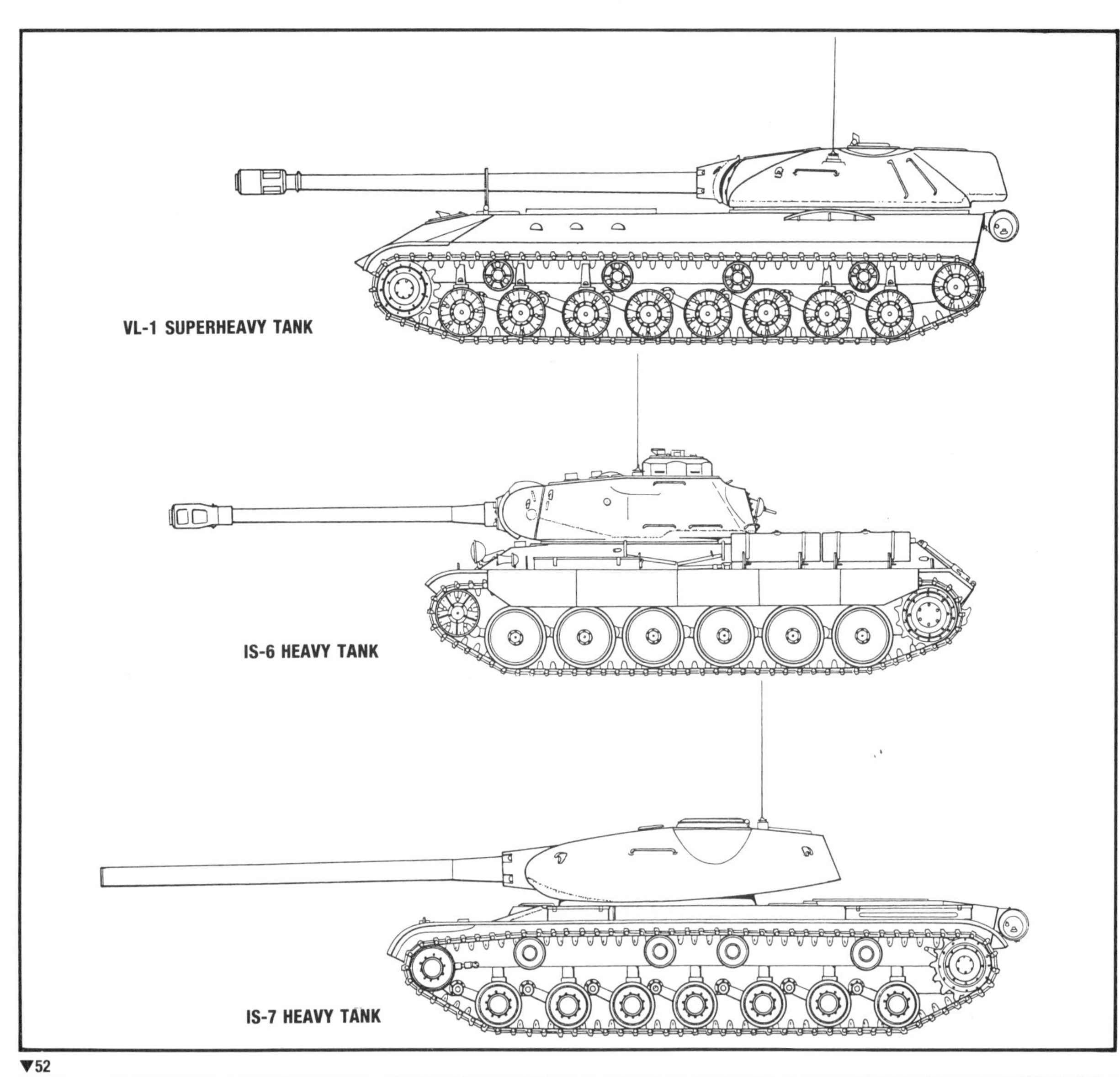

▼52

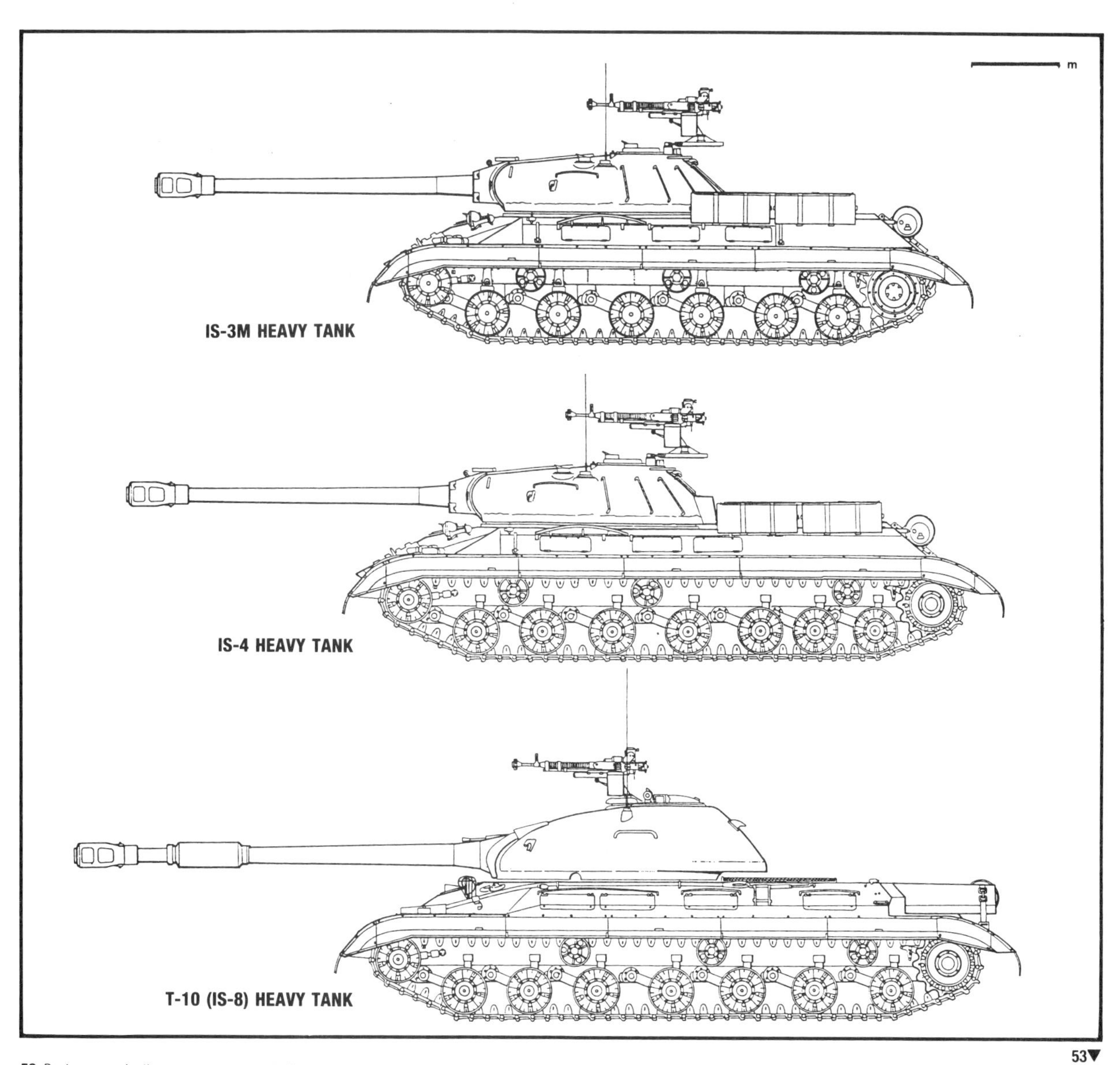

53▼

52. Post-war production improvements led to the IS-3M. This tank had originally been in Egyptian service and was captured by the Israeli Army in the 1967 war. (Israeli Government Press Agency)
53. Artist's impression of the IS-7 heavy tank, with its radical internal trunnion turret design.

▲54

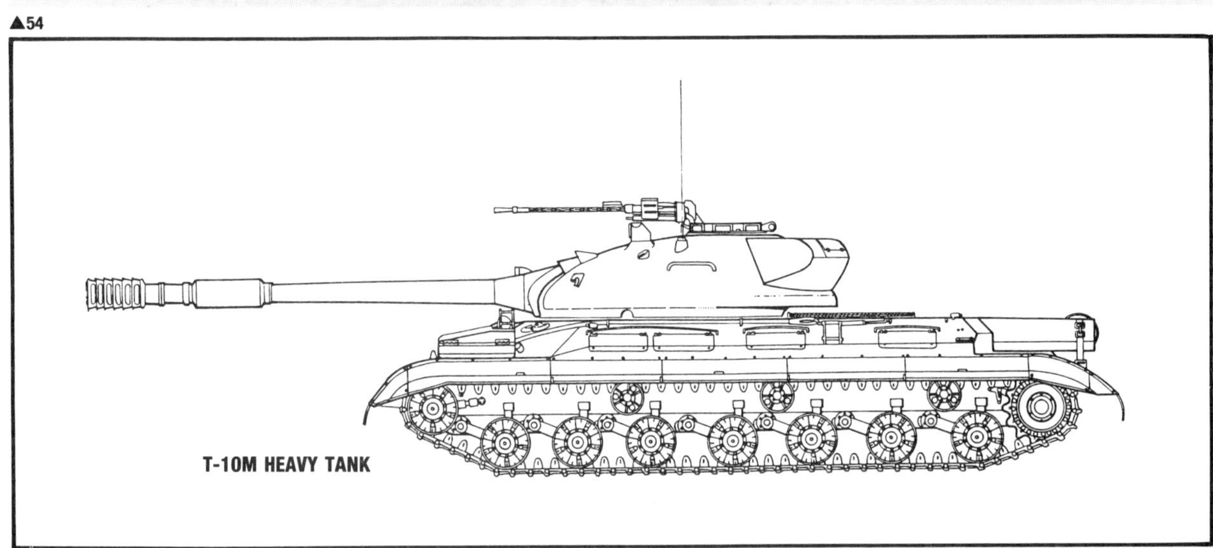

army support, and by the late 1970s were withdrawn into the reserves or emplaced as static pillboxes on the frontiers.

The demise of the heavy tank paralleled similar developments in the British and American armies where the Conqueror and M-103 heavy tanks were also disappearing. These two NATO tanks had been developed in response to the IS-3 and T-10. However, in the early 1960s, medium tank development simply outpaced heavy tank design. The Soviet U-5T 115mm gun had better anti-armour performance than the 122mm gun used on the T-10, and likewise, the British L7 105mm gun adopted for the Centurion and the US M60 series, was perfectly adequate to defeat any existing armour configuration. While heavy tanks could have been fitted with even larger guns, such as the 130mm and 152mm guns that the Soviets had been testing, adoption of such enormous weapons came at a stiff cost. Such a large gun inevitably meant a very large vehicle to absorb the considerable recoil, and the use of split ammunition which meant that reloading was slow and cumbersome. Heavy tanks like the T-10M carried very little ammunition (30 rounds), and it was unlikely that a new design could carry any more. The armour on the T-10M was not significantly better than that on the T-55, nor were the fire controls. It would seem that the Soviets were moving in another direction at this time: fielding a standard medium tank, the T-62, and developing a premium medium tank, the T-64.

New Guns, New Tanks

In the mid-1950s, Petrov's artillery design bureau (GAKB) in Perm began development of new smooth-bore guns for potential use as a tank gun, or in a towed role as an anti-tank field gun. The project was called *Rapira* (Rapier), and the initial design, the U-5 (2A20), was of 115mm

54. The T-10M was the standard heavy tank of Soviet Ground Forces during the 1950s and 1960s.

55. The initial production model of the T-62 tank had an engine deck very similar to that of the T-55, and a loader's flush hatch like that on the T-55.

calibre. The Rapira were the first Soviet tank guns to experiment with armour-piercing, fin-stabilized, discarding sabot (APFSDS) ammunition. This type of ammunition uses a sub-calibre 'arrow' projectile which gives exceptionally good armour penetration. The Soviets have preferred such kinetic energy rounds to the HEAT shaped charge ammunition favoured by NATO at the time, because this type of ammunition has a flatter ballistic arc that does not require as elaborate a fire control system as HEAT ammunition requires.

The new U-5T gun proved to have much better anti-tank characteristics than the D-10T gun used in the T-55. Although a HVAPDS round was developed for the D-10T, to get performance close to that offered by the U-5T's APFSDS round with its cheap steel penetrator, an expensive tungsten carbide penetrator was required. The Morozov bureau began design work to incorporate the U-5T into the T-55. The increased volume of the 115mm ammunition precluded use of the standard T-55 hull since it would have lowered the amount of ammunition the tank could carry below acceptable limits. Instead, a .43m (17in) section was added in the centre of the hull to accommodate a new, and larger, turret. This allowed 40 rounds of 115mm ammunition to be carried compared to 43 on the T-55. The initial prototypes of the *Obickt 162 Yubileyniy* (Jubilee) tank were completed in 1957–58, and it entered quantity production in 1960 as the T-62. In many respects the T-62 programme closely resembled the American M-60 programme, where an existing design (the US M-48 or Soviet T-55) had a new

55▼

▲56

▲57 ▼58

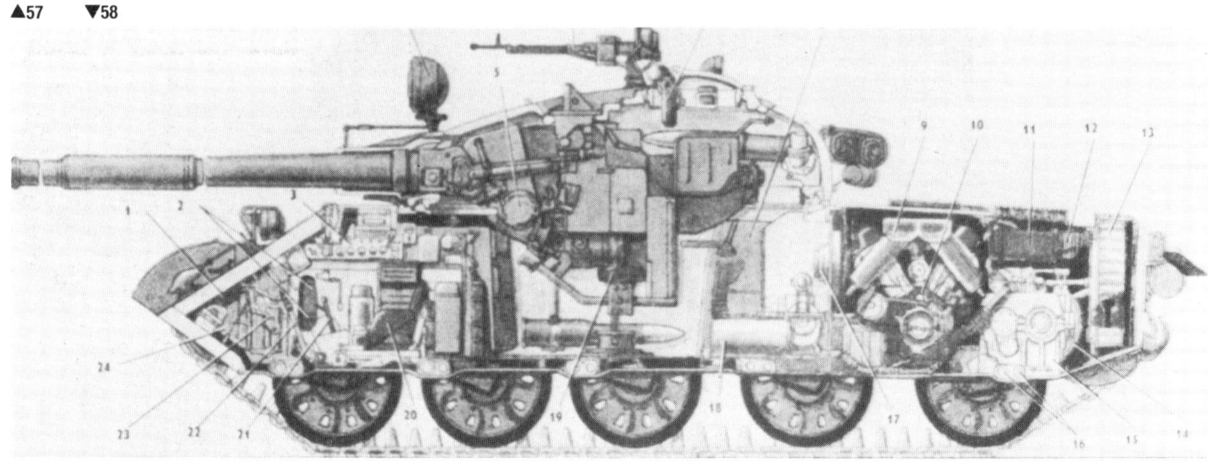

59▲ 60▼

56. This T-62 has the later style engine deck with the folding cover for deep wading operations. The hydraulic cylinders on the front of the tank are for the KMT-4 mineclearing rake.
57. A Soviet T-62M tank, fitted with the improved KMT-6 mineclearing blades.
58. Soviet drawing of the interior configuration of the T-62M.
59. The T-62M, often called the T-62A in NATO, had a loader's revised hatch on the right turret roof, configured for the 12.7mm DShK anti-aircraft machine-gun. The attachments below the hatch are for ammunition boxes, not carried on this Afghan tank.
60. View from the commander's seat in a T-62M tank, looking forward towards the gunner's seat and his fire controls. (Zaloga)

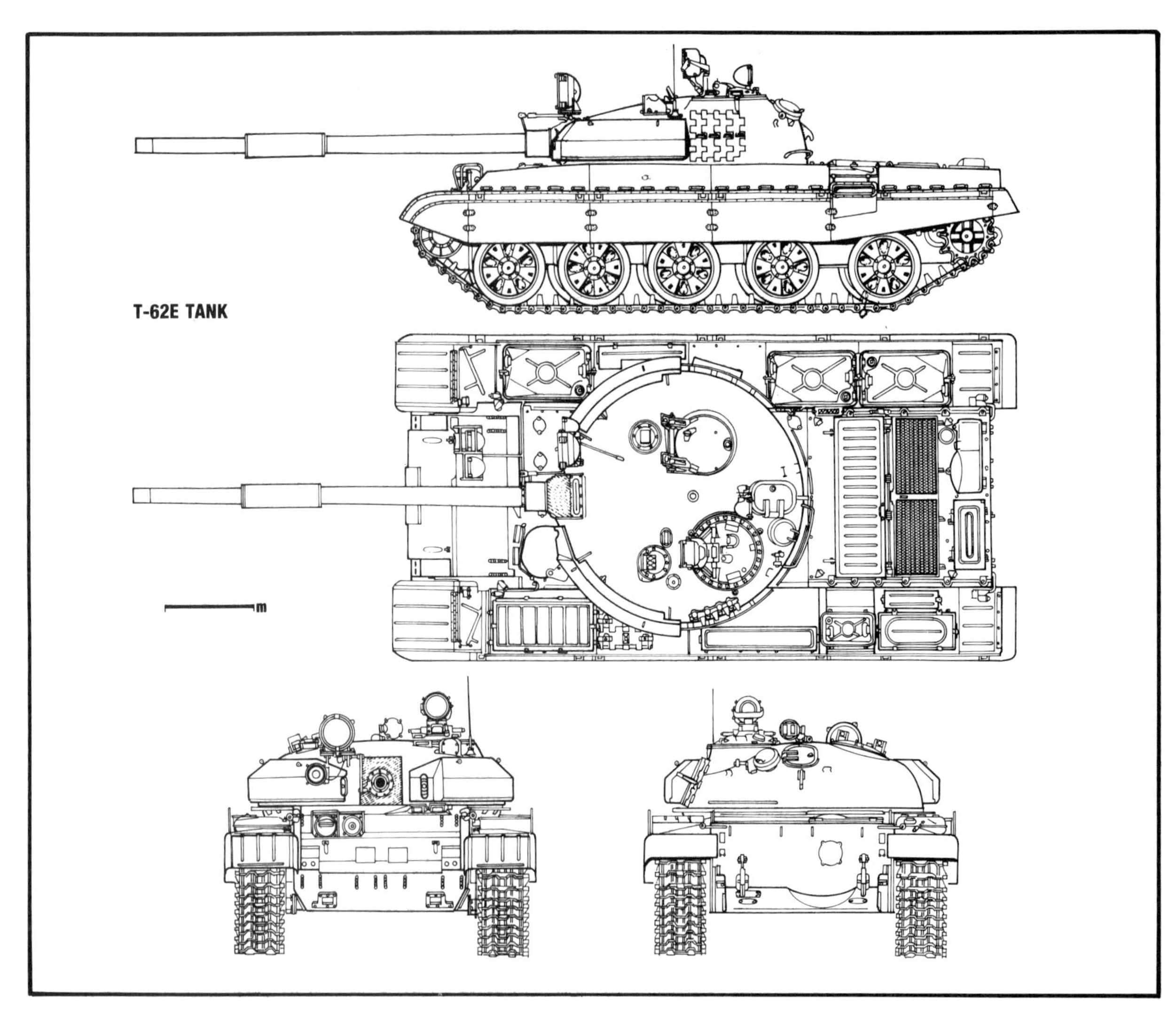

weapon system added while retaining many features of the preceding model.

The extremely cramped conditions of Soviet tank interiors led to some unique features in the T-62's design. The interior was too small to permit shell cases to be ejected inside, so a unique, automatic system was incorporated to eject the cases out of a hatch in the turret rear. This system slightly slows the firing cycle; after each firing the gun must be depressed, the case ejected, and the original elevation restored. There have also been some problems with the spent cases failing to clear the rear port, careening into the turret and injuring the crew. Nevertheless, this system highlights the Soviet predilection to keep overall tank size very compact.

In about 1965, a slightly improved version of the T-62 appeared which had a reconfigured engine deck. This permitted easier access to the transmission and facilitated the fitting of the engine seals for deep wading. In about 1968, the T-62M appeared (called T-62A by NATO). This version also carried the new engine deck, but had a modified turret with a ring for the 12.7mm DShK machine-gun over the loader's station in place of the earlier flush hatch. This corresponded with the move to re-equip the T-55 with additional anti-aircraft protection mentioned earlier. As with the T-55, a command version is also produced, the T-62K. This has the same features as the T-55K and also carries a TNA-3 land navigation device. In the late 1960s and early 1970s, the Ground Forces appear to have experimented operationally with the fitting of guided anti-tank missiles on the T-62 to supplement the main gun in long-range engagements. This system was normally fitted in a container on the rear of the turret roof. This may have been adopted for a secondary role of helicopter protection. A version of this system, but without the main gun, may have led to the enigmatic IT-1 tank destroyer, mentioned in the chapter on tank destroyers. The Ground Forces also appear to have fielded another version of the T-62 tank, known as the T-66. The vehicle appears to have been armed with a conventional gun tube, but this system may have been either the 125mm of the T-64A or a guided missile-launching system such as the AT-8 Kobra.

The T-62 remained in production from 1960 until about 1975 in the USSR and from 1973 until about 1978 in Czechoslovakia. Total production in the USSR was probably about 20,000 and in Czechoslovakia probably 1,500 tanks. One of the enigmas of the T-62 is that no significant numbers were deployed with Warsaw Pact forces outside the Soviet Union itself, even though Czechoslovakia eventually manufactured it. The main drawback was probably cost. The price of the T-62 was reportedly 250,000 roubles, which was about 50 per cent greater than the cost of the T-55 at the time. Having just retooled to produce the T-55 in 1960–64, Poland and Czechoslovakia probably were uninterested in another expensive reconversion, and additional licensing fees to the USSR. The only significant advantage offered by the T-62 was superior anti-armour penetration and this capability could be approached by using newer (albeit more expensive) ammunition such as the BR-6 HVAPDS round. Czechoslovakia's entire T-62 production run was exported to the USSR and to foreign clients in the Middle East.

The T-64 Tank

As production of the T-62 began, work was also under way on a radically new tank, which would eventually emerge as the T-64. The T-64 is probably the most controversial post-war Soviet tank design. Some of the controversy stems from the lack of details of its development or its development rationale. It is not known whether it was a product of the Morozov medium tank design bureau, or of Dukhov's heavy tank bureau. In many respects, the T-64 appears to be a follow-on to Soviet heavy tanks. Although not significantly heavier than the T-62, the T-64 is a much more expensive tank, incorporating a much improved gun and fire control system. Traditionally, heavy tanks have been used by the Soviets to provide long-range firepower, and to act as a counterweight to heavier or more capable NATO tanks. The advent of tanks such as the Chieftain and the M60A2 may have prompted the Ground Forces to issue a TTT for a new premium tank to deal with this threat.

The central element of the T-64 was the new fire control system. In contrast to earlier Soviet tanks, which used a stadiametric rangefinding system, the T-64 used a coincidence rangefinder. This offered improved accuracy at ranges above 1,000m. A typical Soviet stadiametric rangefinder of the period had a probability of a hit of about 33 per cent at 1,500m compared to about 50 per cent using a coincidence rangefinder and firing HEAT ammunition. Western Intelligence sources claim that the original version of the T-64 used the same 115mm U-5TS (2A20) gun as the T-62, though this is denied by Soviet expatriates such as Viktor Suvorov who insist that the initial production model was armed with a 125mm gun from the

61. The T-64A tank entered service in the late 1960s. This vehicle is fitted with the mounting for the KPVT anti-aircraft machine-gun, but the gun itself is not fitted in this view.

▲62

▲63 ▼64

62. Interesting overhead view of the T-64A. The turret is pointed rearward for travel, and the tube stowed on the turret roof is an OPVT deep wading snorkel. (US Army)
63. The T-64K command tank is not normally fitted with the KPVT AA machine-gun, and has a roof attachment for a special antenna to improve radio transmissions. (US Army)
64. In the mid 1970s, T-64As that went through periodic rebuilding had smoke mortars added to both sides of the turret front. (US DoD)
65. In the late 1970s, T-64A that underwent rebuilding had smoke mortars and fabric armour skirts added. (US DoD)

65▲

outset of production. The most significant of the other improvements in the T-64 design was the incorporation of an automatic loader.

There were many other novel features in the T-64 design. It was powered by a new 5-cylinder opposing piston design, possibly derived from the British Leyland Motors L60 used with the Chieftain tank. There is some confusion as to whether the T-64 is fitted with a torsion bar suspension system or a hybrid hydro-pneumatic system. The new suspension and powerplant were probably specified by the TTT since the T-64 was expected to be used with the new BMP infantry vehicle. The new BMP was considerably faster than the T-62, and the Ground Forces probably planned to develop the T-64 as a counterpart to the BMP in the tank divisions. The T-64 was also the first Soviet tank to incorporate laminate armour. The hull glacis plate incorporated a layer of ceramic armour beneath the initial layer of conventional steel armour, to offer better protection against the HEAT rounds that were so popular with NATO at the time. The T-64 also used a rather unique form of spring-loaded side armour panels which could be folded outwards like fish gills to offer a measure of stand-off protection from shaped charge rounds being fired towards the frontal quadrant of the tank from slightly off-centre.

The first T-64 prototypes were completed in 1961–62 (in the West they are sometimes mistakenly called T-67 or T-70 stemming from the original NATO temporary designations such as Model 1970 Tank). They do not appear to have been a major success. The engine was the source of considerable problems, as was the new suspension. A contributory factor in the delay in T-64 production was the development of the D-81T (2A46) 125mm gun. It is not clear if the T-64 was held-up pending completion of the development of the 125mm gun, or if the cost of the T-64 led the Main Armour Directorate to insist that the vehicle receive a larger gun than that used on the T-62, initiating the development of the 125mm gun. In either case, the improved T-64 with the 125mm gun, called T-64A by NATO, passed its state trials in about 1965, and entered initial series production. The T-64A was issued to the 100th Guards Tank Training Regiment in 1967 for operational trials, and began actively to equip the 41st Guards Tank Division shortly afterwards.

At the time, the Ground Forces were also receiving the T-62 tank. The decision to press ahead with two medium tank designs simultaneously is traceable to the high-low mix philosophy described earlier. The Ground Forces cannot afford to fill out all their divisions with the highest quality vehicles, and so are obliged to obtain both a standard vehicle and a premium vehicle to fulfill their needs.

The T-64A was not without its problems. Although the engine and suspension difficulties appear to have been solved, the new 125mm gun suffered from extreme dispersion problems, lowering its accuracy at long ranges. These problems were probably traceable to thermal distortion of the barrel, crosswind interference, and

66. The T-64B is designed to fire the laser-guided Kobra missile. This is a version of the T-64B, shown in May 1985 in Moscow, which does not have the normal T-64B command sight fitted under the KPVT machine-gun mount, but which has other features including the enhanced anti-radiation lining on the roof, and fabric armour skirts. (Sovfoto)

67. Although often misidentified as a T-64A, these tanks are in fact T-72 from the initial production batch. This version had the searchlight on the same side of the gun tube as the T-64, hence the common misidentification. However, the tracks and suspension details show it to be a T-72.

▲66 ▼67

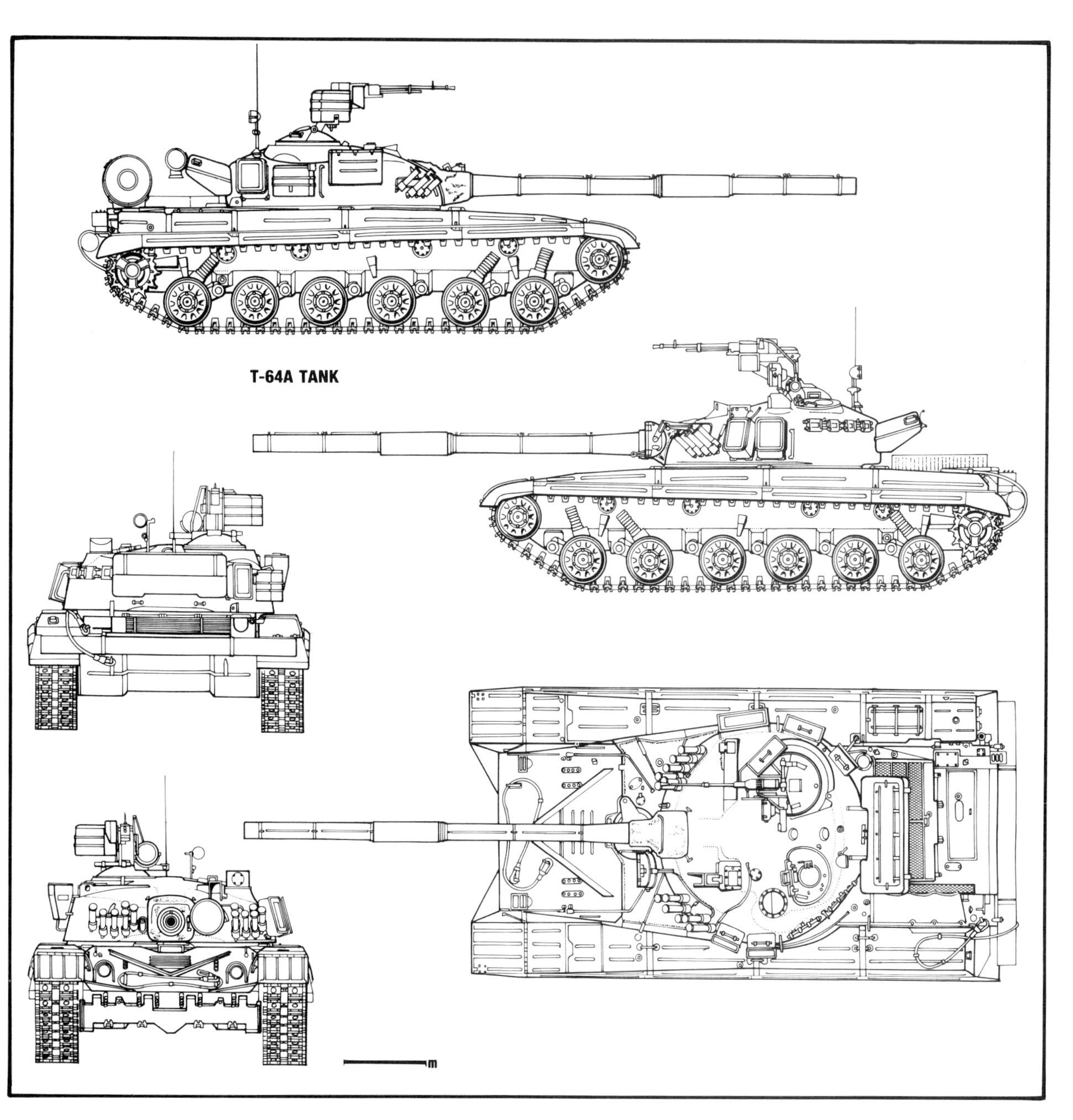

quality control problems with the new consumable case ammunition. These frustrations were not peculiar to Soviet tanks of the period. Despite fire control improvements, many NATO tanks of the period also lacked real accuracy in long-range engagements above 1,500m. Like the Americans and the French, the Soviets attempted to circumvent these problems through the use of guided anti-tank missiles.

The Soviets began development of tube-fired, anti-tank guided missiles using a laser-beam riding guidance system. The 125mm or 130mm version developed for the T-64 was codenamed *Kobra* (and is known by NATO as AT-8). The new version of the T-64 with this missile system is called T-64B by NATO. Externally, it closely resembles the normal T-64A, but has a large sight aperture in front of the commander's station which houses the laser designator. The Kobra gun can fire both the Kobra missile and conventional ammunition. This system is somewhat similar to the US Shillelagh which was used on the M551 light tank and the M60A2 main battle tank. It is not clear how the T-64B was initially deployed. In the early 1970s, General Potapov, later to head the Soviet Armoured Force, proposed an expanded tank battalion, from the normal 31 tanks to 35 tanks, of which four were to be the T-64B in a separate platoon to provide long-range fire support for the rest of

▲68 ▼69

68. The T-72 was the standard production model of the T-72 in the early 1970s. It has the searchlight moved to the right side of the gun tube. (US Army)
69. The T-72M had a number of improvements including the incorporation of a laser rangefinder. Externally this version is distinguishable from the T-72 by the absence of the optical rangefinder port on the right turret roof in front of the commander's hatch. These Polish-manufactured T-72M differ from the Soviet version in that they still use the old folding 'gill armour' in place of fabric armour skirts. The vehicle in the foreground is fitted with a KMT-6 mineclearing blade. (Eastfoto)

the battalion. Initially, the Potapov plan was rejected, but it may have come into effect in the late 1970s.

There was some further experimentation with the T-64 at this time. The T-67 is believed to have been a T-64 with a new armament system. The T-70 has been variously described as a new heavy tank design, or as another experimental variation of the T-64. The T-66 is believed to have been a variant of the T-62M, possibly with a new gun system such as the 125mm used on the T-64. Some T-64A were later refitted with smoke mortars, and some have also been refitted with fabric skirt armour in place of the older gill armour panels. According to US sources, the T-64A remained in production until 1981. An unclassified US DIA estimate placed T-64 strength in 1984 at 7,900 tanks.

In about 1966, work began on a further version of the T-64 in an endeavour to simplify the basic design and so lower its cost. The prototypes of this tank, the T-72, appeared in 1970, and production began in the USSR in 1971. The T-72 bears a striking resemblance to the T-64 as well it should. The modification to it were more regressive than evolutionary. The opposed piston engine was replaced by the cheaper V-46, a turbo-charged version of the V-2 diesel engine that has been powering Soviet medium tanks since 1938. In place of the complicated suspension of the T-64, with its resilient steel wheels and two-pin track, an ordinary torsion bar system was adopted along with a new live track originally conceived for retrofitting the T-55 and T-62 series. The rationale for the T-72 was probably one of cost. By 1970, the T-62 was growing obsolete compared to NATO tanks of the period such as the Chieftain, M60A1 and Leopard 2. While the T-64 could hold its own with these tanks, it was not available in large enough numbers due to its cost. A cheaper version could serve as the standard tank replacement for the T-55/T-62, and could be exported outside the USSR.

There were some differences between the pre-series T-72 and the standard production T-72. The production T-72 closely resembles the pre-series T-72, but the infra-red searchlight is fitted to the right of the main gun barrel on the T-72 and to the left (like the T-64) on the original T-72. T-72 production was also initiated in Poland and Czechoslovakia in 1978. In 1975, the Soviets began development of further improvements for the T-72M. These included the substitution of a laser rangefinder for the optical rangefinder, thickened frontal armour on the turret, and substitution of fabric armour skirts on the hull side in place of the older gill armour. The rationale for the fabric skirts is not entirely clear. They were probably added to boost overall side protection enough to prevent the side armour from being penetrated by newer automatic cannon such as the M242 Bushmaster used on the American M2 Bradley infantry fighting vehicle. They may have had a secondary role of reducing the conspicuous glint of moving track which makes tanks visible to certain types of air-based surveillance radars. These skirts are not always fitted to the tanks during peacetime training, as they get in the way of suspension maintenance. The most distinctive external feature of this model is the deletion of the rangefinder housing on the right forward roof of the turret. This version, designated T-72M1, probably entered production in about 1978, and was first publicly shown in 1980. It is also produced in Poland and Czechoslovakia. The Czechoslovaks and the Poles have both produced early versions of the T-72M lacking the fabric armour skirts. Production of the T-72M was also started in 1984 in Yugoslavia and in 1985 in India.

In1982, some Soviet T-72M began appearing with smoke mortars on the turret front. These created some controversy, because the US DoD initially identified these vehicles as the long-awaited new T-80 tank. Subsequently, this was retracted. This version is the T-72M1 and it has thicker hull frontal armour and significant internal improvements. In 1984, a further variation of the T-72M1 was displayed, but with additional anti-radiation lining on the roof of the tank. This version, probably designated T-74M, was developed in response to US and French work on enhanced radiation weapons (neutron bombs), designed to overcome the radiation protection offered by the earlier generation of Soviet PAZ equipment. The new top armour may also have some utility in defeating shaped-charge bomblets relying on stand-off probes, like the US Mk 20 Rockeye cluster bombs used so successfully by the Israelis against the Syrians in Lebanon in 1982. The lead/plastic sheeting is of a different density from the steel roof, which may shatter the probe before the warhead detonates. It is believed that a version of the T-72 exists armed with the same Kobra gun/missile system as the T-64B. US sources estimate that as of January 1984, the Soviet Ground Forces had 6,200 T-72 of various models. Production of T-72 and variants has averaged about 2,000 tanks annually in the USSR alone.

The T-72M does not compare particularly badly with the types of NATO tanks that entered service in the early 1970s. It has mobility on par with tanks such as the Leopard 1, and it is

▲70 ▼71

70. This frontal view of a Soviet T-72M1 clearly shows the absence of a rangefinding port on the right turret side, and also shows the peculiar ditching blade fitted under the bow to help tanks entrench themselves.
71. A Soviet T-72M1, showing the fabric armour skirts over the suspension. This fabric armour also extends upwards to protect the external fuel tanks and stowage bins from smallarms or machine-gun fire. (Sovfoto)

72. Later production batches of the T-72M1 have smoke mortars added to turret front. This type was originally misidentified as the T-80 by the US Army. (US DoD)

72▲

armoured to a level comparable to the US M60A3. If suffers from mediocre fire controls and other disadvantages. Although incorporating laminate armour in the bow, Israeli forces had no particular difficulty in knocking out T-72M of the Syrian Army in 1982 in the Bekaa valley using 105mm APFSDS tank gun ammunition or TOW anti-tank missiles. After the fighting Israeli tankers noted that the T-72 was prone to burn, probably due to presence of so much ammunition and fuel in close proximity in the hull. The 125mm gun is a very potent weapon, but seems to suffer serious dispersion problems at ranges above 1,000m. Details are not available on an unclassified basis, but there is reason to believe that the performance of the 125mm APFSDS round is not significantly better than that of later production US APFSDS ammunition for the 105mm gun, such as the M833 round. In any event, the Soviet 125mm gun and the NATO 105mm guns seem equally able to defeat the armour of one another's tanks from the mid-1970s period. The fire controls are comparable in many details to NATO laser rangefinder-based systems, but the quality of the laser rangefinder itself is suspect. The T-72M is most backward in night fighting equipment, using infra-red or passive image intensification sights instead of the more effective thermal imaging FLIR systems introduced on such US tanks as the M60A3. Soviet tanks are most equal to NATO tanks in close (under 1,000m) combat, and badly overmatched at longer range.

Nevertheless, the real issue in comparing NATO and Soviet tanks is their performance in the hands of their crews. A good tank, handled by a poor crew can be easily overcome by a decidedly inferior tank with a skilled crew. Soviet tank design philosophy does not foster crew training. Although the T-72 probably has better maintainability and durability than the T-55/T-62 generation, it is still inferior to NATO tanks. This inevitably means that Soviet tank crews receive fewer hours of training each year to prevent the tanks from wearing out prematurely. While the use of tank simulators can help crews keep their basic tank skills well honed, there is no substitute for actual tanks when training for target engagement skills, small and large unit tactics and crew interaction. The Soviets have consciously sacrificed crew quality in order to ensure low tank costs, low tank crew annual training costs, and the resultant ability of the Ground Forces to acquire and maintain a large tank force. Soviet military experiences have led to a decided preference for a large mediocre force rather than a smaller, more skilled force. NATO units believe that they can exact a dispro-

▲73

▲74 ▼75

portionate kill rate against Soviet tank formations. The Soviets believe that even though they may suffer high tank attrition, in the end, quantity has a special quality all its own. A phrase popular in the Soviet military is 'Numbers annihilate'.

The T-80 Tank

Development of an improved version of the T-64 tank began in the early 1970s as the T-80 tank. The T-80 incorporates many of the design improvements introduced into the later production batches of the T-64, including smoke mortars, and enhanced armour. The main change between the T-64 and T-80 is in the area of mobility. The T-80 is fitted with a 1,000hp turbine engine and a new suspension system. The T-80 uses the more conventional rubber-rimmed roadwheels in place of the unusual Tseits resilient steel wheels used on the T-64. The T-64 suspension caused difficulties with noise and vibration levels when moving at full speed. The turbine engine was added mainly to bring up the cross-country speed of the tank. Other T-80 improvements include a new laser rangefinder, and an anti-PGM electronic warfare system. According to US sources, the T-80 entered production in 1979 and by 1984, there were 1,400 in Ground Forces service.

At least two versions of the T-80 exist: one version with the normal 125mm 2A46 gun and another capable of firing the URS Kobra missile (like the T-64B). The version with the Kobra has two roles: long-range fire support, and a secondary role of anti-helicopter defence. The continued use of a guided missile-firing tank is partly due to the latter requirement, but is also attributable to lagging technology in the field of tank gun fire controls.

The only army to have adopted a tank-fired guided anti-tank missile was the US Army, with its ill-fated Shillelagh missile on the M60A2 and M551 tanks. This system was adopted since it provided higher long-range accuracy than gun systems of the early 1970s, but such a system is cumbersome and quite expensive. The missiles cost about fifteen times more than conventional tank ammunition. Tactically, they are a burden, since the tank must continue to track and guide the missile to target. At a range of 3km, the missile would take about seven seconds to reach the target, about double the time for a conventional tank round. The tank cannot fire during this launch-hit interlude, which reduces the rate of fire.

The US Army dropped the Shillelagh system in the late 1970s. By this time, there had been a

73. The T-72M1 is manufactured in Yugoslavia as the M-84. It has a number of changes, including a different laser rangefinder and modified fire control system.

74. In 1984, the Soviets first showed this improved version of the T-72M1, believed to be designated T-74M. It differs from the later production T-72M1 in being fitted with added anti-radiation sheeting on the roof. (Sovfoto)

75. The first photograph of the T-80, released in 1986, shows that the T-80 is a derivative of the T-64. This rear view clearly shows the new exhaust port for the turbine engines, as well as the new road-wheels. This one seems to be lacking the usual rear turret stowage bin. (DoD)

technological revolution in tank fire control which had invalidated the expensive and cumbersome guided-missile approach. A whole range of new technologies came to fruition in the late 1970s which had a synergistic effect on tank fire control accuracy. Laser rangefinders provided a higher degree of accuracy and were simpler to use than earlier optical rangefinders. Wind sensors, barrel thermal sleeves and barrel warp sensors, combined with new digital ballistic computers, could largely remove these sources of distortion in accuracy. By the late 1970s, the new generation of NATO tanks emerging from the factories, such as the M1 Abrams, Challenger and Leopard 2, were as accurate using conventional (and inexpensive) ammunition as expensive and complicated guided missiles, even at long ranges.

The other major tactical shortcoming of the guided missile systems was their reliance on shaped charge (HEAT) warheads due to the relatively slow speed of the missile. The speed of these types of missiles are too slow to permit the use of heavy-metal kinetic energy penetrators like those used on conventional tank guns. This was a particularly serious handicap with the advent of stratified Chobham armour. Chobham armour had been specifically configured to reduce greatly the effect of shaped charge warheads such as those used on man-portable anti-tank rockets (such as the Soviet RPG-7) on guided anti-tank missiles. The newer generation of NATO tanks which began to appear in the late 1970s such as the M1 Abrams, Leopard 2 and Challenger, were all fitted with this armour. These types of tanks are nearly impervious (in the frontal quadrant) to existing Soviet shaped charged warheads, as used on the URS Kobra fired by the T-80. Conventional tank guns offer more flexibility since they can fire both shaped charge (HEAT) and kinetic energy penetrator (APFSDS/dart) projectiles.

In this technological race, Soviet tanks fell behind. Their fire control systems are not as effective as those on the newer NATO tanks, forcing Soviet designers to accept the tactical and economic shortcomings of the Kobra system in order to provide Soviet tank formations with a modicum of long-range firepower accuracy. The discrepancy in Soviet tank fire control becomes much less important at short ranges where the relative accuracy of the Soviet and NATO systems are closer to equivalence. Nevertheless, Soviet tanks of the T-72 and T-80 generations still suffer from shortcomings even at this range.

The newer generation of NATO tanks incorporate two other important innovations: fire-on-the-move capability and thermal imaging sights. Another aspect of the fire control revolution of the late 1970s was the incorporation of full three-axis turret stabilization which permits a tank like the M1 Abrams to fire as accurately, while moving across country at 40mph, as an older tank from a stationary position. This is an important advantage in tank combat since a fast-moving target is more difficult to track and hit than a stationary one. Soviet tanks do have some fire-on-the-move capability, but not with the degree of accuracy offered by the M1 Abrams or Leopard 2. These new NATO tanks are also fitted with thermal imaging sights. Thermal imaging sights were developed originally to provide tank night vision. They were adopted in the mid-1970s to overcome problems with the earlier passive, image-intensification night sights which required ambient moonlight to operate, and which were ineffective on overcast nights. Thermal sights operate by detecting the slight differences in thermal emissions from man-made and natural objects. A thermal sight can easily distinguish a tank, even without its engine running, from the cooler natural background. An unanticipated advantage of these sights is their utility in daytime. In contemporary tank combat, targets are often obscured by smoke and dust. Thermal sights allow a tank to see through much of this atmospheric obscuration, and this permits novel tactics, such as screening friendly tanks with smoke. Since Soviet tanks of the T-72/T-80 generation are not believed to be fitted with thermal sights, the NATO tanks can engage them accurately, while Soviet tanks are unable to see their opponents.

The T-80 is an incremental improvement which failed to bridge the generational gap. It is most comparable to NATO tanks such as the US M60A3(TTS) or Leopard IA4 which are improved versions of 1960-era tanks with 1970s technology enhancements. The Soviets have already begun to retrofit the 1960-generation tanks and the T-80 with new incremental improvements in an effort to close the gap with the new NATO generation of M1 and Leopard 2. Among these improvements is the addition of reactive armour bricks to degrade infantry anti-tank rockets and missiles. This type of armour was pioneered by the Israelis and first used in combat in the 1982 Lebanon fighting. Small, independent panels of plastic explosives are attached over the conventional steel armour of the tank. These panels are largely impervious to small arms fire and shrapnel, but when struck by a shaped charge warhead, such as that used on anti-tank rockets and missiles, the panel explodes outwards. The explosion interrupts the proper formation of the high-pressure jet of the shaped charge warhead, thereby rendering it incapable of deeply penetrating the tank's conventional steel armour. This system is not as effective as Chobham armour in defeating shaped charge warheads, since it can probably be overcome by forcing a premature detonation. But until new warheads with this feature become available in the late 1980s, reactive armour arrays offer a cheap, quick counter to the proliferation of infantry anti-tank weapons.

The Soviets will probably attempt to circumvent shortcomings in fire control by gradually retrofitting thermal pointers, or perhaps even thermal imagers to their tanks. The main drawback to thermal imagers is their high cost, and the Soviets may be reluctant to retrofit them to older tanks.

The Soviet Ground Forces have rarely suffered so serious an imbalance in the quality of their tanks compared to newer NATO tanks as was the case in the early 1980s. Efforts to circumvent this imbalance probably began in the mid-1970s. A new Soviet tank, with stratified, Chobham-style armour, appeared with the Soviet Central Group of Forces in the spring of 1986, and probably entered service in the western military districts of the Soviet Union in about 1983. Nothing is known of this tank, not even its designation. It will probably supplant the T-64B and T-80 on the assembly lines in the next few years, with the T-72M1 continuing to fill out Soviet tank units and export requirements.

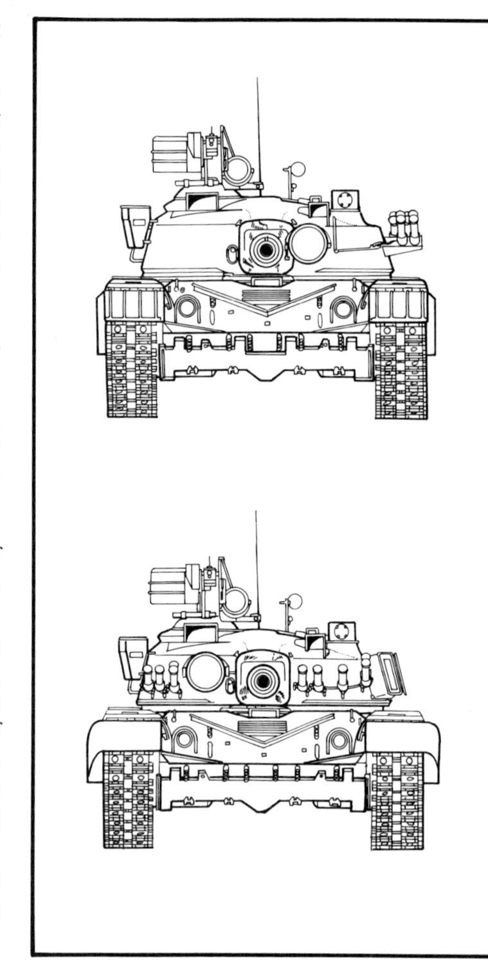

Improving the Breed

In view of the 10-year delay between the first appearance of a new Soviet tank and its issue to a significant proportion of the tank fleet, it is not surprising that existing tanks are frequently updated with new features. In the case of the T-54/55 family, tanks sent for periodic rebuilding often had newer features, such as active infra-red night fighting equipment, added. Other improvements have included a new live track, and the retrofit of laser rangefinders on some vehicles. Similar incremental improvements have been made to the T-62, including the same live track, and laser rangefinder additions.

During the past few years, work has also taken place to permit the incorporation of smoke-mortars and added armour. Initially the added armour was simply a large appliqué of thicker homogeneous steel, a number of plates being added to the glacis and two quarter-round slabs added to each side of the turret front. This package also included fabric armour skirts added over the suspension and side stowage containers, to give better protection against heavy machine-gun fire. The main aim of the package is to offer protection against the proliferating anti-tank rockets and missiles carried by modern infantry. These weapons rely on shaped charge (HEAT) warheads which can probably cut through even the added armour, but by the time their fiery tongues enter the crew compartment, the energy will have been largely dissipated. These added armour configurations also give additional protection against modern kinetic energy penetrators. The added armour is cheap to produce and its only disadvantage is that the additional 2 tons or so of weight further reduce the automotive performance of the tank and the durability of the powerplant components. This type of armour has been seen on Soviet T-54, T-55 and T-62 tanks in Afghanistan, and the drawing of the T-62 shows it configured with it. This version has been labelled T-62E, but its actual Soviet designation is not yet known. Soviet tanks in Europe are not ordinarily fitted with such armour in peacetime, but it would probably be added in time of war. The Poles have developed similar kits for the T-54 and T-55 tanks.

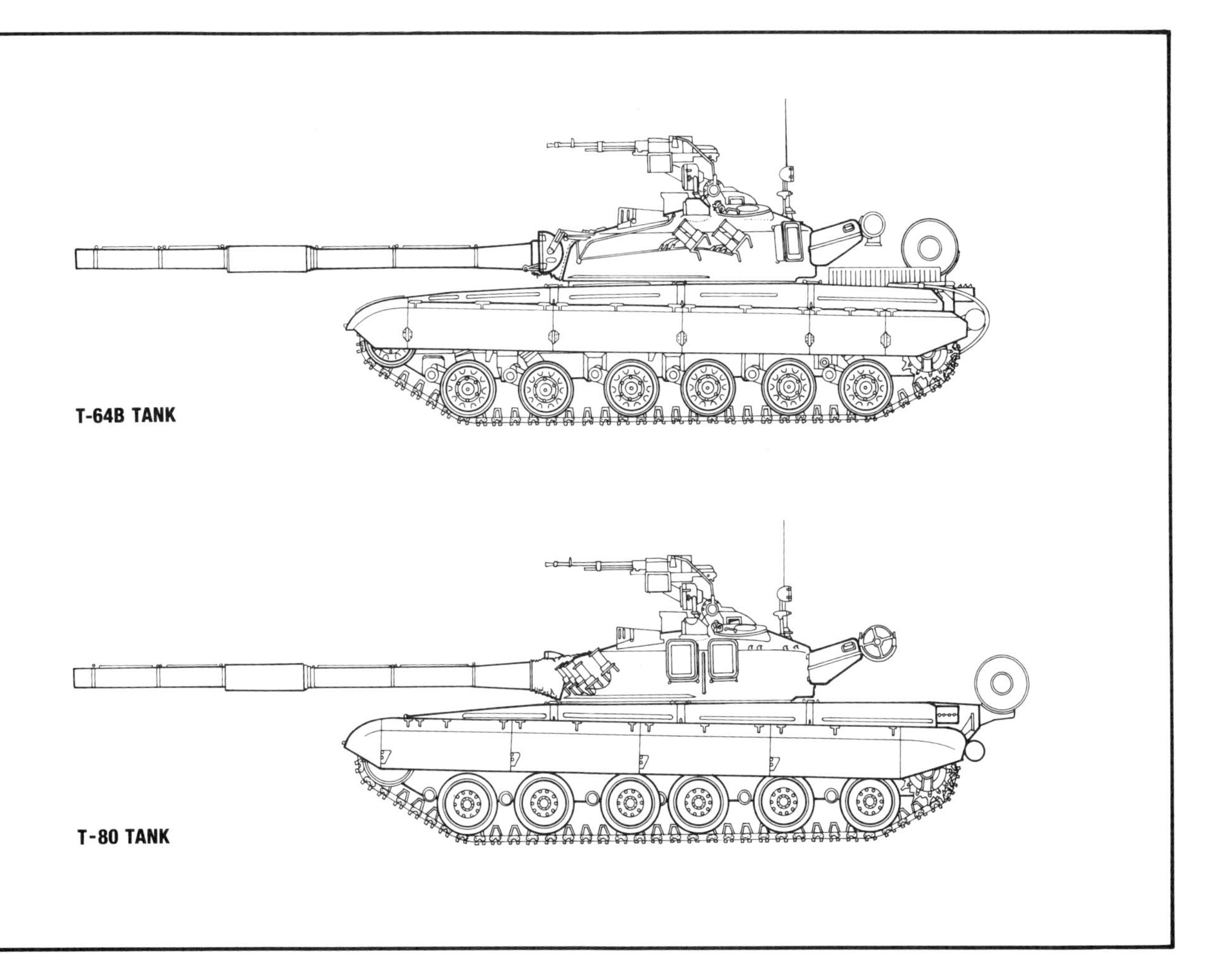

76. This view, released by the British Army in 1986, shows more clearly the new road-wheel pattern of the T-80.

The Soviets are also believed to be pursuing the deployment of active armour systems, similar to Israeli Blazer armour. The Syrians are known to have captured several Israeli tanks with this type of armour in 1982, and presumably the Soviets have had ample opportunity to examine them. The armour consists of small panels containing a sheet of plastic explosives which are fastened to the turret and hull. When the panel is struck by the blast of a shaped charge warhead, it detonates. The detonation interrupts the proper formation of the gas jet of the shaped charge, thereby considerably reducing its effective penetration. The attraction of this type of armour is that it weighs much less than homogeneous steel appliqué, and it may be more effective against shaped charges. The disadvantages are that proper detonation of the explosive panels is not assured, the system is more expensive than homogeneous steel, and can endanger nearby friendly infantry.

In the 1940s and early 1950s, Soviet tanks were fitted with the BDSh series of smoke-dispensing canisters on the hull rear which were intended to conceal daytime movement. In the early 1960s, the TDA system was developed which involved spraying small amounts of diesel fuel on to the engine manifold to generate a cloud of dense white smoke. This system was used on the T-55, T-62, T-64 and T-72 medium tanks as well as the PT-76B scout tank and other light armoured vehicles. The main drawback is that it really only obscures tanks behind the lead vehicles, since the cloud streams out from the rear engine exhaust area. In the 1970s, the Soviets began to imitate the NATO practise of fitting smoke-mortars to some of their tanks. They first appeared on production models of the T-72M1, but they have also been retro-fitted to the T-62, T-64 and earlier models of the T-72. It is likely that many Soviet armoured vehicles will eventually sprout these devices. Unlike the TDA system, smoke-mortars hurl a small smoke-grenade about 200 metres in front of the tank, effectively hiding it from hostile weapon sights. Although current types are not effective in obscuring FLIR thermal imaging sights, it is possible that future smoke-grenades will be capable of obscuring these sights as well.

SOVIET TANK CHARACTERISTICS

	T-10M	PT-76B	T-54A	T-55	T-62A	T-64A	T-72M1	T-80
Crew	4	3	4	4	4	3	3	3
Weight (combat loaded, tonnes)	50	14	36	36	37.5	38	41	42
Overall length (cm)	1067	762	900	900	933	910	953	920
Width (cm)	344	314	327	327	330	340	346	360
Height (cm)	235	219	275	240	240	230	239	230
Ground clearance (cm)	43	37	42.5	42.5	43	43	43	43
Ground pressure (kg/cubic cm)	0.71	0.50	0.80	0.81	0.75	0.77	0.83	0.85
Armour (Thickness in mm @ angle from vertical)								
Upper hull front	120 @60	11 @80	110 @60	100 @60	100 @60	200 @80	200 @80	250 @80
Lower bow plate	100 @55	14 @45	100 @55	100 @55	100 @55	100 @60	100 @55	100 @55
Hull side	90 @60	14 @0	80 @0	80 @0	80 @0	80 @0	80 @0	80 @0
Rear upper plate	60 @30	7 @0	60 @17	50 @17	45 @0	45 @0	45 @50	45 @50
Rear lower plate	30 @50	7 @45	30 @70	20 @70	20 @70	20 @70	20 @55	20 @55
Hull top	35 @90	7 @90	20-30 @90	16-33 @90	16-30 @90	15-30 @90	15-30 @90	15-30 @90
Hull belly	20 @90	20 @90	20 @90	20 @90	20 @90	20 @90	20 @90	20 @90
Turret front	250*	16 @33	210*	205*	230*	250*	350*	450*
Turret sides	75-115*	11-16 @33	95-110*	120-130*	120*	120-200*	120-300*	120-400*
Turret rear	60*	11 @33	60*	60*	60*	60*	60*	60*
Turret roof	30*	8 @90	30*	30*	30*	30*	45*	60*
Gun mantlet	250*	11 @33	210*	205*	230*	250*	250*	250*
Gun designation	D-49T	D-56TS	D-10TG	D-10T2S	U-5TS	D-81T	D-81TM	D-81TM
Gun industrial designation					2A20	2A46	2A46	2A46
Gun type	rifled	rifled	rifled	rifled	smooth	smooth	smooth	smooth
Gun calibre (mm)	122	76	100	100	115	125	125	125
Depression/elevation (degrees)	3/17	4/30	4/17	5/18	5/18	5/18	5/18	5/18
Maximum rate of fire (rounds/min)	2-3	10-12	5-7	5-7	3-5	6-8	6-8	6-8
Ammunition stowed (total)	30	40	34	43	40	40	39	40
HE rounds stowed (avg)	20	14	17	21	14	22	22	22
HEAT rounds stowed (avg)		6	6	7	6	12	11	12
APHE/HVAPDS/ APFSDS stowed (avg)	10	20	11	15	20	6	6	6
Gunner's telescopic sight	TSh-17	TShK-66	TSh2-22	TSh2B-22P	TSh2B-41U	TShS-49	TShS-49	
Gunner's periscopic day/night sight	TPN-1-17	TPN-1-66	TP-1-22	TPN-1-22-11	TPN-1-41	TPN-1-49	TPN-1-49	
Stabilization (planes)	2	2	na	2	2	2	2	2
Commander's range-finding sight	TPK-1	TPKU-2	TPK-1	TPKU-2B	TKN-3	TPD-2		

SOVIET TANK CHARACTERISTICS

	T-10M	PT-76B	T-54A	T-55	T-62A	T-64A	T-72MI	T-80
Rangefinder type	stadia	stadia	stadia	stadia	stadia	coin.	laser	laser
Coaxial machine-gun	KPVT	SGMT	SGMT	SGMT	PKT	PKT	PKT	PKT
Coaxial MG calibre (mm)	14.5	7.62	7.62	7.62	7.62	7.62	7.62	7.62
Machine-gun ammunition stowed	250	1000	1750	3500	1500	2000	2000	2000
Anti-aircraft machine-gun	KPVT	na	DShK	na	DShK	NSVT	NSVT	NSVT
Anti-aircraft MG ammunition stowed	250	na	200	na	250	200	200	200
Engine Designation	V-2-T	V-6	V-54	V-55	V-55V		V-46	
Horsepower	700	240	520	580	580	750	780	900
Integral fuel (internal+ external) (L)	910	380	817	965	960	1000	1190	1000
Supplemental external fuel (litres)	na	190	na	400	400	400	400	400
Transmission	mech. constant mesh	mech. constant mesh	synchro. constant mesh	synchro. constant mesh	synchro. constant mesh		synchro. constant mesh	
Final drive	spur gear	spur gear	single reduction	planetary	planetary		planetary	
Max. range, integral fuel (km)	250	400	440	500	450	450	450	450
Max. range, added fuel (km)	na	600	na	715	650	600	600	600
Max. speed (km/h)	48	44	50	50	50	60	60	70
Unprepared fording depth (cm)	120	amphib.	140	140	140	140	140	140
Trench crossing (cm)	300	280	270	270	285	270	280	270
Vertical obstacle (cm)	90	110	80	80	80	80	120	80
Max. gradient (degrees)	32	38	30	32	30	30	30	30
Turning radius (m)		4.7	2.6	2.6	2.6			
CBR protection	limited	PAZ	na	PAZ	PAZ	PAZ+PBZ	PAZ+PBZ	PAZ+PBZ
Fording	unknown	amphib.	OPVT	OPVT	OPVT	OPVT	OPVT	OPVT
Smoke	BDSh-5	TDA	BDSh-5	TDA	TDA	TDA	TDA/ mortar	TDA/ mortar
Night vision	active IR	active IR	driver IR	active IR	active IR/ passive II	active IR/ passive II	active IR/ passive II	
Radio	10-RT	R-113	R-112	R-113	R-123	R-123M	R-123M	

*Angle varies due to curved surface

SOVIET TANK AND ARMOURED VEHICLE GUN PERFORMANCE

Gun calibre (mm)	73	76	85	100	115	122	125
Gun designation		D-56T***	D-70S	D-10T	U-5T	D-25T	D-81TM
Industrial designation	2A28				2A20		2A46
Barrel length (calibres)	L/32	L/42	L/55	L/58	L/55	L/47	L/48
Rate of fire (rds/min)	8-10	6-8	7-8		3-5	2-3	6-8
Armour-piercing projectile (APT or APCT)							
Projectile designation	none	BR-350B	BR-365K	BR-412B	none	BR-471B	none
Projectile weight (kg)		6.5	9.4	15.8		25.0	
Initial muzzle vel. (m/sec)		655	800	900		885	
Armour penetration* (mm)		60	125	180		185	
High-velocity, armour-piercing, discarding sabot projectile (HVAPDS-T)							
Projectile designation	none	BR-354P	BR-365PK	BM-8	none	?	none
Projectile weight (kg)		3.0	5.1	5.7			
Initial muzzle vel. (m/sec)		965	1030	1100			
Armour penetration* (mm)		50	180	200			
Armour-piercing, fin-stabilized, discarding sabot projectile (APFSDS)							
Projectile designation	none	?	?	?	BM-6	?	BR-11
Projectile weight (kg)					5.4		6.5
Initial muzzle vel. (m/sec)					1615		1615
Armour penetration* (mm)					230		300+
High-explosive, anti-tank projectile (HEAT)							
Projectile designation	PG-9	BP-350M	BK-2	ZBK-5M	BK-4M	BK-6M	BK-11?
Projectile weight (kg)	2.6	3.9	7.3	12.4	11.8	21.6	23.0
Initial muzzle vel. (m/sec)	294**	325	800	900	1000	900	1000
Armour penetration* (mm)	400	120	400	390	450	460	475+

*Armour penetration against vertical steel armour at 1000m **Velocity with rocket ignited ***Designations also printed as D56-T, D70-S, etc.

▲77

▲78 ▼79

77. The BTR-152 was simply a ZiS-151 truck with an armoured body added. This BTR-152 of the Polish LWP shows the simple bench seating arrangement.
78. An Egyptian Army BTR-152V abandoned during the 1967 Sinai campaign with Israel. (Israeli Government Press Agency)
79. The BTR-152V used a tyre pressure regulation system to reduce ground pressure, and improve vehicle traction as on this Afghan Army vehicle.

Armoured Infantry Vehicles

The Red Army was very slow to grasp the need for armoured infantry vehicles to support tanks. In the 1930s experiments had been conducted with armoured infantry vehicles, but none was ever accepted for quantity production. The problem became extremely evident in the 1940 war with Finland, and led to the adoption of improvised armoured sledges towed behind attacking tanks, carrying prone infantrymen. Beyond a few more experimental infantry vehicles, no further attempts were made to begin mechanization of the infantry as was occurring in France, Britain, Germany and the USA. During the Second World War, the need for armoured infantry vehicles became even more manifest. Tanks, unaccompanied by infantry, were very vulnerable to close-in attack by enemy infantry. Tanks were also fairly blind, and often unable to identify and suppress anti-tank gun positions. Foot infantry could not keep up with tanks, and infantry mounted in trucks were unable to follow tanks in rough terrain and in snow. Although the Soviets had witnessed the considerable success of German *panzergrenadier* tactics using armoured infantry halftracks, they were unable to emulate these tactics because of industrial constraints. The Soviet automotive industry was hard pressed to provide sufficient vehicles and light tanks, and could not afford the diversion of resources to armoured infantry vehicles. As a result, during the war, the Soviets produced no armoured infantry vehicles apart from a few experimental models, while nearly a third of German, American and British armoured vehicle production consisted of armoured infantry vehicles. The Red Army did receive British and American armoured infantry vehicles through Lend-Lease, such as the Universal carrier, US armoured halftracks and M3A1 scout cars. However, these were never available in large enough numbers to develop motor rifle regiments, and so they were used as scout vehicles or as armoured transporters for unit commanders.

Soviet limitations in this field led to the development of improvised tank-infantry tactics, notably that of 'tank desant'. Tank desant troops were trained to ride tanks into combat, using hand-holds on the turret and hull sides. The idea was often successful, but was extremely costly because the soldiers were completely unprotected. Shortcomings in infantry mechanization was one of the singular failures in Soviet operational doctrine during the war, and many German officers felt that it was a major contributory factor to German defensive successes against Soviet mechanized offensives during the 1943–45 period.

After the war, attention began to be paid to the requirement for infantry vehicles. In May 1946, the ZiS automotive plant completed the first prototype of its new 2.5ton army truck design, the ZiS-151 which was copied from Lend-Lease American International Harvester K designs. A new design bureau, headed by B. M. Fitterman, was assigned the task of developing an armoured infantry transporter (*bronetransporter* or BTR) called *zavodskoe izdeliye 140*, or Project 140. It was to use a modified version of the ZiS-151 chassis, the ZiS-123, and carry an infantry squad of 17 men (plus two crew). Concurrently with Project 140, an infantry support vehicle was also developed. This was equipped with a new twin heavy machine-gun mount; the new Vladimirov KPV 14.5mm machine-gun on a ZPU-2 mounting. The vehicle was intended to provide fire support for mechanized infantry both against low-flying aircraft and ground targets. In May 1947, the first two prototypes of Project 140 were completed and were sent to state trials, authorized as the BTR-152 (transporter) and BTR-152A (fire support vehicle). Initial series production was initiated and in 1949, the Army operational trials were conducted by N. E. Kaledin's laboratory. The BTR-152 was officially accepted for Soviet Army service on 24 March 1950 and entered service later in that year. The BTR-152A was not accepted until 1952.

In comparison with armoured infantry transporters in service elsewhere at the time, the BTR-152 was a regressive design. It was open-topped, exposing its squad to overhead artillery airbursts, grenades and smallarms fire. The chassis was not significantly different from the normal truck chassis, except that it was encumbered with five tons of armour. As a result, it was a very sluggish vehicle with no real cross-country ability. In contrast, the US Army of the time was adopting the M75 armoured infantry transporter which was tracked and fully armoured. The BTR-152 was probably selected by the Soviet Army for its low cost. It was an easy vehicle for the ZiS Automotive Plant to manufacture, and it served as a worthwhile first generation infantry vehicle with which the Soviet Army could experiment with motorized infantry tactics.

In 1951, design work on the BTR-152 series was transferred to two of Fitterman's subordinates in the ZiS design bureau, V. F. Rodionov and N. I. Orlov. Work was begun on a PUA (*punkt upravleniya artilleriyei*-artillery command post) version. This was completely armoured, and had raised sides to permit artillery command officers to stand within the rear hull and read maps. It was accepted by the Soviet Army in 1952 as the BTR-152B. At the time, the ZiS Automotive Plant in Moscow (renamed ZiL in 1953) was developing a tyre-pressure regulation system on the basis of American systems received in the Lend-Lease programme. These systems could lower tyre pressure from the driver's station, thereby increasing vehicle traction in poor terrain or snow. Wheeled vehicles like the BTR-152 had ground pressures at least five times higher than comparable tracked vehicles. Theoretically, the tyre-regulation system could reduce this ground pressure to levels similar to tracked vehicles, but the vehicle could not be used at high speeds in this mode for fear of damaging the tyres. The system was first used on the ZiL-157 truck, and was adapted to the BTR-152 in 1954 as the BTR-152V. The first twenty pre-series BTR-152V were used during the 1954 Belorussian army manoeuvres, where they won the personal endorsement of Marshal G. Zhukov who was impressed by the cross-country performance improvements and who pushed to adapt this system for all infantry transporters. The BTR-152V had very noticeable external air lines running from the hull to the wheel hubs, and had a winch added to the front bumper; it was accepted for Army use in October 1955 and entered quantity production at the end of 1955. In 1959, the system was improved using internal air lines, and together with infra-red driving lights, resulted in the BTR-152V1. Earlier versions of the BTR-152 were rebuilt with the new tyre-regulation system, rebuilt BTR-152 becoming the BTR-152V2 and rebuilt BTR-152V becoming the BTR-152V3.

Development also proceeded on further support and command vehicles. An improved version of the BTR-152A fire support vehicle, based on the BTR-152V chassis, was accepted for production as the BTR-152D. Another version based on the BTR-152V, using a quad KPV 14.5mm heavy machine-gun system was also produced in small numbers as the BTR-152E. Two further command versions of the BTR-152V were developed: the BTR-152I being a counterpart to the earlier BTR-152B artillery command post, and the BTR-152S being a new command post vehicle, designed for motor rifle commanders. In 1963, after production had ceased, some BTR-152 were rebuilt as fully armoured infantry vehicles. These were designated BTR-152K. Production of the BTR-152 ceased in about 1959–60 in favour of the newer BTR-60. Total production was about 15,000 vehicles of all types. The BTR-152 disappeared as a troop transporter in the late 1960s and early 1970s when the BTR-60 became available, but many were retained and rebuilt as armoured ambulances, command vehicles,

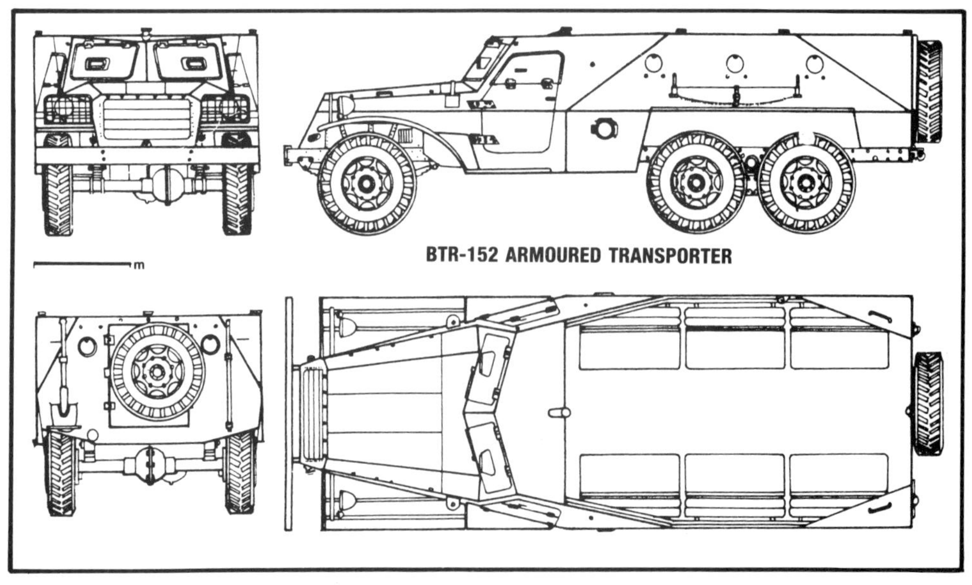

BTR-152 ARMOURED TRANSPORTER

80. The fire support version of the BTR-152 was the BTR-152A. It was fitted with twin KPV 14.5mm heavy machine-guns in a ZPU-2 mount. (Chris Foss)
81. The fire support version of the BTR-152V was the BTR-152D which carried the same armament as the BTR-152A. This one served with the German NVA in the 1950s.
82. Many BTR-152V were later rebuilt as fully armoured command vehicles, like this Polish example.

80▲

81▲ 82▼

▲83

▲84 ▼85

86▲

83. The BTR-152V1 introduced a new central tyre pressure regulation system which did away with the fragile external air pressure lines.
84. The BTR-152K was originally intended as a fully armoured infantry transporter. In later years, after it was retired from motor rifle units, it was often used as an armoured field ambulance, like this vehicle of the German NVA.
85. Two command versions of the BTR-152V1 were built: the BTR-152I for artillery officers, and the BTR-152S for motor rifle units. It is not clear if these vehicles had any external differences.
86. Some exported BTR-152V1 were refitted as improvised fire support vehicles like this PLO vehicle which has had a ZU-23 welded into the rear compartment. This vehicle took part in the 1982 fighting in Lebanon, where it was knocked out by Israeli forces. (Chris Foss)
87. The initial version of the BTR-50P was open-topped. Two versions were built: the basic BTR-50P with two 7.62mm machine guns, and the BTR-50PA with a 14.5mm KPVT heavy machine-gun. (US Army)

mobile radio stations and engineer mining vehicles, thereby serving well into the 1970s.

The BTR-50 Tracked Infantry Vehicle

Experience with the BTR-152 had made it clear that simple armoured trucks had serious shortcomings as infantry transporters. This was especially evident in the tank divisions, where the infantry vehicles were expected to keep up with the tanks. In 1951, work began on a tracked infantry transporter for the motor rifle regiments of the tank divisions, using the new PT-76 scout tank chassis. This vehicle, the BTR-50P, was a straightforward adaptation of the PT-76; in place of the turret, a simple, open box superstructure was added on the hull front. The BTR-50P was accepted by the Soviet Army in 1954 and entered production that year. The basic BTR-50P was designed to carry either troops or equipment. When used in the troop-carrying role, it could carry twenty men on four benches. As an equipment transporter, it could carry a ZiS-2 57mm anti-tank gun or ZiS-3 76mm divisional gun, 5 men and 25 rounds of ammunition. In this role, the gun was loaded up on the rear engine deck using two integral folded ramps. Other possible loads included the D-44 85mm anti-tank gun and two men, a GAZ-69 jeep and 7 men, or a 120mm mortar and its crew. The BTR-50PA was similar, but in lieu of the two mountings for 7.62mm machine-guns on the BTR-50P, the BTR-50PA was fitted with a 14.5mm KPVT heavy machine-gun and stowage racks for 800 rounds of ammunition. Due to doctrinal debate over tactical use of nuclear weapons, it was felt prudent to incorporate an armoured roof into the BTR-50P; this appeared in about 1959 as the BTR-50PK. The BTR-50PK became the standard production model of the family. The BTR-50PK was fitted with the PAZ filtration system. The final production batches of the BTR-50PK had a GPK-59 gyrocompass in place of the earlier GPK-48, a new fire extinguisher system, the improved V-6V engine, new headlights, the SGMB machine-gun and a new mounting system in place of the SGMT, and modified firing ports.

During the development of the BTR-50PK, it was decided to develop a corresponding command vehicle, akin to the BTR-152B/I or BTR-152S, designated the BTR-50PU. This command version resembled the BTR-50PK, but had a modified armoured roof with oval doors and additional vents to dissipate the heat from added electronics. The original version had a single bay on the left side of the hull glacis for the driver, but the subsequent, and more common, production model of the BTR-50PU had two bays.

87▼

▲88

▲89 ▼90

88. The BTR-50P was quickly superseded by the BTR-50PK which had an armoured roof. This one is being used by a heavy weapons team armed with two B-10 82mm recoilless rifles.
89. BTR-50PK of the Central Group of Soviet Forces on parade in Czechoslovakia in the 1970s. The BTR-50PK was never available in sufficient numbers significantly to affect Ground Forces mechanization.
90. Although the BTR-50PK faded from use, the command version, the BTR-50PU, remained in production into the 1970s. It can be distinguished from the BTR-50PK by the oval roof hatches and the additional generator equipment on the rear deck. This Romanian ASR BTR-50PU is of the later type with twin bays on the hull front.

91. A German NVA BTR-50PU showing the many whip antennas on the command vehicle. These are used in motor rifle and tank units.
92. The GT-T amphibious tractor was used in some Soviet Arctic motor rifle units instead of the BTR-152 or BTR-50 because of better performance in snow, or in the boggy marshlands of northern Russia.
93. The Czech OT-62 TOPAS was an improved version of the BTR-50PK manufactured in Czechoslovakia. The TOPAS-2A had a small turret added over the right hull front bay, armed with a machine-gun and Tarasnice 82mm recoilless rifle.

91▲

92▲ **93▼**

▲94

▲95 ▼96

94. The Polish LWP purchased the OT-62 TOPAS from Czechoslovakia, and modified them with a locally developed turret to create the OT-62 TOPAS-2AP.
95. Command versions of the TOPAS are called TOPAS-VS by the Czechoslovak CSLA. These vehicles are Polish-modified command vehicles which differ in a number of respects from the Czech model.
96. A pair of Czech CSLA OT-62 TOPAS-2A on autumn exercises, wearing the colourful Czech temporary summer/autumn camouflage paint.
97. The initial version of the BTR-60 series, the BTR-60P, had a completely open roof. (Sovfoto)

The BTR-50P series was not entirely satisfactory as an armoured infantry vehicle. It was certainly more mobile than the BTR-152, but the design was poorly configured for troop entrance and exit. The men had to climb up the sides, which was a time-consuming nuisance when field equipped. Exit was equally slow, and far more dangerous if under fire since the troops had to clamber over the roof. In addition, the Soviets were coming to realize that armoured infantry vehicles should be tailored to squad size. The BTR-50P carried two squads, or 20 troops. Since Soviet motor rifle companies were triadic (three platoons of three squads each), there was inevitably a bit of confusion mixing squads from different platoons together in the same transporter.

As in most NATO countries of the period, the 1960s saw a general shift away from large armoured troop carriers to slightly smaller carriers suitable for a single squad. The next step (in the Soviet case) occurred in the late 1960s when the motor rifle battalions' armoured transporter companies were abolished in favour of each motor rifle company having its own armoured infantry transporters.

Due to the shortcomings in the BTR-50PK design, its production ended in the late-1960s, but the BTR-50PU command vehicle had proved very useful and production continued until 1972–73. Total BTR-50 production was much lower than BTR-152 production, amounting to about 6,500 vehicles of all types. The BTR-50 was produced in too small a number significantly to affect the mechanization of the Ground Forces; it was never available in sufficient numbers to equip the motor rifle regiments of all the tank divisions.

The BTR-60

Experience with the BTR-152 provided the Ground Forces with critical experience in armoured infantry tactics. With the decision in 1956–57 to start converting all rifle and mechanized divisions to motor rifle divisions, a new vehicle was needed to make this possible. The principal shortcoming of the BTR-152 was its poor cross-country ability, and in 1959, a new TTT was issued for the development of an armoured transporter with improved mobility, including amphibious capability. It would seem that a tracked chassis was ruled out on the grounds of cost. Tracked chassis, although offering better mobility in poor terrain, are more expensive to produce, operate and maintain than

97▼

▲98

98. Another example of the BTR-60P showing the standard SGMB 7.62mm machine-gun armament.

wheeled systems. It would appear that the TTT for the new *zavodskoe izdeliye 49* was issued to two design teams: Dedkov's OKB at GAZ in Gorkiy, and probably the Rodionov/Orlov team at ZiL. The Dedkov team had already developed a four-axle, all-terrain chassis in the winter of 1956, the Project 62B, which formed a basis for their work on Project 49. The TTT called for the use of gasoline (since diesel fuel was still relatively scarce in the USSR), and the use of an existing engine. The Dedkov team selected the GAZ-49 engine which they had employed already in the earlier BRDM scout vehicle design. The Dedkov team proposed several novel technical features in the design, but most of these were rejected at the state trials in favour of simpler automotive components which would be less trouble to manufacture. The prototypes were submitted for state trials in 1960, and the Dedkov entry was selected. It was authorized under the designation BTR-60P.

The initial version of the BTR-60, the BTR-60P, had an open roof. It is not known why such an archaic feature was retained in view of the general trend in the Ground Forces towards sealed vehicles which could be fitted with nuclear-protective equipment. In any event, the BTR-60P was short-lived. In 1963, it was supplanted by the BTR-60PA which had an armoured roof. In this version, the troop size was reduced from 16 (14+ 2 crew) to 12. The main shortcoming of the BTR-60PA was that the squad machine-gun could not be fired from within the protective shell of the vehicle. There was also some criticism that the armoured transporters were becoming increasingly 'toothless' and could not deal with hostile infantry transporters on the battlefield. As a result, in1964, work was undertaken on an improved version mounting the 14.5mm KPVT heavy machine-gun in a small turret. The first production model of this vehicle appeared in 1965 as the BTR-60PAI, but it was quickly replaced by a slightly improved type, the BTR-60PB, which had an improved sighting system for the gun. The BTR-60PB became the standard production model of the family. The turret adopted for the BTR-60PB was the same as that which appeared later on the BRDM-2 in 1966.

The turmoil in BTR-60 development highlighted the tactical ferment in the Soviet Ground Forces at the time. There was still some controversy over the tactical requirements for an armoured transporter for the new motor rifle divisions. The BTR-60P represented the last trace of a doctrine which viewed armoured transporters as nothing more than taxis to bring infantry close to the battleline. The BTR-60PB, which appeared only four years later, represented the first glimmers of a new view that an infantry transporter had to be survivable on a nuclear battlefield and that the troops had to be

99▲

100▲ 101▼

99. The BTR-60PA was similar to the BTR-60P, but had a fully armoured roof. This is a BTR-60PA of the German NVA.
100. The armoured roof of the BTR-60PA.
101. Side view of an Iranian BTR-60PB showing side firing ports and relative lack of exit ports.

▲102

▲103 ▼104

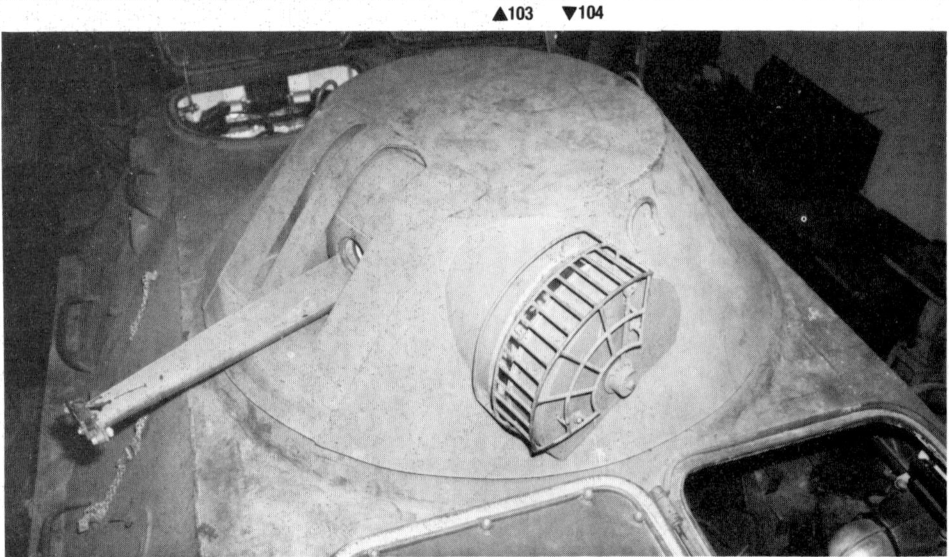

102. Closeup of the hatch arrangement and armament on the BTR-60PA. Note that on this version, the armament was increased to a 12.7mm DShK heavy machine-gun and two 7.62mm SGMB machine-guns.
103. The BTR-60PB introduced a turret 14.5mm KPVT machine-gun to the BTR-60 series, as well as an improved hatch layout.
104. The Romanian TAB-72 is a close copy of the BTR-60PB, differing externally by this modified turret sight arrangement.

able to fight from within its confines. The BTR-60PB was not an infantry fighting vehicle in the current sense of the word, since only 6 of its 8 squad members could fire their weapons from within the armoured vehicle. But it was a step in that direction. The BTR-60PB has a normal complement of 11: 3 crew (including the machine-gunner) and an 8-man squad.

In comparison with NATO designs of the day, such as the US M113 or the British FV438, the BTR-60PB was not terribly impressive. The design turmoil between the open-topped BTR-60P and the closed BTR-60PA and BTR-60PB had resulted in a vehicle poorly suited to crew entrance and exit. The doors on the BTR-60PB were small and badly situated. A squad disembarking under hostile fire was extremely likely to suffer casualties. In contrast, the NATO designs had large rear doors which permitted easy entrance and exit, and a modicum of protection for the squad if exiting under fire. The only advantage offered by the BTR-60PB was the turret machine-gun station. In contrast, the machine-gun on the American M113 was completely exposed. Automotively, the BTR-60PB was inferior to the M113. The BTR-60 was powered by two engines, and a complicated powertrain with four powered axles. Engine synchronization was a frequent problem, as were other powertrain failures. Due to the hull shape, the fire-prone petrol engine, and its automotive shortcomings, the BTR-60PB was known as the 'wheeled coffin' (*kolesniy grob*) among Russian motor riflemen.

The BTR-60 was designed to be amphibious without preparation. It uses a hydrojet system similar to that employed on the PT-76 tank. This offers good swimming capability in rivers so long as the current isn't above 8km/h. The BTR-60 has a water swimming speed of 10km/h. The BTR-60 series is faster and has better handling in water than NATO systems such as the track propulsion used on the M113, but the BTR-60PB has problems in getting out of the water.

As has been the case with so many Soviet light armoured vehicles, the BTR-60 fostered a very large family of derivative types. Besides the basic troop-carrying varieties, a number of specialized BTR-60PU command vehicles have also been fielded. Not all the Soviet designations for these command vehicles are available. One version, used as a command post for air defence units, is designated the BTR-60PU-12. Depending on the radio configuration, each of these OTR-60PU variants has a three-digit radio designation preceded by an 'R' (R-XXX). The Forward Air Control (FAC) version of the BTR-60PB has a large generator on the rear of the hull and a plexiglass window replaces the armament in the turret. Another FAC version of the BTR-60 has a new, higher turret than the normal BTR-60PB, but without armament.

These turretless vehicles are primarily intended as radio vehicles for battalion and regimental command staffs. The earliest versions were usually simple adaptations of the turretless BTR-60 with additional whip antennas. In about 1972, a new, standardized configuration appeared. This BTR-60PU has a clothesline antenna running around the hull, at least one additional generator in a rectangular container in lieu of the turret, and may have a telescoping antenna (NATO codename: Hawk Eye) to improve transmission. The antenna fit and internal arrangements are tailored to meet the requirements of the user. A typical BTR-60PU,

105▲ 106▼

105. This Soviet BTR-60PU is a modified BTR-60PB with no fewer than four radio antennas added.
106. This Hungarian BTR-60PU is simply a BTR-60PA with added radio equipment and antennas. (Chris Foss)

107. There is a wide range of BTR-60 command vehicles. This BTR-60PU is based on a BTR-60P.

108. The standardized BTR-60PU has a clothes-line antenna added around the hull, a telescoping Hawk Eye antenna (seen folded here) and a generator added in lieu of the normal BTR-60PB turret.

▲107 ▼108

109. This German NVA BTR-60PU, attached to a ZSU-23-4 Shilka unit, is a modified BTR-60PB with four radio antennas and a box generator added on the rear.
110. This forward air control BTR-60PU is a modified BTR-60PB with the gun removed, antennas added, and a large generator mounted over the rear to power the many new transmitters added inside the vehicle.
111. The BTR-60PU with the Hawk Eye antenna fully erected.
112. Closeup of a Hawk Eye antenna on a BTR-60PU before being telescoped upward.

109▲

110▲ 111▼ 112▼

113. The TAB-73 is a Romanian version of the BTR-60, fitted with an 82mm mortar.

used by a motor rifle battalion chief of staff, would be fitted with an R-130 high-frequency (AM) transceiver to communicate with regimental HQ on the regimental AM radio net; an R-107 very-high-frequency (FM) amplifier-equipped transceiver to communicate on the regimental FM command net; another R-130 to operate on the battalion AM command net; an R-123 very-high-frequency (FM) transceiver to communicate on the main battalion net used by all battalion vehicles; and finally an R-311 high-frequency AM receiver to listen in on the regimental or divisional CBR and air-warning network. In contrast to this staff vehicle the commander of a motor rifle battalion would have a BTR-60KSh with an R-107, R-123, R-126 and R-130 transceiver. A company commander's vehicle would have a similar fit, minus the R-130.

The BTR-60 series was in production from 1960 to about 1976. Total production of all models is believed to have reached about 25,000 vehicles. Final production models had a number of small improvements over the earlier BTR-60PB including a new roof-mounted periscopic sight for the KPVT heavy machine-gun. BTR-60PB with the Limited Contingent of Soviet Forces-Afghanistan have been seen in some cases with an AGS-17 30mm grenade-launcher mounted in place of the normal KPVT machine-gun.

The BMP Infantry Fighting Vehicle

The first Soviet infantry vehicle to be developed from the outset with the needs of the nuclear battlefield in mind was the BMP (*Boyevaya Mashina Pyekhota*: Infantry Fighting Vehicle). It was intended to replace the BTR-50. Design of the BMP began in about 1959 as *zavodskoe izdeliye 765 Korshun* (Kite) in the wake of the doctrinal changes in the Soviet Ground Forces that stressed the need to be able to fight on a nuclear battlefield. These doctrinal requirements necessitated a rethinking of infantry vehicle design. This re-evaluation began in the late 1950s, and was manifest in designs such as the BTR-50PK and BTR-60PB. However, both these variants were designed on the basis of earlier vehicles conceived before the doctrinal changes had occurred. As a result, certain of the features on these vehicles were of an improvised nature.

The requirement for Project 765 stressed high vehicle speed, good armament and the capability for all members of the squad to fight from within the confines of the vehicle. The armament issue was quite controversial. The original TTT apparently called for a 23mm autocannon, which was felt adequate to defeat comparable infantry vehicles such as the German Marder. However, in view of the likely costs of Project 765 when it reached production, the Main Armour Directorate, or another element of the Ground Forces, insisted that the vehicle have anti-tank capability.

The infantry squad configuration selected for Project 765 was unique at the time, though it has since become commonplace. Eight members of the squad were seated in the rear, back-to-back, facing outwards. Six firing ports and associated periscopes were positioned on each side, and two more towards the rear. The turret of the vehicle was in front of the crew compartment. The driver was positioned in the front left of the vehicle, and the squad commander behind him beside the turret. Entrance and exit from the vehicle could take place through roof hatches or two rear doors. This layout clearly reflected the experiences of Soviet motor rifle units with the inferior layout of the BTR-50 and BTR-60. The layout allowed the crew to fire its weapons from within the vehicle without exposure to an outside (and potentially contaminated) environment. The internal compartment was protected by a nuclear protection (PAZ) system relying on a detector, filtration system and atmospheric over-pressure to keep out airborne contaminants.

The armament system for the Project 765 was even more novel. The primary armament selected was a new gun/rocket design, the 2A28, which used a new recoilless system developed for the SPG-9 anti-tank rocket-launcher. A conventional anti-tank gun was out of the question since it would have been too heavy, and its recoil too severe, for use from a light armoured vehicle. A recoilless rifle system was overruled because of the usual problems associated with back-blast and reloading. The gun/missile system was a hybrid, having certain features common to both. The projectile was ejected from the gun tube by a PG-15 propellant casing, as with a normal gun, but as the projectile itself was a rocket (derived from the RPG-7 rocket-propelled grenade), it was not necessary to use a large propellant casing to boost it to a high initial muzzle velocity. Hence, recoil was very modest. On leaving the gun tube, the rocket engine of the PG-9 projectile ignited, boosting the projectile to its cruise speed. The gun tube was of the smoothbore type, and projectile stabilization was accomplished by folding fins which popped out as the projectile cleared the tube. In a sense, this weapon provided the infantry squad with a variation of the normal squad RPG-7, but a variation that could be fired from within a vehicle without the danger of the normal RPG-7 back-blast. In addition to the novel nature of this weapon, the design incorporated an automatic loader in order to limit the turret crew to one man. The main weakness of the 2A28 system is that it has a very short effective range (700m). To supplement the gun/rocket launcher, a 9M14 Malyutka (AT-3 Sagger) wire-guided anti-tank missile-launcher was added above the gun tube. This missile had a greater effective range than the 2A28, and a larger warhead, but it was considerably larger than the 73mm ammunition of the 2A28 and had a very low rate of fire due to time-consuming reload procedures. Nevertheless, the turret design on the Project 765 offered a remarkable amount of firepower for a light armoured vehicle.

Many of the other features of the Project 765 were fairly novel. The vehicle was designed with a new type of track, similar to that adopted by the contemporary medium tank, the T-64. Since Project 765 was expected to keep up with the T-64, it was designed for high speed. It was the first Soviet tracked armoured vehicle to use a simple driving yoke steering system. It was also designed to be amphibious, but the hydrojet system was dropped, due to its space demands, in favour of the track propulsion system commonly used on American armoured infantry transporters. In many respects, Project 765 was the most novel and radical departure in Soviet armoured vehicle design since the war, and it was the world's first true infantry fighting vehicle.

Project 765 was subjected to state trials in 1965 and entered limited scale production as the BMP-765, or BMP (called BMP-76PB by NATO initially). It first appeared in 1966 for operational trials and these were protracted because of faults in the design. The suspension had to be strengthened, especially in the front, due to the speed of the vehicle. The swimming vanes on the fenders had to be modified, and the internal venting system, which expelled fumes when the crew fired their AKM assault rifles, had to be improved. In addition, the Ground Forces decided that besides protecting against nuclear contaminants, the BMP would also have to have a PBZ chemical protection filter system. There were at least four subvariants of the BMP between 1966 and 1969 as these difficulties were ironed out. Finally, in 1970, the definitive version of the BMP emerged as the BMP-1 (called BMP-A by NATO). The BMP-1 incorporated the new chemical filter system to the left of the turret, and had a number of other improvements as well. A 20cm extension was added to the bow to shift the centre of gravity aft, and to prevent the BMP from 'submarining' in

114. Undoubtedly the most radical Soviet armoured infantry vehicle to appear in the 1960s was the revolutionary BMP which combined speed, mobility and armoured protection together with considerable firepower.

the water while swimming. Also, a new swimming air intake was added with a low, erectable snorkel, to prevent water from flooding the air intake as had happened on the earlier BMP. The BMP-1 also incorporated the improved 9M14M missile.

The decision to adopt the BMP in the Ground Forces provoked vigorous debate. It was an extremely expensive vehicle, and many tank officers questioned whether it was prudent to spend so much money for a vehicle which, in the end, was still very lightly armoured and lightly armed compared to a tank, when the cheaper BTR-60 could be obtained in larger numbers. The debate was also sparked by continuing doctrinal development in the Ground Forces. By the early 1970s, the Ground Forces had begun to shed their obsession with nuclear operations. The USSR was approaching strategic weapons parity with the USA. The chances of either side provoking each other into full-scale nuclear exchange via an escalating series of tactical nuclear weapon exchanges, was viewed as unlikely. Nuclear parity implied that a European war might be confined to purely conventional weapons, with both sides fearing the provocative consequences of the use of tactical nuclear weapons. With this in mind, attention again shifted to conventional tactics and doctrine.

In the eyes of many Soviet tacticians, the BMP was not entirely suited to the conventional battlefield. On a nuclear battlefield, NATO anti-tank guided-missile and rocket teams would be severely inhibited by the contaminated environment. The BMP could range freely over the battlefield at the head of combined tank/motor rifle groups. On a conventional battlefield, there would be a profusion of anti-tank teams. The BMP, with its light armour, was especially vulnerable to the wide range of infantry anti-armour weapons available to NATO. The Soviet debate questioned how the BMP could be employed in these different conditions, and concluded that new tactics were required.

The new tactics accepted the use of mounted infantry BMP actions where there was little resistance, such as during the breakout phase of an offensive, or during pursuit of a disorganized enemy. But where resistance was stiff, the BMP would be used as a part of a tank-infantry team with the infantry dismounted. A platoon of tanks would be placed in a wave in the vanguard, since they were better able to absorb the blow of anti-armour defences. Infantry would follow 200m behind the tanks to help rout out hostile infantry anti-armour teams. The BMP would follow no more than 300–400m behind the infantry, providing fire support for the tanks, and preparing to

115. In the BMP, the commander sits behind the driver, to the left front side of the turret. In the rear compartment is the 7–8-man squad.
116. The BMP was replaced by the BMP-1 in about 1970. The BMP-1 had a redesigned and lengthened nose to stop the vehicle from submarining in the water. (Sovfoto)
▼115

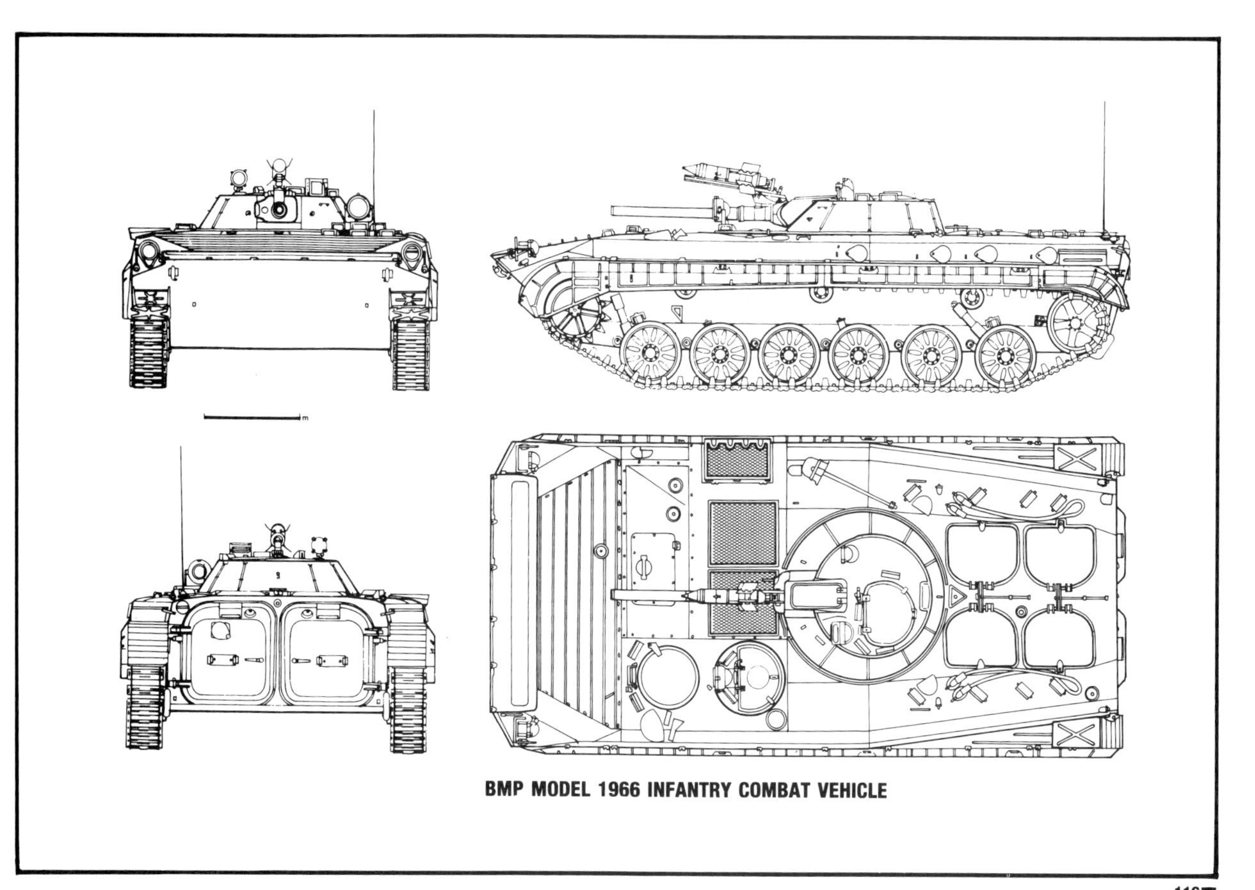

BMP MODEL 1966 INFANTRY COMBAT VEHICLE

116▼

move forward to pick up the infantry once the opposition was overcome.

Actual experience with these tactics highlighted the technical shortcomings of the BMP-1 in dismounted combat. It is so low that its gun/rocket-launcher and coaxial machine-gun are only 1.75m above the ground; so low that they would hit friendly infantry advancing in front of the vehicle. This forced the adoption of tactics where each infantry squad would leave a 50m zone of fire between it and the squads on either side to permit the BMP to fire its weapons. This is easier to perform in training than to carry out in the confusion of a modern battlefield. Furthermore, the use of the BMP to the rear of the tanks and infantry precluded use of its main weapon, the 2A28 low-pressure gun. The 2A28 had an effective range of about 700m and a maximum range of about only 1,300m. The Soviet assault wave would form up about 1,000m from the forward edge of the enemy lines, which would place the BMP as much as 1,500m away from its targets. The BMPs' low-pressure gun would only come in range of hostile targets as the tanks approached a scant 200m from the forward edge of the enemy lines. The PG-9 round was fin-stabilized, and had an alarming tendency to fly into a headwind due to the large size of the fold-out fins. This degraded its accuracy, especially at longer ranges.

The supplementary 9M14M Malyutka missile-launcher was of little consolation. It was not easy to control because of its primitive joystick steering. Effective use required constant practise, and the probability of hitting a small or moving target, especially from a moving vehicle, was very low. It was also painfully slow to reload. The gunner had to crawl into the lower hull to collect the missile, and after reseating himself, slide it out onto its launch rail. He then took a metal rod and carefully prodded the four folded tail fins out to their extended position for firing. This reduced the effective rate of fire to about one missile a minute, and the gunner's preoccupation with reloading kept him from using other turret weapons. There are reports that later models of the BMP incorporated a semi-automatic guidance system instead of the simple joystick control used in the standard model. However, this only slightly ameliorated the difficulties. In the final production models of the BMP-1, the BMP-1M, introduced into service in about 1974–75, the 9M14M Malyutka launcher was removed in favour of a 9P135M launcher for the 9M111 *Fagot* (Bassoon) missile (AT-4 Spigot). This launcher is semi-automatically guided, but the mounting is improvised, and to use it, the gunner must open his hatch, and fire the missile from outside the turret.

In the early 1970s, work began on an improved BMP, the BMP-2. The primary change was in the substitution of a new 2A42 30mm autocannon for the 2A28 low-pressure gun, and the substitution of a 9M66 (AT-5 Spandrel) missile-

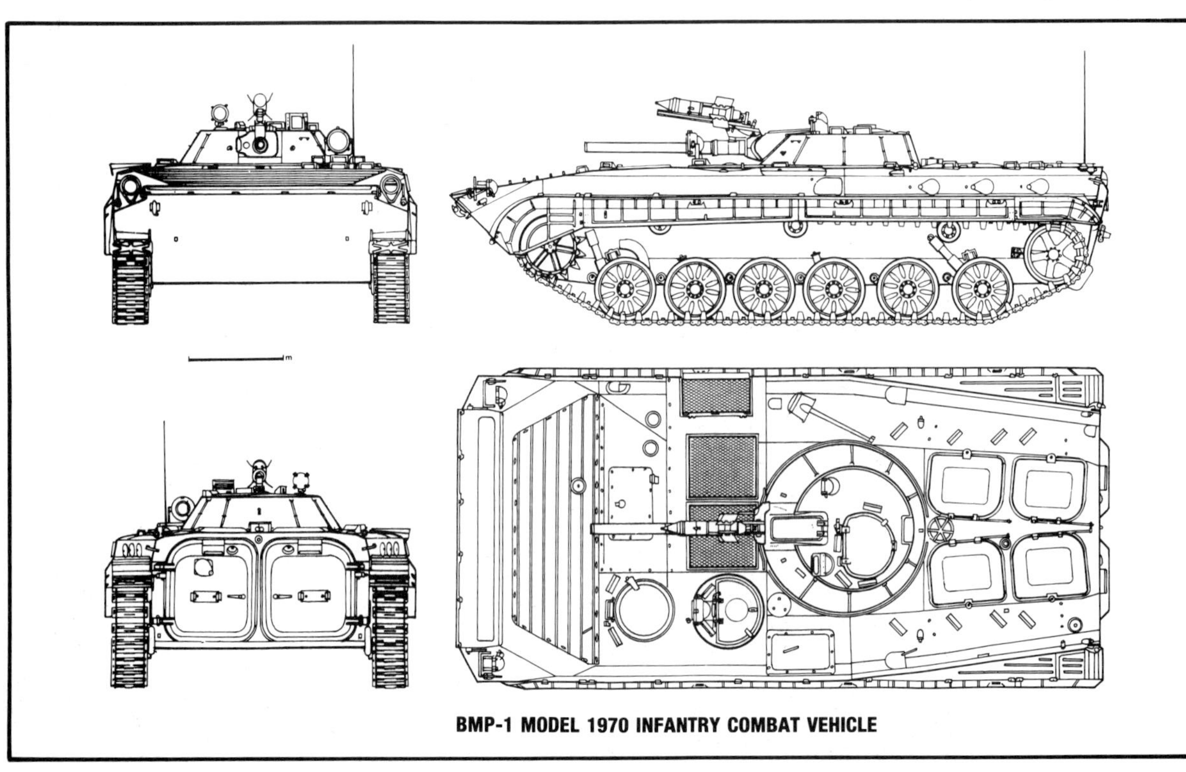

BMP-1 MODEL 1970 INFANTRY COMBAT VEHICLE

117. A BMP-1 on winter exercises. The BMP-1 had reconfigured troop hatches in the rear roof, and many other improvements over the BMP. (Sovfoto)
118. The BMP-1 first saw combat with the Syrian Army in the fighting against Israel on the Golan Heights in 1973. This vehicle has suffered an internal explosion and is completely burned out.
119. The BMP-1 is manufactured in Czechoslovakia as the BVP-1. Some of this production is shipped to the Soviet Union for Ground Forces' use or export.

117▲

118▲ 119▼

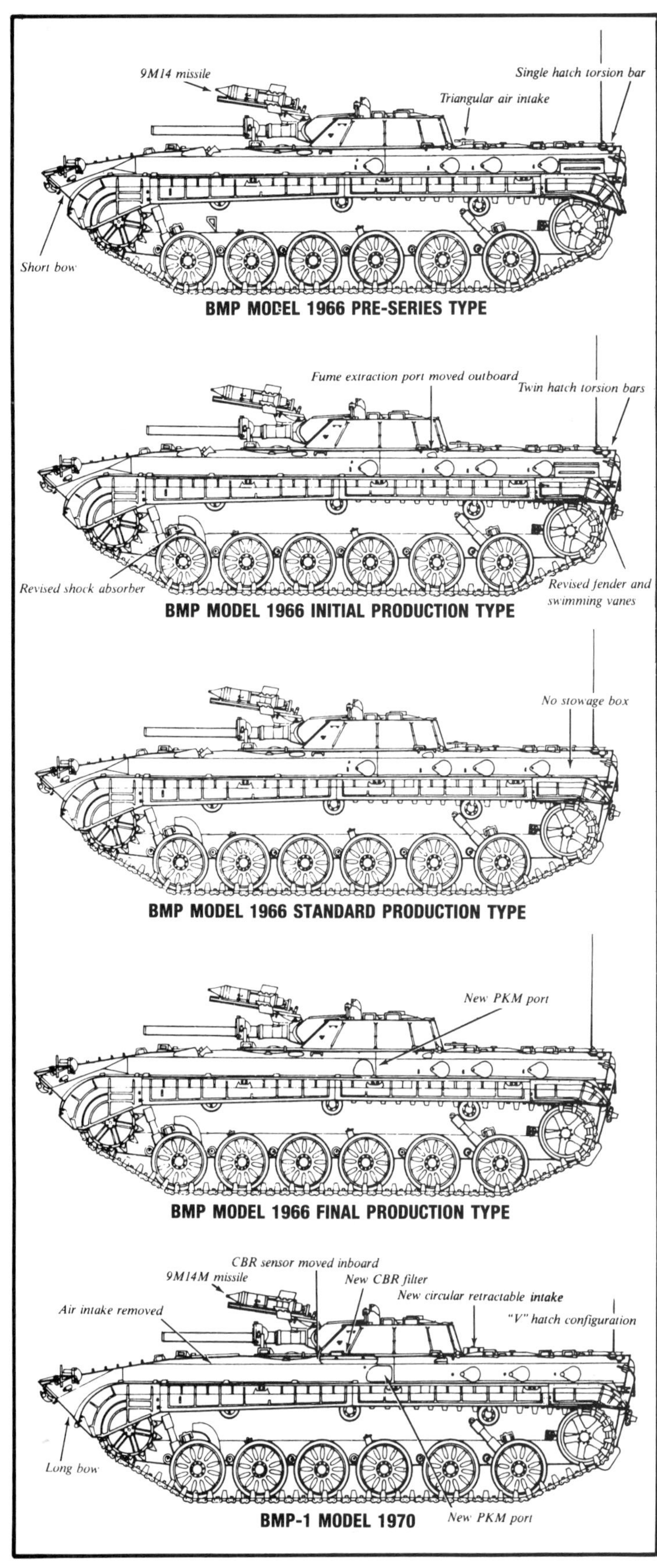

launcher for the Malyutka/Fagot types. The main advantage of the 2A42 30mm gun was that it offered far better range (2,000–4,000m), which made fire support of the lead waves of tanks more practicable. It displayed a pragmatic re-evaluation of the utility of low-pressure gun systems, which seem to offer a useful anti-armour capability, but which in fact have significant range and accuracy shortcomings when used to provide overwatch fire support. Although the 30mm gun cannot penetrate the frontal armour of a main battle tank, the weapon is highly effective against the profusion of light armoured vehicles on the battlefield, including infantry fighting vehicles and APCs. The 2A42 is fitted in a high-elevation mounting with reasonably fast turret traverse, offering a measure of protection against low-flying anti-tank helicopters.

The AT-5 Spandrel system, similar to the Euromissile HOT, is semi-automatically guided. Unlike the 9M14M Malyutka, which the gunner actually steers into its target, with the Spandrel, the gunner merely keeps the target aligned in his sights, and the launcher feeds course corrections to the missile over the connecting wire. This offers a far higher probability of hitting a tank-sized target at long ranges. Unlike the improvised AT-4 mounting on the BMP-1 Model 1974, the BMP-2's AT-5 launcher can be fired from within the protective confines of the vehicle. There is some controversy over the issue of the AT-5 on the BMP-2. The BMP-2 manufactured in Czechoslovakia are fitted with the 9M111 Fagot (AT-4 Spigot) in place of the 9M66 (AT-5 Spandrel). It may be that the vehicle can fire either missile, or that only Soviet vehicles carry the larger AT-5 missile.

The BMP-2 also incorporated a 2-man turret in place of the 1-man turret on the BMP-1 family. This shifted the squad commander from his previous position to the left of the turret in the hull, up into the turret. This was done for two reasons. On the BMP-1, the commander's station is fitted with an infra-red searchlight. This obstructed the turret armament, and the gun had to be elevated to clear it if engaging targets to the left front corner of the vehicle; it created a dead zone in the front left corner. The squad commander also had very poor vision in his hull location. The turret over his right shoulder precluded any vision in that direction. By moving the commander into the turret, the obstruction was removed, and the commander gained a 360° view. It is interesting to note that the US Army came to the same conclusion at this time. Its original infantry fighting vehicle, the XM723 MICV, had the same crew configuration

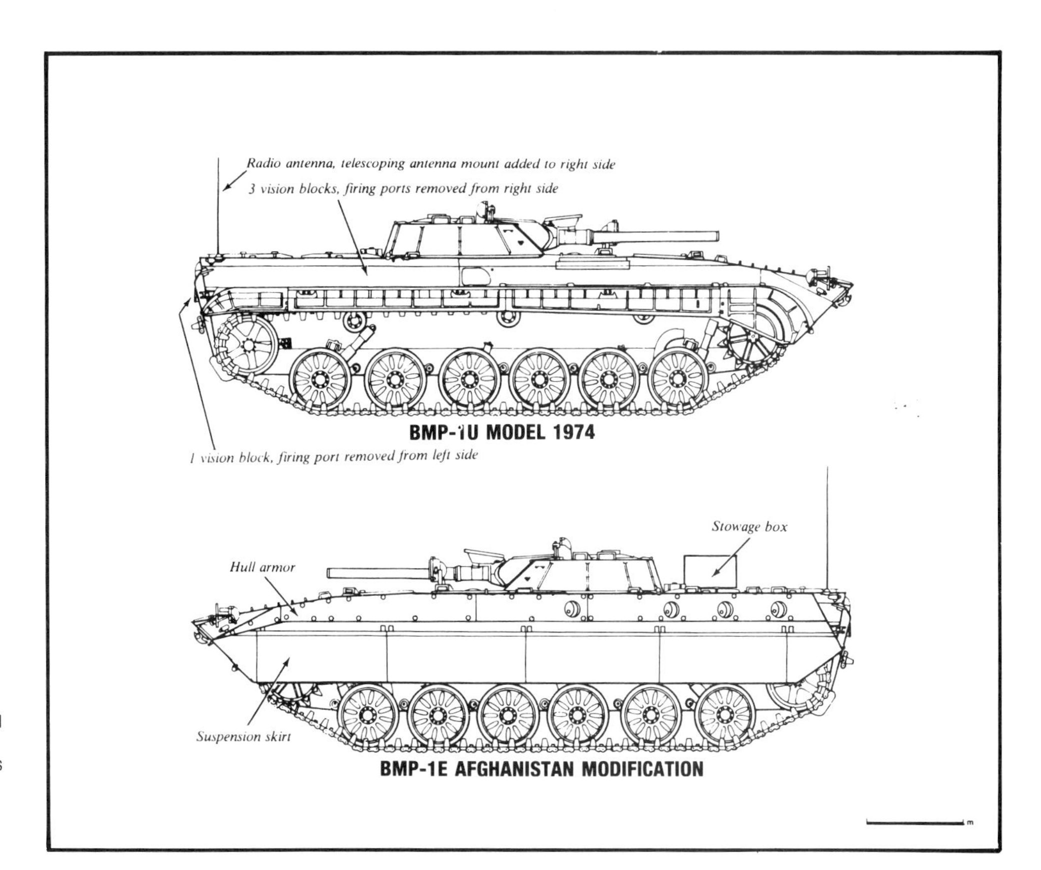

120. This BMP-1M has the mounting post for the 9P135M launcher on the roof, but the launcher is not fitted. This was the final production version of the BMP-1 series, prior to the introduction of the BMP-2. (Sovfoto)

▲121

▲122 ▼123

121. The BMP-1M has an improved rear stowage rack to keep the squad stowage from fouling the forward roof troop hatch. This version also has the 9P135M launcher for the 9M111M Fagot (AT-4 Spigot) anti-tank missile fitted in lieu of the older 9M14M Malyutka (AT-3 Sagger).

122. The BMP-1K is the command version of the BMP-1 designed for company commanders. The firing ports on the right side have been deleted, along with some of the periscopes, and a radio aerial has been added at the right rear corner of the hull. (US Army)

123. Internal view of the BMP-1 showing the cramped seating. The periscopes are very evident (upper left) as are the firing ports. (US Army)

124. A Finnish Army BMP-1K showing the reconfigured right side with the deleted firing ports. (K. Moilonen)

as the BMP-1. Before production began, however, it was reconfigured with a 2-man turret and entered service in the early 1980s as the M2 Bradley IFV. The main drawback of a 2-man turret is that it tends to take up a disproportionate amount of hull room, forcing a reduction in squad size; but infantry squad sizes have been shrinking in most European armies due to the increasing amount of firepower available to them. The BMP-2 probably entered production in about 1976-77.

In configuration and features the BMP-2 is very similar to the new US M2 Bradley or the British MCV-80. By comparison with the American vehicle, it is somewhat less heavily armoured, though either vehicle can penetrate the armour of the other at a range of 2,000m. Squad size of both vehicles is similar, although the US vehicle is roomier and can carry more ammunition, stores and missiles. The US vehicle has better turret stabilization and night-fighting capability, having a FLIR thermal night sight instead of the image intensification sight used on the BMP-2. The Bradley is a more robust vehicle than the BMP-2 and probably has significantly better cross-country mobility.

As with the BTR-50 and BTR-60, there are command versions of the BMP. The BMP-1K, called BMP-M1974 in NATO, is a company command vehicle with R-123, R-126 and R-107 transceivers. The company commander's BMP-1K carries the company commander and a company staff officer on the left side, and a radio operator on the right. Due to this configuration, the firing ports and periscopes on the right side are blanked off, as are one firing port and periscope on the left side. A small telescoping antenna is carried on the right rear hull side. The more elaborate communication requirements of the battalion and higher staffs led to the development of the BMP-1KSh. This vehicle is fitted with a fixed turret without the usual gun. A large, telescoping Top Ball antenna is carried in front of the turret, and can be folded up or down. There are only two rear roof hatches, and an extra generator is fitted on the rear roof to power the radios. There is also stowage for additional radio antennas on the hull rear. Like the BTR-60PU, the BMP-1KSh is fitted with a varying assortment of radios, often including the R-130, R-123, R-311 and R-107. The vehicle is used by battalion commanders, battalion chiefs of staff, and by higher command elements. There are probably other BMP command vehicles as well.

There have been persistent reports of BMP mortar vehicles. For example, there have been

124▼

125. Soviet drawing of internal layout of the BMP-1.
126. Soviet drawing of internal layout of the BMP-2.
127. A BMP-2 of the Czechoslovak CSLA on parade in Prague in 1985.
128. Rear view of a Czech BMP-2 showing the buoyancy cells added to the fenders. This vehicle does not have the smoke mortars fitted.

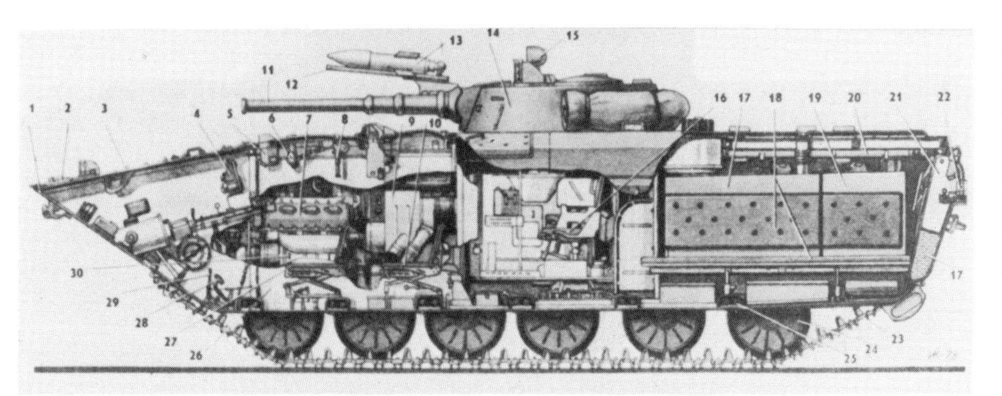

▲125

▲126 ▼127

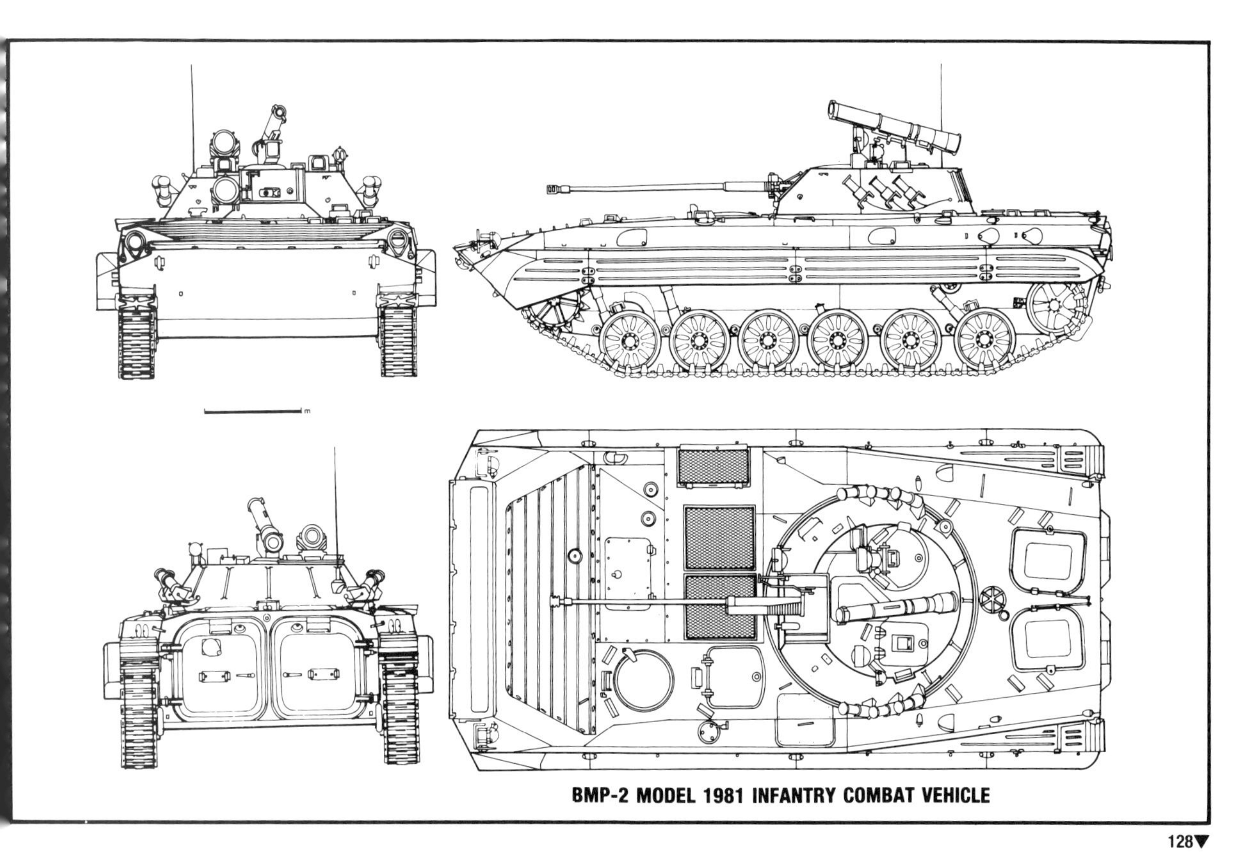

BMP-2 MODEL 1981 INFANTRY COMBAT VEHICLE

128▼

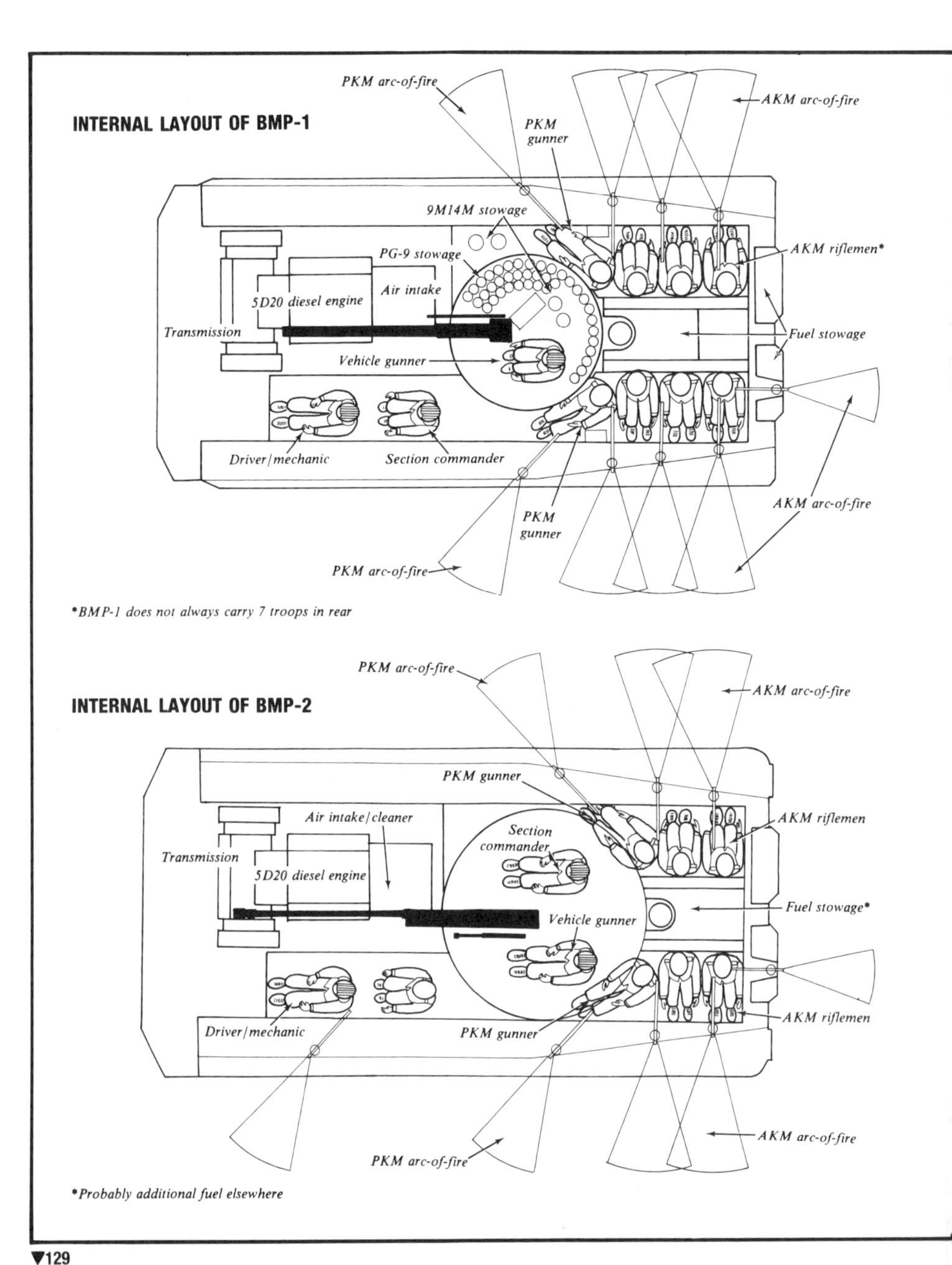

▼129

129. This unusual vehicle appeared on parade in Sofia, Bulgaria in 1985. It consists of a BMP-2 turret mounted on a modified SO-122 (2S1) hull, and may represent a Polish attempt to develop a BMP substitute, or the new BRM-2 Soviet scout vehicle.

130. In 1984, the Soviets displayed a modified version of the BMP-2, fitted with additional anti-radiation sheeting over the turret sides to protect the crew from the blast of enhanced radiation (neutron bomb) warheads. (Sovfoto)

131. The BMP-1KSh is the battalion and regimental staff command version of the BMP. It is fitted with added communication equipment, including a Top Ball antenna which is erected at the front of the false turret (and can be seen here in folded position).

130▲ 131▼

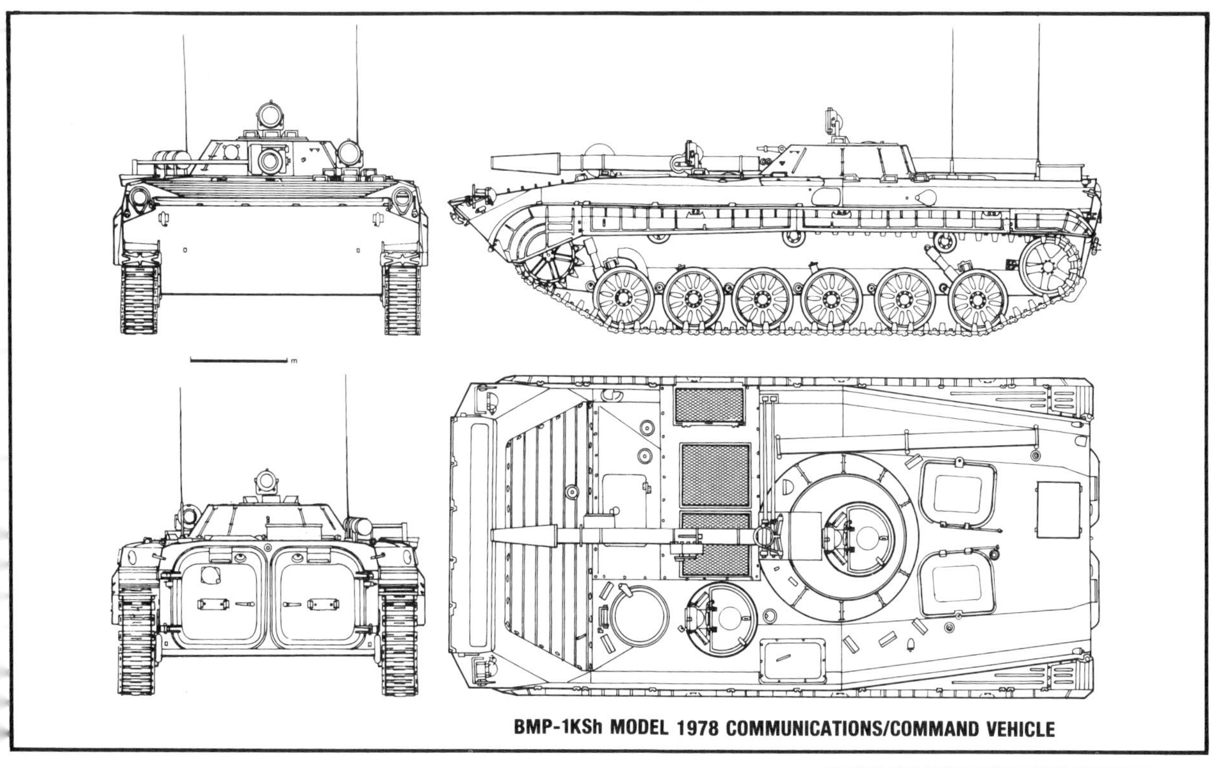

BMP-1KSh MODEL 1978 COMMUNICATIONS/COMMAND VEHICLE

reliable reports of a BMP-1 variant with a drop ramp in the rear instead of the usual split doors. It has been suggested that this vehicle is associated with a BMP mortar vehicle. There have also been reports of a BMP-2 variant fitted with the same 120mm hybrid gun/mortar turret as the BMD-derived SO-120, possibly designated 2S12. BMP-1 in Afghanistan have been refitted with additional armour and side skirts to prevent penetration of the hull sides by 12.7mm heavy machine-guns. The BMP has also served as the basis for a variety of specialist vehicles, some of which are covered in detail elsewhere in this book. These include the BRM scout tank, the PRP-3 radar artillery scout vehicle, the BMP-PPO training vehicle and a Czechoslovak light recovery vehicle with crane.

The BMD Airborne Assault Vehicle

In the wake of the Cuban missile crisis embarrassment in 1963, the Armed Forces were instructed by the Central Committee of the Communist Party that a major emphasis would have to be placed in developing the means to project power outside traditional regions of Soviet influence. A major offshoot of this effort was a rejuvenation of the VDV (Air Assault Force) which was an element of the Ground Forces at that time. Under the new policy, it became a semi-autonomous element of the Army to be used as a special strategic strike force. Until 1964, the VDV had been a conventional light paratroop force. Its divisions had modest numbers of armoured vehicles such as the ASU-57 and ASU-85 assault guns, and achieved strategic mobility through the use of paratroop landing tactics. Once on the ground, however, the mainstay of its tactical deployment was the foot infantryman. Soviet studies of airborne operations during the war had concluded that the inability of lightly armed paratroops to deal with contemporary mechanized infantry or tank forces severely limited their utility except for peripheral operations, so the Armed Forces decided gradually to mechanize the VDV. The aim was to offer the new air assault divisions a greater degree of tactical mobility on the ground, better protection against artillery and anti-personnel weapons, and to increase their firepower, especially anti-armour firepower.

The centrepiece of this new effort was the development of an airborne counterpart of the BMP, called the BMD (*Boyevaya Mashina Desantnaya*, Airborne Combat Vehicle) a scaled-down version of the BMP. The turret and its associated weapons were to remain the same, but a smaller hull was designed to fulfill the requirement that the vehicle be air-transportable and air-droppable from normal VDV transports such as the An-12. The BMP was too large for this role, and wasn't designed to withstand the impact of parachute landings. The new hull has a pneumatic suspension system which can be folded up for air dropping. A modernized version of the PRS rocket-braked airdrop pallet, the PRSM-915, was developed at the same time. Its suspension retracted, the BMD is loaded on to a PRS pallet with the PRSM-915 retrorocket and

▼132

132. The BMD-1 is the VDV (Air Assault Forces) counterpart of the Ground Forces (SV) BMP. Both vehicles use the same turret and engine, but otherwise the vehicles are distinctly different. This is the initial version of the BMD-1, and differs from the earlier BMD in the configuration of the circular air filter intake and other details. (Sovfoto)
133. Soviet drawing of the internal layout of the BMD-1.
134. This intermediate model of the BMD-1, first seen in the mid-1970s, was reconfigured with new road-wheels, a front bow grill for better vehicle ventilation, and a number of other small changes. (Sovfoto)
135. The BMD-1M corresponds to the BMP-1M, and has the 9P135M launcher for the 9M111M Fagot (AT-4 Spigot) missile in lieu of the 9M14M Malyutka (AT-3 Sagger).

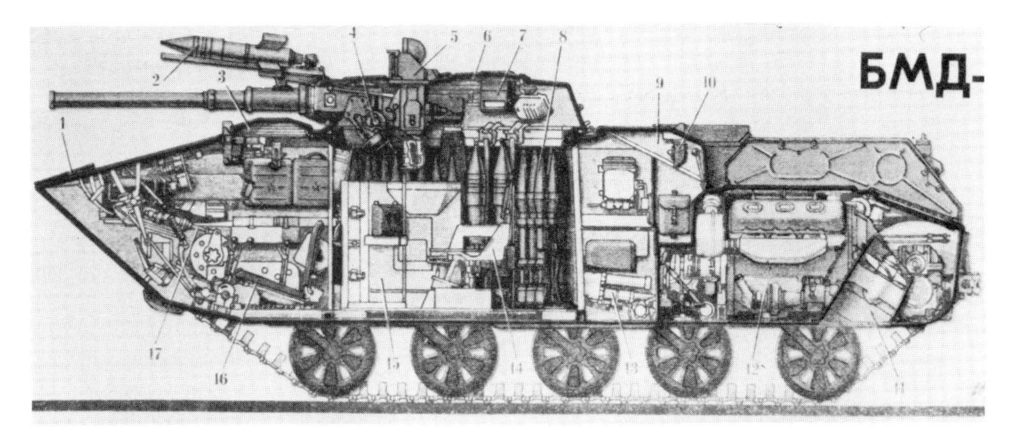

133▲

134▲ 135▼

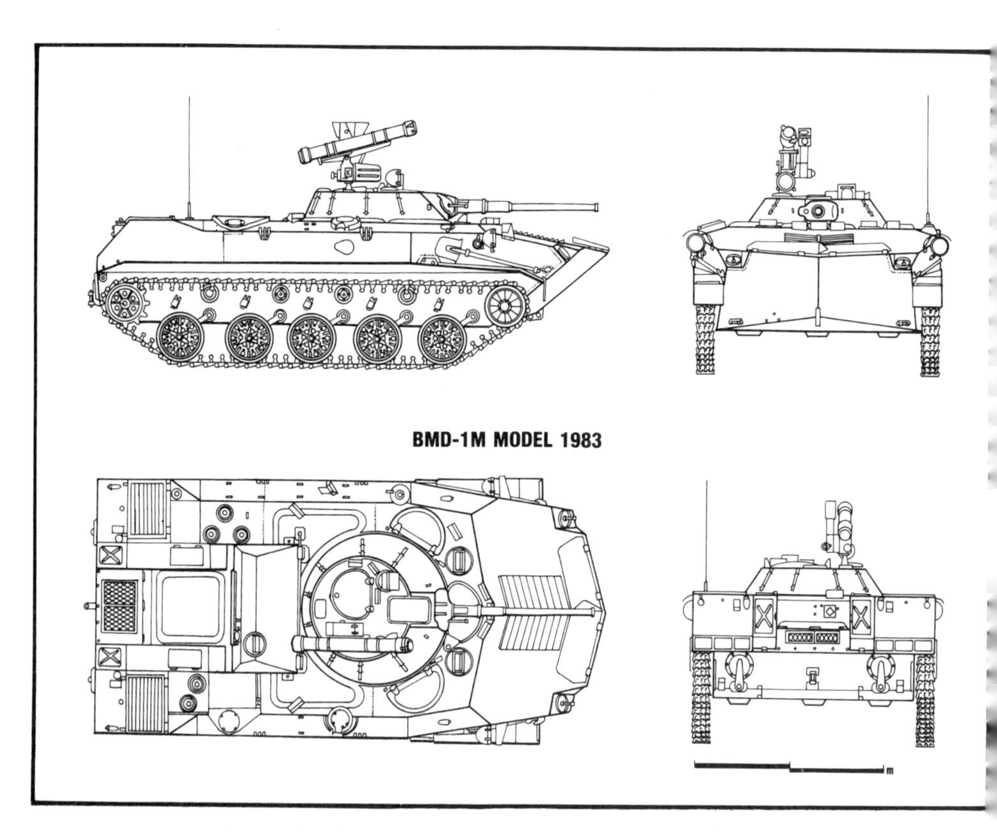

parachutes stowed above. After being pulled out of the rear of the Il-76 or An-12 transport aircraft by a drogue chute, the main canopy deploys, and four probe poles unfold beneath the pallet. When the first of these contacts the ground, the PRSM-915 retro-rocket system is fired to brake the descent of the vehicle. The BMD is fitted with a radio 'bleeper' which enables the crew to find their vehicle on the ground. The crew jumps separately, and on joining the vehicle, start the engine, detach the pallet restraints, extend the suspension to normal running position, and drive the vehicle away.

The smaller hull size of the BMD inevitably reduced the size of the squad. The BMP-1 seats up to eleven troops; the BMD seats seven. In the hull front is the driver, to his left the squad commander and to the right, the squad machine-gunner with his PKM machine-gun. In the centre is a 1-man turret, and to the rear is seating for three riflemen. There are firing ports for the commander, squad machine-gunner and riflemen, two facing forward, two to the sides and one to the rear. As in the case of the BMP, the BMD is fully sealed for operations on a nuclear-contaminated battlefield. It is also fully amphibious, and uses a hydrojet propulsion system.

The BMD first entered service in 1970, probably limited to operational trials. As was the case with the initial BMP versions, there were a fair number of technical problems which had been rectified by the time that the standard production model appeared in 1973 as the BMD-1. The BMD-1 differed in a number of details from the initial BMD, and among its improvements was a new filtration system for chemical defence of the crew compartment. Production was very modest, and was insufficient to equip all eight air assault divisions completely. Consequently, throughout the 1970s, most divisions received only sufficient BMD to equip one of their three air assault regiments. It was not until the mid-1980s that enough BMD had been produced to equip all three air assault regiments of the divisions.

Development of a support version of the BMD followed. This vehicle, the BMD-2, is a turretless version with a longer hull. Two basic versions were developed. The BMD-2KSh is a staff vehicle like the BMP-1KSh or BTR-60PU. It has a 'clothesline' radio antenna around the hull superstructure. The other version is a support vehicle which can be used to tow light field guns, ZU-23 air defence guns or mortars such as the 82mm *Vasilek* automatic mortar, and can be used to transport special weapons teams. It is nearly identical with the BMD-2KSh, but is not fitted with the external clothesline antenna.

As is the case with most Soviet armoured vehicles, the BMD-1 underwent evolutionary development. In the mid-1970s, a slightly improved model appeared which was fitted with new wheels, and an armoured grill on the hull

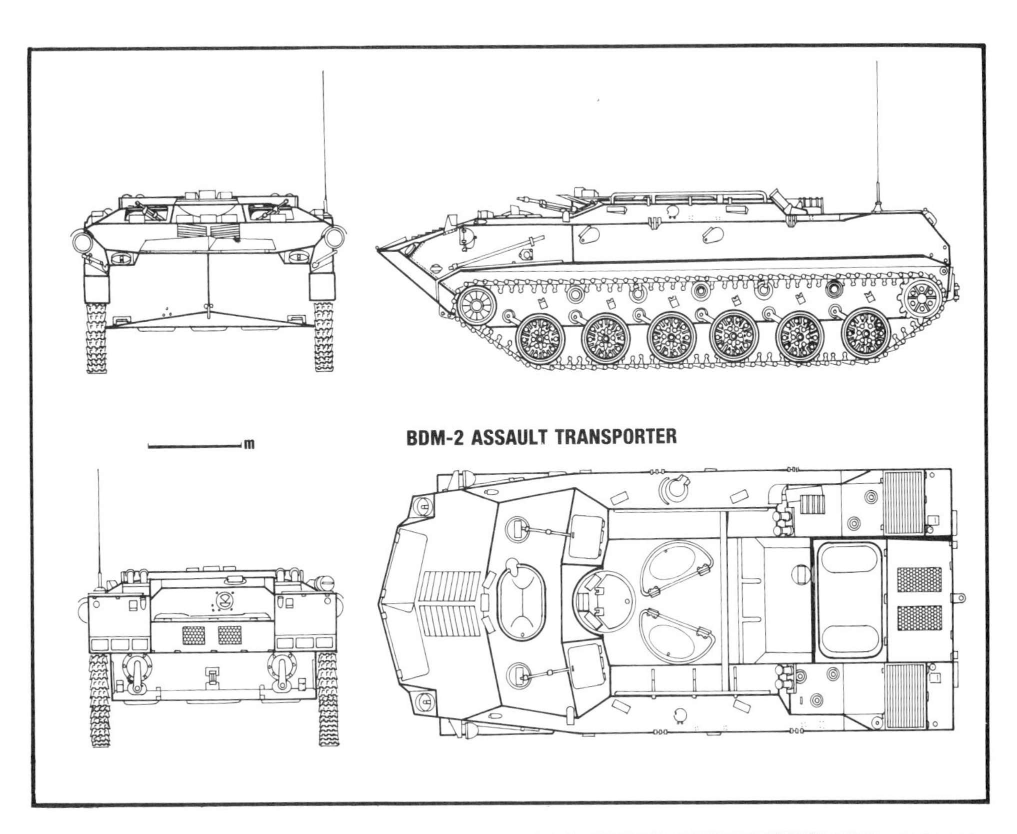

136. The BMD-2KSh is the command version of the BMD, and has a lengthened hull. It is fitted with a 'clothes-rail' folding antenna around the hull.
137. The BMD-2 is the transport counterpart of the BMD-2KSh. It is used to carry heavy weapons teams, or to tow light weapons like the ZU-23 air defence gun.

136▲ 137▼

138. Some Soviet motor rifle units in Arctic areas adopted the MT-LBV in place of the BTR-60 because of poor ground conditions. These replaced the earlier GT-T. (Sovfoto)

139. The MT-LB may have been designed as a fall-back in case the revolutionary BMP did not work out. These MT-LB are operated by a US Army OPFOR unit to simulate Soviet units in National Training Center exercises. (Michael Green)

140. The MT-LB can carry up to 8 men in the rear, but the compartment is not configured to allow all the troops to fire their assault rifles from within the vehicle. (Michael Green)

front to improve interior ventilation. The BMD-1 armament system has also been the subject of improvement. As on the BMP-1, in the late 1970s, the 9M14M Malyutka missile was replaced by the 9M111M Fagot missile, and its associated 9P135M launcher. This is also an improvised fitting, as the turret gunner must lean out of his hatch to fire the missile. There is some controversy as to whether a new version of the BMD-1 has already been fielded with a 2A42 30mm autocannon as in the case of the BMP-2, but this evolutionary development seems likely. Total production of the BMD and its variants to date has probably been about 3,000 vehicles.

In about 1981, to provide heavy fire support for the air assault regiments, the Soviets deployed a peculiar mortar/howitzer version of the BMD, the SO-120(259). This is based on the lengthened BMD-2 hull, and is fitted with a new, high turret. The weapon appears to be a breech-loading 120mm mortar that can fire high-explosive rounds at normal or high elevations, and special HEAT anti-tank rounds. This vehicle appears to be a replacement for the ASU-85 assault gun, since it can be used both in the anti-armour role, and for general artillery fire support.

▲138 ▼139

The MT-LB Armoured Transporter

In the late 1970s, the Central Auto and Tractor Directorate embarked on a development programme to replace the AT-L, AT-S and AT-T tractors with a new generation of vehicles. The light tractor requirement resulted in the MT-L, as well as an armoured derivative, the MT-LB which was probably developed as a cheaper alternative to the BMP for utility roles. The BMP is well armoured, but its sleek, low shape was not designed for carrying cargo or similar roles. The MT-LB was based around many existing components including a commonplace truck engine. The road wheels, though resembling the PT-76 type, are of a new design. Although not its primary function, the MT-LB can be used as a troop carrier. The MT-LBV uses a special wide track which makes it especially suitable for operations in snow. As a result, some Soviet motor rifle divisions in the Arctic regions use the MT-LBV in lieu of the BTR-60PB. The MT-LB went into production in 1966 in the USSR and, later, Poland. It is used as the basis for the SA-13 Gopher launch vehicle, for the SNAR-10 artillery radar vehicle and in many other roles. The use of MT-LB variants in these roles is covered in other sections of this book.

140▲
MT-LB ARMOURED LIGHT TRACKED TRANSPORTER
337

141. The BTR-70 is the successor to the BTR-60, and is very similar in appearance. This rear view of a German NVA vehicle shows the rear contours of the vehicle which are significantly different in appearance from the BTR-60.
142. Rear view of a German NVA BTR-70 showing the reconfigured upper deck.
143. One of the main advantages offered by the BTR-70 is improved entrance and exit using these lower hull doors, but they are still not as easy to use as the large rear doors on the Czechoslovak/Polish OT-64 SKOT.
144. View of the turret armament of the BTR-70 from the inside. The turret is too small for the gunner to sit inside it. This same turret is also used on the BRDM-2, BTR-60PB and SKOT-2A.

▲141

▲142 ▼143

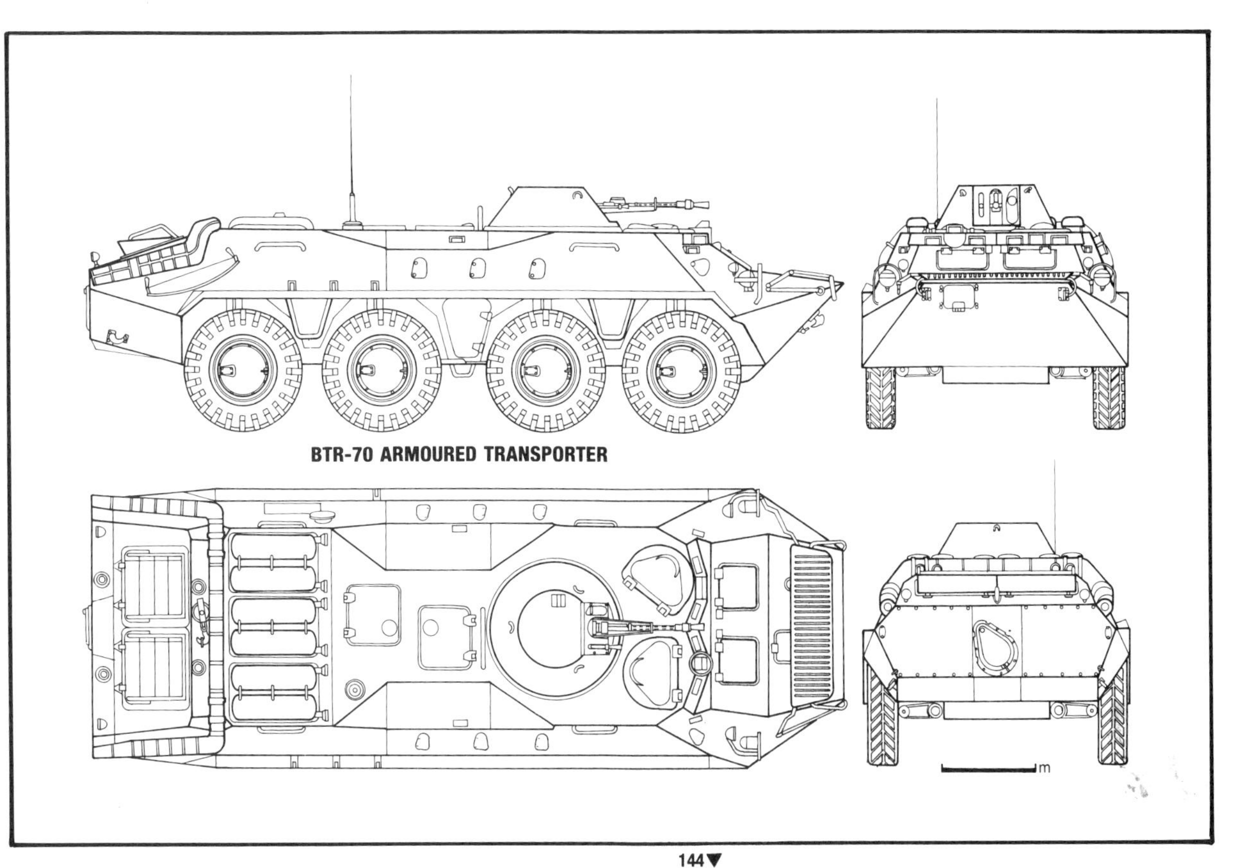

144▼

The BTR-70 Armoured Transporter

If the BMP is one of the most radical vehicles developed in the Soviet Union since the war, the BTR-70 is one of the least radical. The BTR-70 is a straight evolutionary development of the BTR-60PB, also designed by the Dedkov OKB in Gorkiy. Development began in the early 1970s to solve some of the problems with the BTR-60. The evolution of the BTR-60 from an open-topped carrier in the BTR-60P model to the closed, turreted version in the BTR-60PB model, left the Soviets with a vehicle poorly configured for troop entrance and exit, and ill-suited to the tactics of the 1970s. The BTR-70 corrected these faults by reconfiguring the hatch and seating arrangements. Rather than go for a complete reconfiguration, such as that offered by the Czechoslovak/Polish SKOT, the Dedkov OKB opted for a simpler change. Exit hatches were provided in the lower hull between the second and third wheel stations. Internally, the BTR-70 offered a reconfigured seating arrangement more in keeping with the mounted infantry tactics being used in BMP motor rifle regiments. In the rear, a bench seat was located down the middle of the vehicle for six riflemen sitting back to back, each with his own firing port. Two more

▲145 ▼146

riflemen behind the driver and vehicle commander face forward, and have side firing ports as well. Apart from these changes, the BTR-70 offers slight improvements in ballistic protection, and most of the main elements of the BTR-60PB design have been retained, including the peculiar twin engine arrangement with its attendant problems.

The BTR-70 is a clear example of the Soviet predilection towards a high-low mix in armoured vehicle procurement. The BMP is issued to motor rifle regiments in tank divisions, and to one of the three motor rifle regiments in each motor rifle division. The remaining two motor rifle regiments in the motor rifle divisions are equipped with the BTR-70 (or the older BTR-60PB). The BTR-70 allows these regiments to emulate BMP mounted and dismounted tactics, but the BTR-70 does not offer the armoured protection, mobility or firepower of its more expensive counterpart.

As with the BTR-60PB and BMP, command versions of the BTR-70 are also in service: the BTR-70KSh command vehicle and BTR-70MS radio vehicle. Some BTR-70 in Afghanistan have been modified with an AGS-17 grenade-launcher mounted on the turret roof to supplement the KPVT heavy machine-gun.

The BTR-70 betrays the flaw in relying on conservative evolutionary development of armoured vehicles. The design clearly did not rectify all of the BTR-60PB's problems, notably the poor exit arrangements and the excessively complicated double engine arrangement. As a

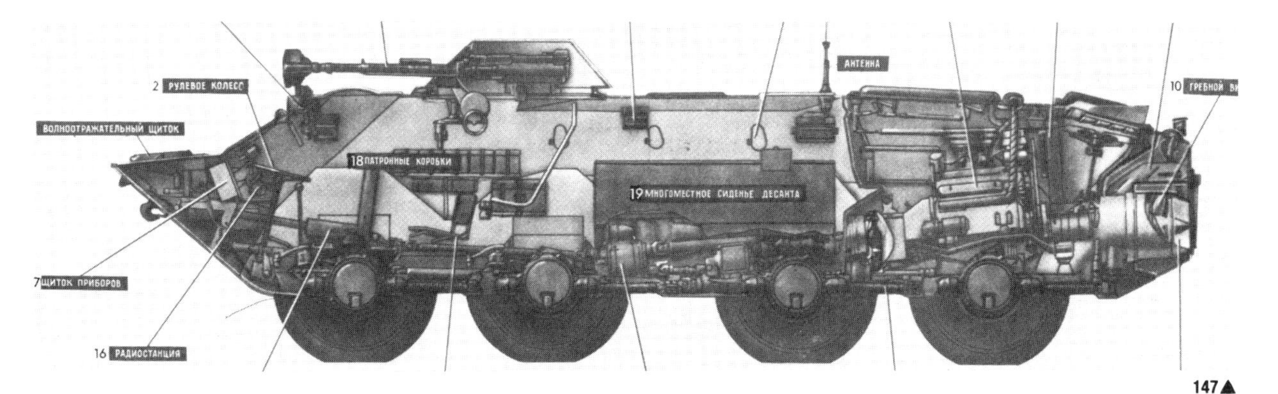

147▲

145. The BTR-70 interior is configured like that in the BMP to permit the rifle squad to fire its assault rifles from within the vehicle. This view looks backwards from the driver's position, past the gunner's seat towards the troop compartment.
146. The BTR-80 is a derivative of the earlier BTR-70, with engine and other improvements. Externally, it is similar to the BTR-70 as is evident from this Soviet illustration.
147. Soviet drawing of the interior configuration of the BTR-70.
148. The TAB-77 is a Romanian-built derivative of the BTR-70 with an anti-tank guided-missile launcher added to the turret sides among other changes.

result, in the early 1980s, a derivative was developed – the BTR-80, with three main changes: the twin engine configuration has been dropped in favour of a more sensible, 260hp diesel engine and a simpler powertrain. The side doors have been improved, and the turret has been redesigned to permit elevation of the KPVT heavy machine-gun to 60°, compared to the 30° on the earlier vehicle, which enables the weapon to be used against aerial targets such as helicopters. There have been a number of other detail design improvements, including the addition of smoke-mortars behind the turret, and improved firing ports. Presumably the BTR-80 has replaced the BTR-70 in production.

Warsaw Pact Armoured Infantry Vehicles

Armoured infantry vehicle design is one of the few areas where the Soviet Union has allowed its Warsaw Pact allies some leeway in local design and production. This may have been permitted in order to take advantage of the more mature automotive industries in some of these countries, and to placate them for the high licence fees for manufacturing other armoured vehicles such as tanks. The most active development of armoured infantry vehicles has been in Czechoslovakia.

Czechoslovak Infantry Vehicle Development

The Czechoslovak Army inherited some expertise in armoured infantry vehicle design from the Germans. The Skoda facility in Plzeň was involved in manufacturing components for German halftracks like the SdKfz 251 during the occupation. Immediately after the war, the Czech government encouraged the rebirth of the national armament industry, and plans were under way to market a modernized export version of the SdKfz 251 Ausf D when the Communist take-over occurred. Under the

148▼

Stalinist policies of the early 1950s these plans were shelved, but in the mid-1950s they were resurrected again. The Czechoslovak People's Army (CSLA) was given permission to develop its own armoured infantry vehicle in lieu of adopting the BTR-152. A number of competitive proposals were considered including an armoured V3S truck developed by Praga, and a rejuvenated SdKfz 251 halftrack carrier developed by Tatra. The latter was selected and entered service in about 1958 as the OT-810. The OT-810 used a Tatra diesel engine and had a number of body improvements compared to its German ancestor. The OT-810 was short-lived, being produced only until 1962. Total production was probably about 1,500 vehicles. In the late 1960s, as more modern vehicles entered service, it was modified as a tank destroyer with the M-59 recoilless rifle.

In the late 1950s, the CSLA was encouraged to emulate the Soviet reorganization and equipment of its infantry forces. The CSLA decided to adopt the Soviet BTR-50P for the motor rifle regiments of its tank divisions, but sought licence production rights. Negotiations were concluded in 1958, but the CSLA decided to develop an improved version rather than a straight copy. The V-6 engine was improved as the PV-6 by turbo-charging which boosted its output, and a new transmission was developed, derived from the wartime German AK 7-200 used on the Panther tank. The body was redesigned with side hatches to permit easier access and exit from the vehicle. This was accepted in 1962 as the OT-62 TOPAS and entered production in 1963. Four versions of the TOPAS were manufactured. The original version closely resembled the BTR-50PK, and carried no special armament. This

149. Praga developed an armoured version of its V3S truck which competed against a Tatra design (the OT-810) in the 1950s for a Czechoslovak CSLA contract. The Tatra design won, but the basic armoured V3S design was used to create an armoured twin 30mm air defence gun vehicle.
150. The Czechoslovak CSLA adopted the OT-810 half-track in lieu of the Soviet BTR-152. It was derived from the German Hanomag SdKfz 251 Ausf D.

▲149 ▼150

151▲

151. The OT-810 offered better cross-country mobility than the BTR-152, and the folding panels on the hull rear could offer overhead armour protection as well.

was followed by the OT-62 TOPAS-2A which carried a small machine-gun cupola over the right bay, also armed with a *Tarasnice* 82mm recoilless rifle. Two command versions were also manufactured, called TOPAS-VS or TOPAS-*Velitelske Stanoviste*; one version as a simple command vehicle, the other as a more elaborate command/staff vehicle with additional radio masts and generators.

The Polish People's Army (LWP) decided to acquire the OT-62 TOPAS in lieu of the BTR-50PK. The basic production model was ordered, with an aim towards modifying it to satisfy Polish requirements. The basic TOPAS was used in some units, but later production deliveries were shipped to LWP workshops where they were modified with the WAT turret developed by the Military Technical Academy for the OT-64 SKOT-2AP. This turret was armed with a 14.5mm KPVT machine-gun with a special high elevation trunnion for secondary use in an anti-aircraft role. This reduced the crew from 18 on the TOPAS to 15 on the TOPAS-2AP. The Poles also converted some of the TOPAS-2AP to a special carrier for mortar squads, carrying two 82mm mortars on external mountings, as well as fitting ammunition racks inside the hull. This version, the TOPAS-2AP (*mozdzierz*) carries a 3-man crew and two 4-man mortar squads. The Poles also developed a light recovery vehicle on the basis of the TOPAS, designated WPT-TOPAS. TOPAS production continued into the early 1970s, and about 3,500 were manufactured. Besides use by the CSLA and LWP, the TOPAS was exported to the Middle East where it has seen combat.

The CSLA also discussed licensed production of the BMP to replace the TOPAS. The negotiations were completed in about 1970, and production of the BMP-1 began in about 1971-72 as the BVP-1. Czechoslovak production was geared not only to CSLA requirements, but was part of a Czech agreement with the USSR to supply armoured vehicles to the Soviet Ground Forces. About 70 per cent of Czech BMP production is shipped to the USSR. Total Soviet import of armoured infantry vehicles from other Warsaw Pact countries (Czechoslovak BMP and Polish MT-LB) has averaged about 600–800 vehicles annually according to US DIA estimates.

The OT-64 SKOT In 1959, Czechoslovakia and Poland discussed the possibility of co-producing a new armoured infantry vehicle in lieu of purchasing the BTR-60PB from the USSR. Responsibility for the work was divided, with the Czechs responsible for the chassis and automotive components, and the Poles for the armoured body and armament. The first prototype was completed in 1961, and production began in about 1963. It is believed that chassis production is undertaken by the Tatra Automotive Factory in Koprivnice, Czechoslovakia and armoured hull work and assembly at the FCS (*Fabryka Samochodow Ciezarowych*) in Lublin, Poland. The initial production version, called OT-64 SKOT-1A, corresponded to the Soviet BTR-60PA and had no armament. The principal differences between the OT-64 SKOT and the BTR-60P were that it could carry a larger number of troops, was configured for more satisfactory troop entrance and exit, and incorporated a CBR protective system from the outset. The OT-64 has two large rear doors to speed troop access, and reduces their vulnerability to small-arms fire. Besides the basic troop-carrying version, a variety of turretless support vehicles were also developed. The Polish WITI (Military Institute of Engineer Technology) developed two engineer versions: the SKOT-1A *inzynierny* (*torujacy*) which was used to carry mine detection and clearing gear, and the SKOT-1A *inzynierny* (*zaporowy*) to carry mines and tow a mine-dispersing trailer. The SKOT-WPT is a light recovery version of the SKOT-1A and entered production in 1969. It uses a small jib crane, and carries various repair equipment inside. There are three command versions of the SKOT, differing in their radio gear and antenna features, and designated SKOT-R1, SKOT-R2 and SKOT-R3. These correspond to the BTR-60PU. The SKOT *artylerjski* is a special weapons carrier, with stowage for mortar crews,

152. Czechoslovakia and Poland jointly developed and manufactured the OT-64 SKOT wheeled armoured infantry vehicle instead of purchasing the Soviet BTR-60. These are Polish SKOT-1A with the early machine-gun crow's nests, armed with the 12.7mm DShK.

▼152

153. The SKOT-1A was superseded by the SKOT-2A which was armed with the same turret as that used on the Soviet BTR-60PB. The SKOT-2A was exported to a number of countries. This one belongs to the Ugandan Army.
154. The definitive version of the SKOT was the SKOT-2AP, fitted with a WAT turret designed in Poland. This offered better anti-aircraft performance than the Soviet BTR-60PB turret because of its higher maximum gun elevation.
155. As in the case of the TOPAS, a variety of command versions of the SKOT were built. The Poles call their vehicles SKOT R-1, R-2 and R-3, while the Czechoslovak CSLA calls them SKOT-VS.

153▲

154▲ 155▼

156. To give the SKOT a measure of anti-tank protection, some Polish SKOT-2A were fitted with 9M14M Malyutka (AT-3 Sagger) anti-tank missile-launchers on the turret.
157. The Polish Army developed a version of the MT-LB fitted with the same WAT turret as used on the SKOT-2AP and TOPAS-2AP as a cheaper alternative to the BMP. It does not appear to have entered production.

▲156

anti-tank guided-missile crews or SPG-9 crews and was developed in 1968. Some of the turretless vehicles used the turret riser developed for the SKOT-2A to provide a little more headroom inside. These have been deployed both as command vehicles, and for internal security forces.

The original version of the SKOT, the SKOT-1A, was a pure 'battlefield taxi'. The only shortcoming of the SKOT compared to the newer BTR-60PB was that it was not armed. In the 1960s, the Poles began to experiment with simple external gun mounts including an armoured crow's-nest around a PKT 7.62mm machine-gun, and a similar arrangement around a 12.7mm DShK machine-gun. Neither was entirely satisfactory. As a result, it was decided to adopt the same turret used on the BTR-60PB (and BRDM-2) as an interim solution. This resulted in the SKOT-2A, which entered service in 1968–69. The Poles were not satisfied with this arrangement, feeling that the machine-gun had too restricted an elevation, which diminished its utility against low-flying aircraft or helicopters. A design team at WAT (Military Technical Academy) in Warsaw developed a new turret, using the same weapons, but with a CGS-90 sight and higher elevation. This was accepted for production as the SKOT-2AP, and the WAT turret was later used on the TOPAS-2AP as well. In the early 1970s, the WITU (Military Institute of Armament Technology) developed a mounting for the 9M14M Malyutka missile on the SKOT-2 turret which offered a measure of anti-tank protection. This was retrofitted to some vehicles. Total SKOT production to date has been fairly large, probably amounting to about 7,500 vehicles. It has been exported to a number of countries and has seen combat with Indian and Ugandan forces.

▼157

The most recent employment of the WAT turret has been on the MT-LB. In the late

1970s, the Poles began experimenting with a locally produced MT-LB mounting a WAT turret either in the middle of the vehicle, or to the rear. This was apparently examined as a cheaper alternative to the BMP, or as an eventual replacement for the OT-62 TOPAS. In 1985, a new troop carrier appeared in a parade in Sofia, Bulgaria. It consisted of the chassis of the SO-122 (2S1) Gvozdika, fitted with the same turret as the BMP-2. Following so closely on the heels of the BMP-2, it seems unlikely to have been a Soviet vehicle. It may be Polish. The Poles currently build the SO-122 (2S1) chassis, and may have felt that such a combination is a cheaper alternative than purchasing an entire BMP-2 from the USSR. In any event, the new vehicle is something of a mystery.

Romanian Armoured Infantry Vehicles

Romania's gradual drift from the Warsaw Pact has led it to seek a greater measure of weaponry independence than might be expected from such an industrially weak state. In the late 1960s, the Romanian Socialist Army (ASR) approached the Military Industrial Committee of COMECON about the possibility of licensed production of the BTR-60PB. The Soviets consented, probably feeling that this was preferable to yet another co-development scheme between Romania and the heretic Yugoslavs. The initial, turretless model, called TAB-71, entered production in 1970, and was basically a BTR-60P with two 140hp engines in place of the normal 90hp engines. This version was not produced in significant numbers. It was soon succeeded by a version of the BTR-60PB with a modified turret and uprated engines, designated TAB-72. The only external difference between a BTR-60PB and the TAB-72 is the protruding gun sight on the left side of the Romanian vehicle. The Romanians also designed a turretless mortar version of the TAB-72, the TAB-73. Total production of the TAB-71/-72/-73 was modest, and probably amounted to about 1,200 vehicles.

In the late 1970s, the Romanians acquired licensed production rights for the newer BTR-70 which entered production in about 1977 as the TAB-77. The Romanian version is essentially similar to the Soviet version, but has launchers for the 9M14M Malyutka missile on the turret sides to give the vehicle some anti-tank protection. A locally developed, shortened version of the TAB-77, with four instead of eight wheels, entered production at about the same time as the TAB-C. This appears to be intended as a scout vehicle rather than a troop carrier.

SOVIET ARMOURED INFANTRY VEHICLES

	BTR-152V	BTR-60PB	SKOT-2AP	BTR-70	BTR-50PK	TOPAS-2AP	BMP-1	BMP-2	BMD-1	MT-LB
Crew+squad	2+17	3+8	2+10	3+8	1+20	2+13	2+9	2+8	2+5	2+9
Weight (tonnes, combat loaded)	9.8	10.2	14.8	11.5	14.2	15.1	13.9	15.0	6.7	11.9
Length (cm)	683	722	744	754	703	700	674	675	540	645
Width (cm)	232	282	255	280	314	322	294	343	363	285
Height (cm)	200	241	206	223	207	272	208	210	197	186
Ground clearance (cm)	28	47	40	40	37	42	39	37	40	40
Ground pressure (kg/cubic cm)	3.7	2.5	2.5	2.8	0.51	0.53	0.60	0.61	0.57	0.46
Armour (mm)										
Turret (front)	–	7	7	7	–	7	23	23	23	7
Turret sides	–	7	7	7	–	7	19	19	19	7
Hull bow	11-15	9-11	10	10	10	10	7-19	7-19	7-15	7
Hull sides	8-9	7-9	9	7-9	9	9	16-18	16-18	18	7
Hull rear	7	7	7	7	7	7	16	16	16	7
Main gun	SGMB	KPVT	KPVT	KPVT	SGMT	KPVT	2A28	2A42	2A28	PKT
Gun calibre (mm)	7.62	14.5	14.5	14.5	7.62	14.5	73	30	73	7.62
Depression/elevation (degrees)		−5+30	−4+89	−5+30		−5+78	−4+30	−5+74	−4+33	−5+30
Ammunition stowed	1250	500	500	500	1250	500	39	250	39	2000
Coaxial armament	–	PKT	PKT	PKT	–	PKT	PKT	PKT	PKT	–
Gun calibre (mm)	–	7.62	7.62	7.62	–	7.62	7.62	7.62	7.62	–
Ammunition stowed	–	2000	2000	2000	–	2000	2000	2000	2000	–
Anti-tank missile	–	–	–	–	–	–	9M14M	9M66	9M14M	–
Rounds carried	–	–	–	–	–	–	4	4	3	–
Engine designation	ZiL-123	GAZ-49B	T-928-14	ZMZ-4905	V-6	PV-6	UTD-20	UTD-20	5D20	YAMZ-238V
Type	petrol	petrol	diesel	petrol	diesel	diesel	diesel	diesel	diesel	diesel
Horsepower	110	2 × 90	180	2 × 115	240	300	300	300	300	240
Fuel stowed (litres)	300	290	330	300	400	407	460	460	300	520
Road range (avg. km)	650	500	750	400	400	550	500	500	500	500
Max. speed (km/h)	65	80	95	80	44	60	80	75	61	62
Amphibious propulsion	–	hydrojet	prop	hydrojet	hydrojet	hydrojet	track	track	hydrojet	track
CBR protection	–	PAZ	PAZ	PAZ	PAZ	PAZ	PAZ+PBZ	PAZ+PBZ	PAZ+PBZ	PAZ+PBZ
Radio (standard)	10RT-12	R-123	R-113	R-123M	R-113	R-113	R-123	R-123M	R-123	R-123

158. The BM-14-17 was a 140mm multiple rocket-launcher based on the GAZ-63 truck. A similar launcher was also mounted on the ZiL-151 truck as the BM-14-16.
159. The BM-13 was a post-war modernization of the wartime BM-13S, substituting the ZiS-151 truck for the Studebacker US6.
160. The BM-24 was a heavy multiple rocket-launcher, designed to replace the wartime BM-31. This example was captured by the Israeli Army from Egyptian forces, and taken into Israeli service. (US Army)

▲158

▲159 ▼160

Mechanized Artillery

In the Russian Army, both Tsarist and Soviet, artillery has traditionally been called *bog voiny*- the god of war. If the Russians have harboured a lingering feeling of technological inferiority to western European armies in most fields, this has seldom been the case in the artillery branch. Since the time of Peter the Great, the Russians have prided themselves on their artillery.

During the Second World War the Soviet artillery arm was respected by its opponents for the quality of its weapons, even if derided for the infatuation with sheer volume of firepower. Mechanization was delayed compared to the process occurring in other European armies of the time. The Soviet Main Artillery Directorate (GAU) showed very little interest in self-propelled artillery during the war. Western observers have frequently mistaken the profusion of assault guns, such as the SU-85, SU-100, SU-122 and ISU-152 for self-propelled artillery. In fact, these assault guns were developed at the request of the Main Armour Directorate, manned by tank troops, and employed as surrogate tanks. They were intended primarily for direct fire, and were ill-suited for the usual artillery role of indirect fire. The only significant design that vaguely resembled American, German or British self-propelled guns was the SU-76, a lightly armoured vehicle mounting the 76mm divisional field gun. But even this had been developed as a tank destroyer, and was used in a role more akin to the pre-war infantry support tanks. The Red Army of the Second World War had no immediate equivalents of the American M7 105mm howitzer motor carriage; M40 155mm gun motor carriage; the British Sexton 25lb self-propelled howitzer; or the German Wespe 105mm or Hummel 150mm self-propelled howitzers.

The only area in which the Red Army showed much interest in mobile artillery was the Guards mortar, better known as Katyusha or multiple rocket-launcher. The Red Army pioneered the use of multiple rocket-launchers for artillery use, and used them in greater profusion than any other army during the war. These artillery rocket-launchers were usually mounted on trucks, and by the end of the war, more than 10,000 had been manufactured. A total of 40 independent battalions, 105 independent regiments, 40 independent brigades and 7 divisions had been equipped with these weapons, not to mention the numerous divisional guards mortar units. The Katyushas were popular with the Red Army for two reasons. On the logistical side, many Soviet artillery factories had been overrun by the Germans during the opening months of the war. Conventional tubed artillery requires elaborate (and expensive) machining. Katyushas, on the other hand, can be readily manufactured by small machine shops with little specialized equipment. The second attraction of the Katyushas for the Red Army was their applicability to the style of massed firepower favoured by Russian artillerymen. A single truck-mounted launcher could ripple fire a rocket salvo, equivalent to a battery of conventional guns. The Katyushas were mounted on trucks because their very distinctive back-blast when fired required them to be moved frequently to avoid counter-battery fire. The limited accuracy of this kind of weapon was not a major concern, since they were intended to supplement conventional artillery, not replace it. Conventional artillery could be used in roles, such as counter-battery fire, where accuracy was demanded.

Post-War Katyushas

In the immediate post-war years, the GAU focused its attention on modernizing its large force of Guards mortars, and a slightly improved, new generation of equipment was developed by the Barmin Design Bureau. Beginning in 1949, the BM-13-16 on the ZiS-151 truck replaced the BM-13N (on the Lend-Lease Studebaker US 6). The long-range BMD-20 was finally introduced, based on wartime experiments with the BM-13SN. In 1955, the BM-14 replaced the BM-13; the BM-24 Guards heavy mortar was introduced the same year and became the standard weapon in its class. The Guards mortars were employed both in independent artillery units, and as organic artillery units in tank, rifle and mechanized divisions. Each division usually had a battalion of Guards mortars to supplement conventional towed artillery.

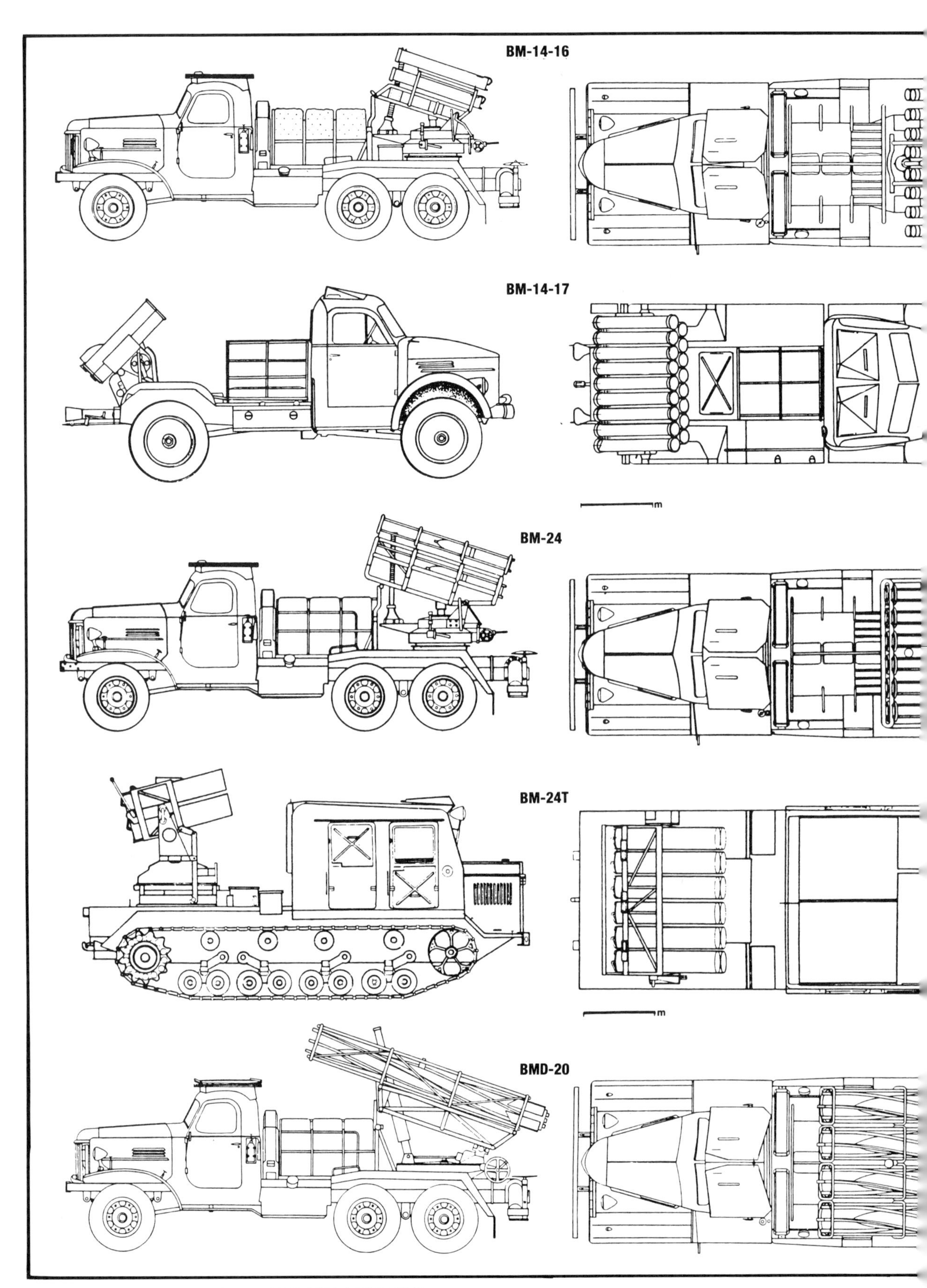
BM-14-16
BM-14-17
m
BM-24
BM-24T
m
BMD-20

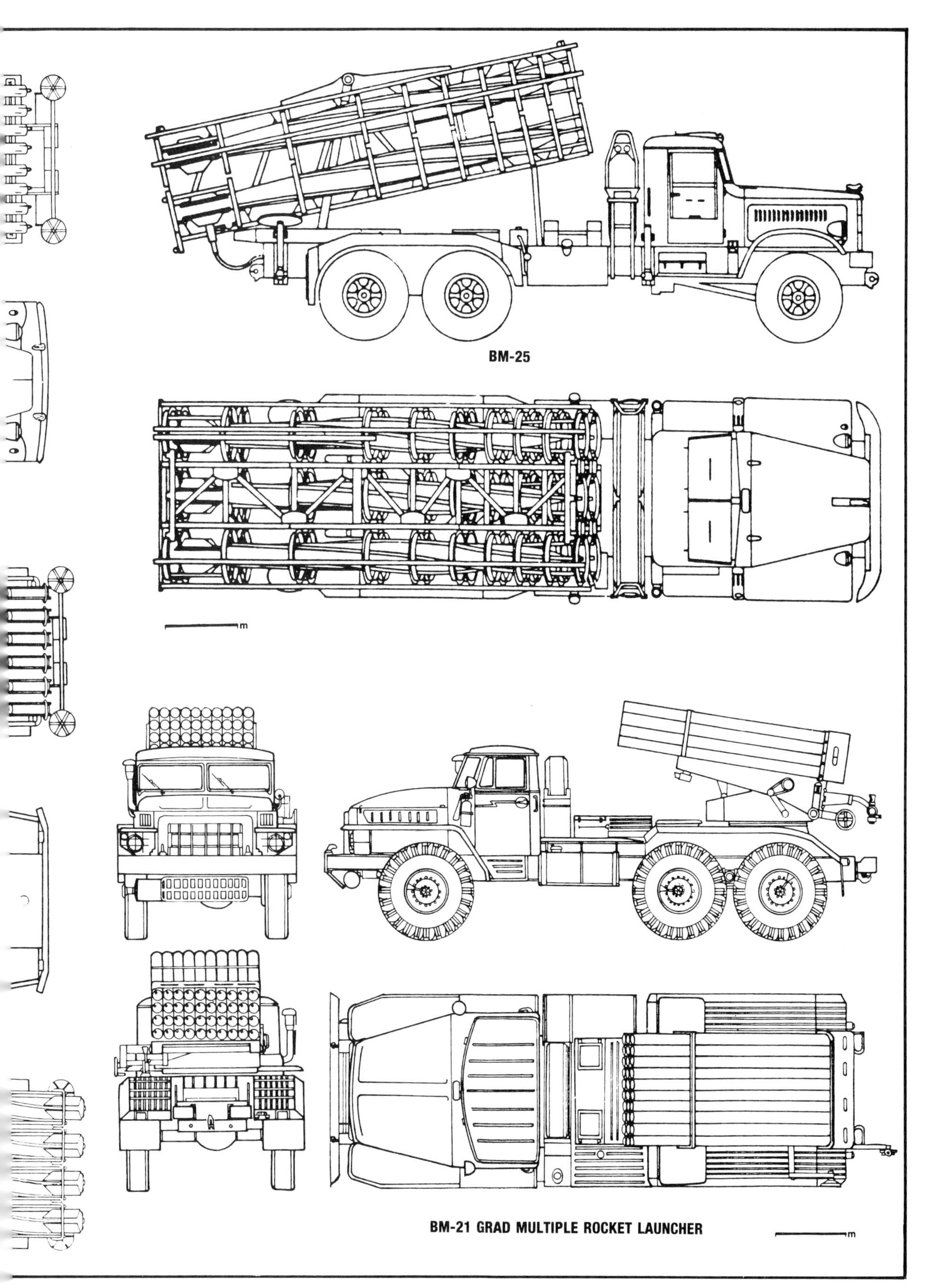

BM-25

BM-21 GRAD MULTIPLE ROCKET LAUNCHER

▲161

▲162 ▼163

161. The BMD-20 was intended as a long-range supplement to the normal multiple rocket-launchers. Each launcher carried only four rounds at a time. (Sovfoto)
162. The BM-25 was another long-range multiple launcher, and fired the largest rocket of all the Soviet multiple rocket-launchers. (Sovfoto)
163. The BM-27 multiple rocket launcher is a new long-range system designed to replace the older BMD-20 and BM-25 long range multiple rocket launchers. (US DoD)

164▲

165▲

164. The Grad-P is a lightweight derivative of the BM-21 system intended for use by airborne units. It is mounted on a modified GAZ-66B truck.
165. In 1964, the Ground Forces began to receive the BM-21 multiple rocket-launcher, based on the Ural 375 truck. It was intended to simplify logistics by replacing a larger variety of outdated launchers like the BM-13, BM-14 and others. (US Army)

The BM-27

Besides the long-range 2S5 and SO-203, Soviet army and front-level artillery units began to receive the new BM-27 in 1977. The BM-27 is intended as a replacement for the obsolete BMD-20 and BM-25 long-range multiple rocket-launchers. It is mounted on BAZ-135 chassis and has sixteen tubes. The new rockets have a maximum range of about 40km, about double that of the divisional-level BM-21. The warhead types available probably include both conventional and chemical munitions. The conventional rounds are probably both unitary high-explosive types, and cargo types with grenade submunitions. The BM-27 is also the first Soviet multiple rocket-launcher to include a reload assistance vehicle. This is also mounted on a modified BAZ-135 chassis. It feeds reload rockets into the empty tubes of the BM-27 in much the same manner as is employed on the Czech RM-70 system. This system was probably adopted for its speed and because the rockets are probably too large to be handled unaided.

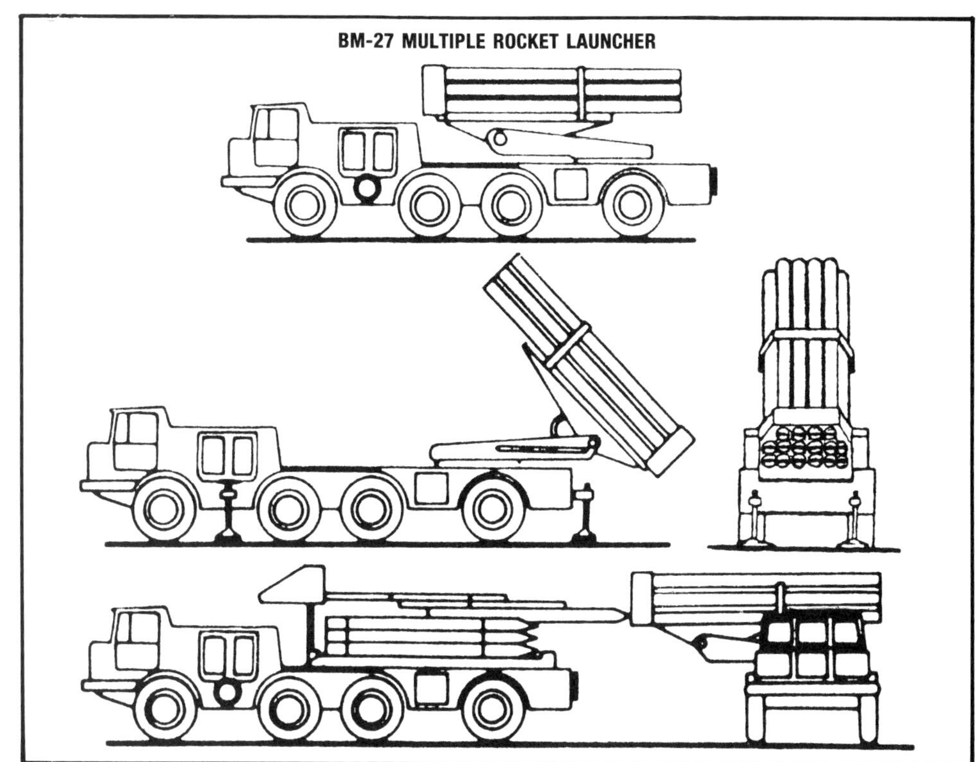

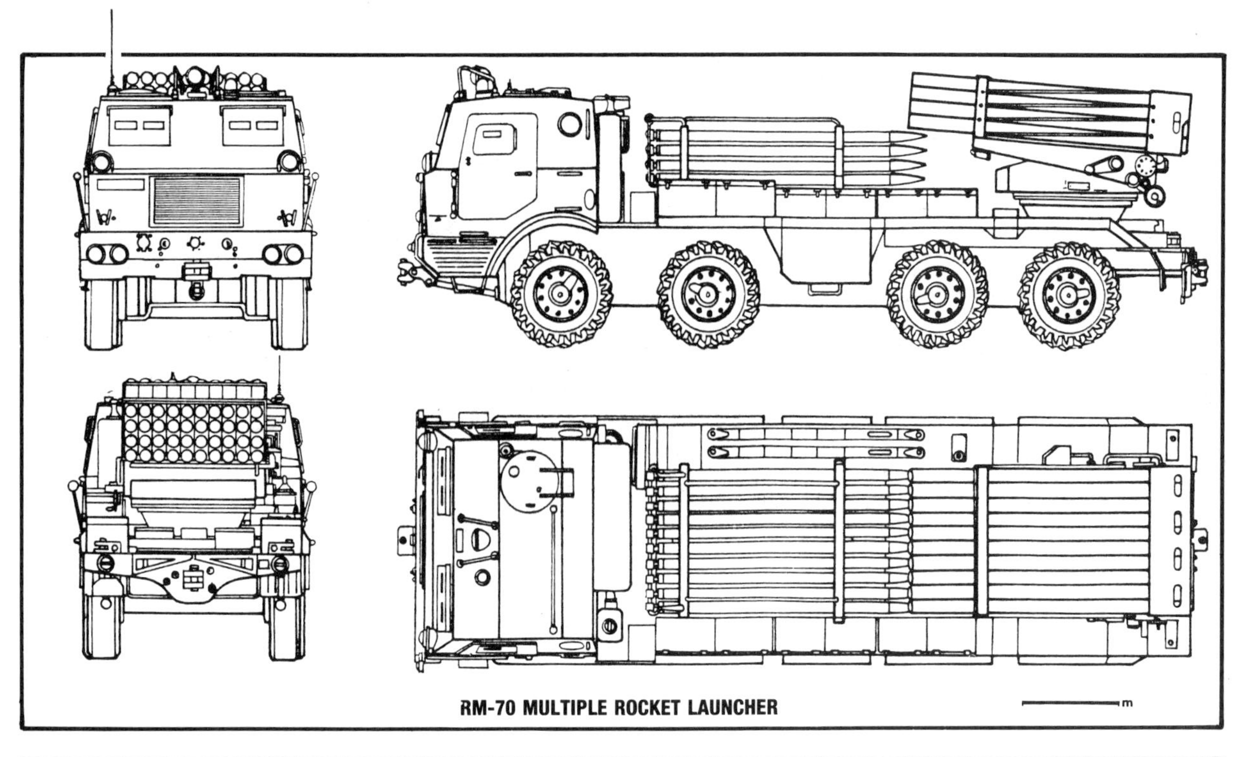

RM-70 MULTIPLE ROCKET LAUNCHER

SOVIET MULTIPLE ROCKET ARTILLERY VEHICLES

	BM-21-36	BM-21	RM-70	BM-14	BM-14-17	BMD-20	BM-24	BM-24T	BM-25	BM-27
Vehicle chassis:	ZiL-131	Ural-375D	Tatra 813	ZiL-151	GAZ-63A	ZiL-151	ZiL-157	AT-S	KrAZ-214	BAZ-135L4
Crew	6	6	6	7	6	6	6	7	6	4
Weight (tonnes)	10.5	13.7	14	8.2	5.3	8.7	8.9	15.2	18.1	22.7
Length (m)	6.9	7.35	7.76	6.92	5.41	7.2	6.7	5.97	9.81	9.7
Width (m)	2.5	2.69	2.5	2.3	1.93	2.3	2.31	2.60	2.7	2.8
Height (m)	2.48	2.85	2.70	2.65	2.24	2.85	2.91	3.1	3.5	3.2
Ground clearance (cm)	40	41	40	26.5	27	26.5	31	40	38	38
Engine type	ZiL-131	ZiL-375	T-930	ZiL-121	GAZ-51	ZiL-121	ZiL-157	V-54T	YaMZ-206B	ZiL-375
Horsepower	150	175	270	92	70	92	109	275	205	360
Max. speed (km/h)	80	75	75	60	65	60	65	35	55	65
Range (km)	525	480	1000	600	650	600	430	380	530	500
Fording depth (m)	1	1	1.4	.8	.8	.8	.85	1	1	1
Number of rocket tubes	36	40	40	16	17	4	12	12	6	16
Max. elevation (degrees)	55	55	55	52	47	50	52	55	60	55
Traverse (degrees)	180	180	180	200	210	20	140	210	20	180
Reload time (min)	10	10	1.5-3	4	2	10	4	4	10	15
Emplacement time (min)	2.5	2.5	2.5	3	3					3.5
Rocket Characteristics										
Rocket calibre (mm)	122	122	122	140	140	200	240	240	250	220
Length (m)	1.9	3.22	3.22	1.08	1.08	3.11	1.29	1.29	5.82	4.8
Weight (kg)	45.8	77.5	77.5	39.6	39.6	91.4	109	109	455	360
Max. velocity (m/s)	699	699	699	402	400	660	465	465		
Range (km)	10.8	20.5	20.5	9.8	9.8	19	16.8	10.2	55.9	40
Stabilization	fin	fin	fin	spin	spin	fin	spin	spin	fin	fin
Rate of fire (rockets/ 10 seconds)	20	20	20	3	3	4	2	2	1	5

The BM-21 Grad

In the area of multiple rocket-launchers, an effort was made to cut back on the bewildering variety of calibres and types with the introduction of the new *Grad* (Hail) system in 1964. Although some older systems such as the BM-13 were modernized, for instance by mounting them on newer trucks like the ZiL-131, the emphasis was on adopting a new common type to replace the bewildering variety in service. The Grad system was a new 122mm rocket system mounted on the Ural-375D truck as the BM-21 and was intended to replace the 140mm rocket systems at divisional level. The BM-21 uses a tube launching system with forty tubes per vehicle. The basic rocket used by the Grad system is the M-21-OF (9M22M), also known

166. The Czechoslovak equivalent of the BM-21 is the RM-70. This uses a larger armoured Tatra 813 truck which enables reload rounds to be carried. It is also used by the East German NVA as seen here.

as the DB-1B high-explosive rocket. Other rocket types with different warheads are available, as is a shorter (1.9m vs. 3.3m) round with reduced range, the M-14-OF (DKZ-B). This system has become the standard Soviet divisional multiple rocket-launcher since 1964. In the 1970s, the slightly modified BM-21-36 version based on the ZiL-131 truck was introduced which apparently uses the shorter M-14-OF round. This is a lightweight version, more suitable for use in mountainous areas, and is fitted with 36 tubes instead of the usual 40 tubes on the BM-21, the two central tubes being eliminated from the two bottom rows. Another special lightweight 12-tube version was also developed, and mounted on a GAZ-66 light truck.

The Czechoslovak People's Army had developed their own multiple rocket-launcher, the M-51 mounted on the V3S truck. The CSLA later decided to adopt the Soviet BM-21 system, but was opposed to using an unarmoured truck. Instead they developed a version of the Tatra 813 truck with an armoured cab. This version entered service in 1972 as the RM-70. It is considerably larger than the BM-21, and besides the advantages offered by its armoured cab, it is fitted with a semi-automatic loading system with an additional 40 rounds of rockets for rapid reload capability. The RM-70 is the standard multiple rocket-launcher of the CSLA and the East German NVA. The Romanian Army used an adaptation of the Czechoslovak M-51 on a ZiL-151/157, but in the 1960s adopted a locally produced version of the BM-21, mounted on the Bucesi SR-114 truck at about the same time.

The BM-21 equips a multiple rocket-launcher battalion in each division's artillery regiment. This battalion has three batteries, each with six BM-21, for a total of eighteen BM-21 per division. The salvo firepower of one of these batteries is massive. A single battery of six launchers can fire 240 rockets totalling eleven tonnes of metal and high-explosive into an area roughly 950m by 600m in a 20-second ripple fire. It takes about ten minutes to reload the BM-21 between salvoes. By comparison, a battery of its 122mm towed howitzer counterpart, the D-30 (2A18) *Sonyushka* (Little Sonya), would take seventy minutes to deliver the same volume of fire. The main disadvantages of the BM-21 compared to conventional tubed artillery is that the rockets suffer from much greater dispersion at range. Taking the oval dispersion footprint of a single BM-21 and D-30 as an example, the linear dispersion of a BM-21 is about 74m deep compared to only 26m for a D-30, while the lateral dispersion is 118m across for the BM-21 and only about 9.7m for a D-30 at 15km range. For this reason, the multiple rocket-launchers are only useful for area bombardment, not for precision artillery attacks.

New Directions

Unlike the armoured infantry vehicles where the lack of wartime development was followed by a blossoming of interest after the war, there was no

167. The SU-310 was a monstrous 310mm long-range gun intended for firing nuclear projectiles. It was too cumbersome, and was supplanted by rocket-launched nuclear warheads like the Luna (FROG) series.
168. The SU-420 was a heavy mortar counterpart of the SU-310, and equally unsuccessful.
169. Closeup of the SU-420 showing the sheer size of the vehicle. It was based on components from the IS-2/3 family of heavy tanks. (George Balin)

sudden spurt of interest in mechanizing the artillery; in fact development focused almost exclusively on evolutionary development of war-time weapons and tactics. The administration of the Soviet artillery branch, under Marshal N. N. Voronov, was preoccupied with other matters.

In 1944-45, Soviet Intelligence became aware of German successes in rocket technology. A Special Technical Commission under General Gaidukov, and including the USSR's premier rocket designer, Sergei Korolov, followed in the footsteps of the advancing Red Army to retrieve such rocket technology and scientists as could be found. Stalin was insistent that the Soviet artillery force incorporate heavy rocket weapons at the earliest possible opportunity. The GAU decided to begin manufacturing the German A-4 rocket (better known as the V-2) for Soviet artillery units as the R-1. These did not become available until the late 1940s. In the interim, it was decided to form temporary units using captured German equipment. The Germans had begun to develop an A-4 rocket launching train in 1944, but had abandoned the project owing to its lack of utility in the face of Allied air superiority. The idea intrigued the Soviet Special Technical Commission, and two such trains, called FMS (a cover name meaning Mobile Meteorological Station) were built under Soviet instruction in occupied East Germany. In 1946, one of these trains was used to form the 'Special Purpose Brigade', the first Soviet missile unit. It was formed on the basis of a Guards mortar regiment, and was put under the command of Major-General A. Tveretskiy, reporting directly to Marshal Voronov. In the late 1940s, as Korolov's NII 88 bureau at Kaliningrad mastered A-4 manufacturing technology, the first Soviet R-1 missiles became available. These were used to form Special Missile Brigades which were deployed at army and front level as a much larger counterpart of the Katyushas. As in the German case, they were fired from wheeled trailers. They received the US/NATO reporting name of SS-1a Scunner.

The Main Artillery Directorate (GAU), later to become the Main Artillery and Missile Directorate (GRAU), was also administratively responsible for the military aspects of the Soviet nuclear weapons programme. The staff of GAU was deeply interested in adapting nuclear weapons to tactical battlefield roles besides their strategic use to counter US and British nuclear weapons development. In the early 1950s, a TTT was issued to Korolov's NII 88 to develop a family of tactical battlefield missiles capable of carrying a small nuclear warhead. At the same time, one of the armoured vehicle design bureau, probably Kotin's or Dukhov's, began work on a massive tracked chassis, derived from the IS-3 tank, for a new self-propelled gun to fire the nuclear projectiles being developed by the Central Artillery Design Bureau (TsAKB) at Kaliningrad on the outskirts of Moscow. The GAU expected that the US Army would employ nuclear weapons on the battlefield, and was intent on developing comparable systems. The main technical drawback faced by Soviet designers was the failure of Kurchatov's nuclear weapons design bureau to miniaturize the nuclear warheads to the extent that the Americans had achieved. While the US Army was already experimenting with artillery-fired nuclear projectiles, the Soviets were having a hard time adapting nuclear warheads, even to fairly large missiles.

Superheavy Artillery

The design requirements of the early 1950s resulted in a spate of new nuclear artillery systems in 1956–57. Two self-propelled artillery systems were developed on a common chassis by the Central Artillery Design Bureau: the SU-310 mechanized superheavy gun, and the related SU-420 mechanized superheavy mortar. Both weapons were paraded in Moscow from 1957, and were crowd pleasers if only for their gargantuan proportions. They did not prove to be tactically successful, and their further production was curtailed by Nikita Khrushchev's personal disapproval.

The R-11/SS-1b Scud A

In the rocket field, Korolov's NII 88 design teams were more successful. A new medium-range missile, the R-11, was successfully tested at the Kapustin Yar proving ranges in 1956–57, to replace the R-1 in the special missile brigades. The R-11 had several advantages over the R-1. It was mounted on a special tracked launcher derived from the IS-2 tank chassis, probably developed by Dukhov's design bureau. Also, it was capable of carrying a nuclear warhead, even if there were very few tactical nuclear warheads available in 1957 due to shortages in fissionable material and the priorities allotted to strategic nuclear missiles such as the R-7. The R-11 was accepted in Army trials and entered service in 1957. It was given the US/NATO codename SS-1b Scud A. The R-11 was issued to special missile brigades at army and front level. Initially these brigades had two launch battalions with six launch vehicles each, but later this was expanded to three battalions in some units, for a total of

167▲

168▲ 169▼

▲170 ▼171

170. The long-range counterpart of the FROG/Luna is the R-11 missile, called Scud by NATO. The SS-1b Scud A launcher, seen here in Romanian ASR service, is based on an IS-2/3 chassis.
171. An SS-1B Scud A launcher of the German NVA.
172. The Luna (FROG-1) was the first of the divisional nuclear-capable rocket-launchers introduced into the Soviet Ground Forces. It was based on the chassis of the IS-2/3 family of heavy tanks. (Sovfoto)
173. The Luna-1 (FROG-2) was launched from the more mobile and compact PT-76 chassis. This launch vehicle is being decontaminated during a CBR exercise. (Sovfoto)

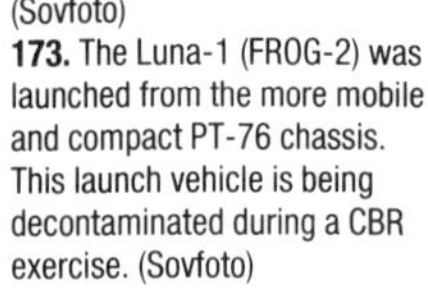

eighteen launchers. At first most of these missiles were fitted with conventional warheads owing to a shortage of nuclear warheads. They were suitably modified as nuclear warheads became available in the 1960s and could also carry chemical warheads. During this period, there were also efforts to develop intermediate-range missiles mounted on mobile, tracked launchers such as the Scamp/Scapegoat and Scrooge, but these were for strategic roles, not for the Ground Forces, and are outside the scope of this book. Also, the Soviet Navy developed a number of mobile coastal-defence missile vehicles on wheeled chassis, but these too fall outside our purview.

The Luna/FROG Rocket

There was some interest in providing each division with nuclear firepower, and this became manifest in the *Luna* (Moon) programme. The first of the Luna ballistic rockets were tested in 1956–57. Two different missile types were developed: the Luna, based on the IS-2/3 chassis, and the shorter-range Luna 1, on a modified PT-76 chassis developed by Kotin's bureau in Leningrad. Both missiles were simple fin-stabilized rockets using solid rocket propulsion. Both were accepted for service in 1957, and became operational in 1958. They received the codenames FROG-1 and FROG-2 by NATO (standing for Free Rocket Over Ground). These missiles were deployed with mechanized and tank divisions (and the later motor rifle divisions) in special missile-launcher battalions with two launch vehicles per battalion. The IS-2/3-mounted Luna proved cumbersome, and in 1960 was supplanted by the Luna 2 which offered similar performance, but which was mounted on a modified PT-76 chassis. This system was designated FROG-3 by NATO. FROG-4 and FROG-5 used the same rocket body as FROG-3, but had different warheads.

172▲ 173▼

174. The Luna-2 had three variants which all used the same rocket, but had different warheads. This particular type received the NATO codename of FROG-3. (Sovfoto)
175. The Luna-2 (FROG-4) had a more streamlined appearance than the other sub-types of this rocket. This side view shows clearly the modified PT-76 chassis used on the Luna-2 launcher which had a higher suspension and a set of return rollers. (Charles Perkins)
176. The Luna-2 was followed by the Luna-M R-75 (FROG-7) rocket mounted on a BAZ-135L4 truck. This launcher was more mobile than the tracked launchers, and had its own crane. (Sovfoto)
177. A Luna M crew preparing the rocket for launch. (Sovfoto)
178. The Luna M can be fitted with a conventional, chemical or nuclear warhead. Here, an R-75 rocket is being loaded onto the launch rail by its German NVA crew using the vehicle's hydraulic crane.

▲174

▲175 ▼176

177▲

178▲

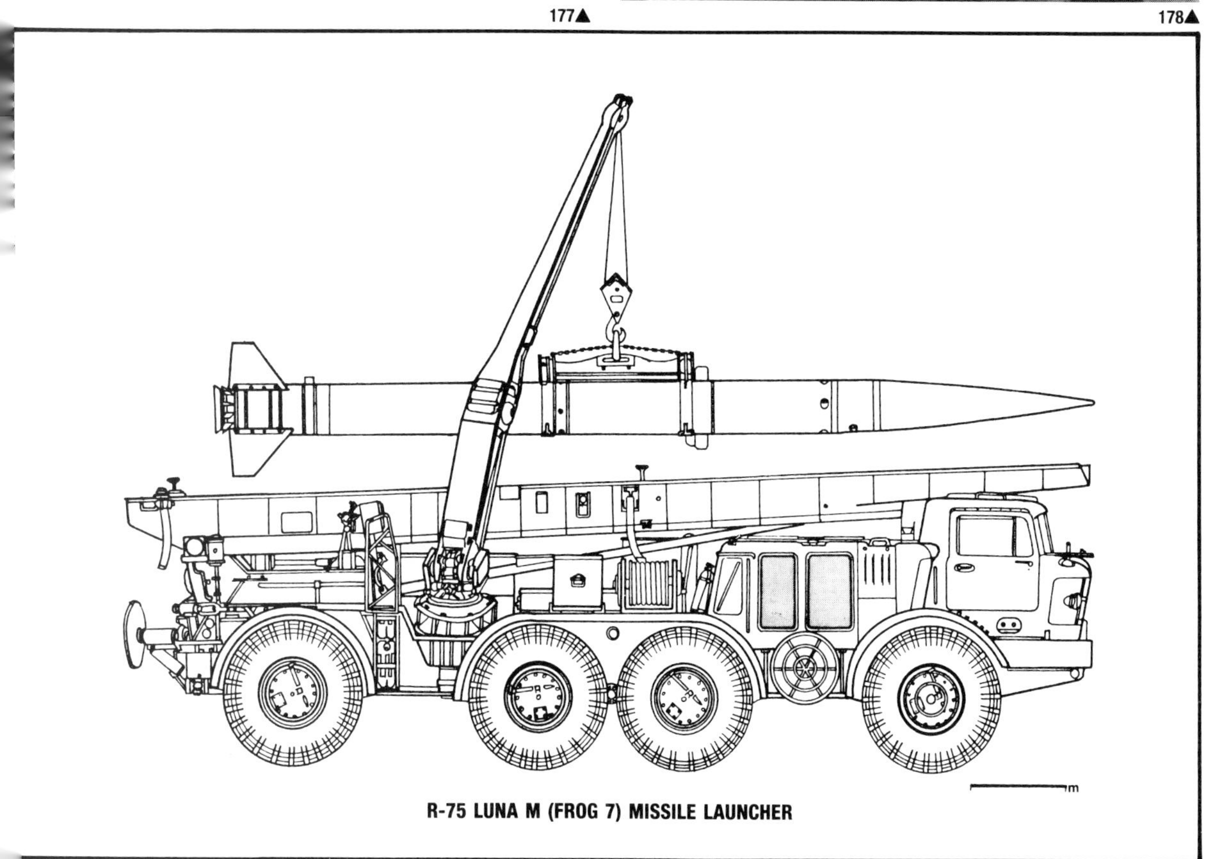

R-75 LUNA M (FROG 7) MISSILE LAUNCHER

▲179

In 1960, the Politburo decided to split the growing strategic missile force off from the Ground Force's artillery branch, to form an independent branch, the Strategic Missile Force (RSVN). Although the formation of the RSVN drew off many of the finest officers of the artillery force, it eased the organizational distractions that had led to the neglect of the more conventional elements of artillery during the late 1940s and 1950s. The 1960s saw the beginnings of a major modernization programme in the artillery. The GRAU remained responsible for three main categories of artillery weapons: towed artillery, multiple rocket-launchers and artillery missiles used at divisional, army and front levels. Missiles used at theatre level (IRBM:Intermediate Range Ballistic Missiles) and at strategic level (ICBM:Intercontinental Ballistic Missiles) were transferred to the new RSVN.

The Luna-M/FROG-7

Improvements similar to those adopted on the R-17E were introduced on the divisional Luna rocket in the 1960s. In 1965, the Luna-M system appeared, using the new R-75 rocket (NATO codename FROG-7). As in the case with the R-17 system, the GRAU opted for a wheeled transporter/launcher instead of the tracked PT-76 launcher used on previous examples of the system. The Luna-M was mounted on a BAZ-135L4 cross-country vehicle. Besides being more mobile and more maintainable than the PT-76 versions, the BAZ-135L4 launch vehicle incorporated other innovations. The launch vehicle has a small hydraulic crane for reloading the launcher. Each launch vehicle is accompanied by a BAZ-135 TZM rocket transport vehicle which carries three reload rockets. The crane on the launch vehicle cuts reload time down to about 20 minutes from an hour using the older method of a separate crane.

With the advent of the Luna-M, the divisional tactical missile battalion was increased to two firing batteries, with two launch vehicles each, from the previous organization of a single battery. Total production for the Soviet Ground Forces amounted to about 700 launch vehicles, and a further 200 for other Warsaw Pact countries. As with the R-17, the Soviet exported the Luna-M to many of the combatant countries in the Middle East. It was used by the Syrian 69th Rocket Brigade in the 1973 war, with unimpressive results. Like the R-17 (Scud) missile, the R-75 (FROG-7) is intended mainly to carry area weapons such as nuclear or chemical warheads. Its CEP is about 400m which is not accurate enough for anything other than general area bombardment when used with a conventional 550kg explosive warhead. Severa improved versions of the R-75 were later developed, including a type identified by NATO as FROG-7b which is .4m longer than the FROG-7a. One of the improved types has a rear spoiler system to reduce the minimum effective range of the missile below the normal 11km.

The R-17/SS-1c Scud B

The 1960s were also a time of modernization fo the tactical missile units of the Ground Forces. In 1960–61, the R-11 missile was supplanted by the improved R-17 (SS-1c Scud B) which had an improved inertial guidance system. The tracked IS-2/3 chassis used with this system proved troublesome and prone to breakdown and led the GRAU to request a more practica

179. The TZM transloader vehicle for the FROG-7/Luna-M is also based on the BAZ-135 chassis, and carries three reload rockets.
180. The improved SS-1c Scud B was mounted on a modified chassis. It can be distinguished from the earlier launch vehicle by its use of two compressed-air bottles on each superstructure side, compared to one bottle on the earlier model. This launcher also carried the improved R-17 missile. (Sovfoto)
181. The R-17E (SS-1c Scud B) launcher was developed on the basis of the MAZ-543P truck instead of a tracked chassis. This shows the initial launch vehicle configuration. (Sovfoto)

180▲ 181▼

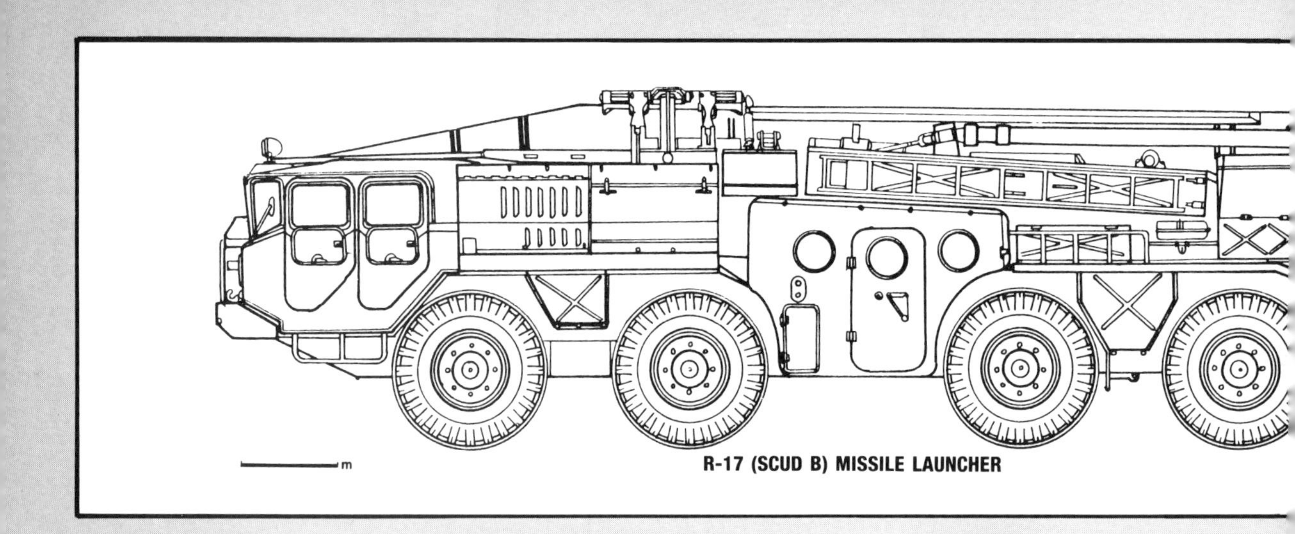

R-17 (SCUD B) MISSILE LAUNCHER

182. An R-17E team preparing to test-fire a missile. This is the initial type of launch vehicle with the hydraulic assist arms on the missile elevating cradle on the roof of the vehicle. (Sovfoto)

183. In about 1973, an improved version of the launcher appeared, as shown here. The launch cradle has been simplified, for example, by the deletion of the hydraulic cylinders. Note that there are still three portholes in the central crew section.

▲183

vehicle. There was really no need for cross-country mobility, so a wheeled vehicle, the MAZ-543P, was selected. This new version of the R-17 launch vehicle first appeared in about 1965, and became the standard launcher type. A few years later, a slightly improved version of the missile, the R-17E, also appeared. There were no fewer than four versions of the MAZ-543P launch vehicle introduced during its production, each with incremental improvements in the launch assembly, fire controls and other features. Total production for the Ground Forces amounted to about 550 launch vehicles. In 1961, the Politburo decided to permit the other armies of the Warsaw Pact to possess these types of weapons (minus the nuclear warheads). These countries received about 130 R-11 and R-17 launchers, both the IS-2/3 launch vehicle and the MAZ-543P. The USSR later exported the R-17, also with conventional warheads, to a number of Middle-East clients, where it has seen action in the war between Iran and Iraq. The missile has a circular error probability (CEP) of about 800m, which makes its utility with a conventional warhead fairly dubious. In the Iraqi case, it has been used mainly to bombard cities and other large targets, in the manner of a latter-day V-2. The dispersion problem with this missile is irrelevant when used with a nuclear warhead, which was its primary design requirement. A later version of the Scud B, referred to by the US temporary designation of KY-3, has also been fielded with this launch system and has a range of 550km with a nuclear warhead

▼184

184. The third launcher model, seen here, is very similar to the second type, but has only a single porthole in the central crew section instead of the three found on the two earlier models.

185. The fourth launcher type is very similar to the third, but the venting system above the first and second wheels is different.

185▲

The SS-12 Scaleboard

The arrival of the R-17E was accompanied by the initial deployment of a new front level tactical missile, called SS-12 Scaleboard by NATO. Like the Scud, the Scaleboard is mounted on a variant of the MAZ-543P cross-country vehicle. The missile is larger than the Scud, and has longer range. A Scaleboard brigade has two–three launch battalions, with 12–18 Scaleboard launch vehicles per brigade. It is nuclear armed and is designed for attacking rear area command and control centres, airfields and other vital rear area targets.

The SM-240 (2S4) Mechanized Mortar

The 1960s saw the first Soviet self-propelled gun developed since the inauspicious SU-310 and SU-420 of 1956. In about 1964, the Ground Forces began to receive a self-propelled 240mm mortar vehicle, believed to be designated SM-240 or SO-240. The basic chassis was a derivative of the GMZ minelaying vehicle, also used with the ZRK-SD Krug (SA-4 Ganef) air defence missile system. The mortar was the 240mm M-240 designed by Boris I. Shavyrin's bureau in 1949–50. The M-240 was used in artillery regiments of rifle divisions in the 1950s, but was withdrawn from divisional use in the late 1950s when the rifle divisions were mechanized as motor rifle divisions. The M-240 mortar was then transferred to army or front level heavy mortar battalions. The M-240 was not a very practical weapon. Its F-864 high-explosive round weighed 130kg (285lb) and so was very difficult for the crew to handle in the absence of a crane.

The rejuvenation of this breech-loaded mortar was probably due to a revival in Soviet interest in nuclear projectiles. Although the Ground Forces were amply supplied with nuclear armed rockets like the R-17 and R-75, nuclear projectiles are not as cumbersome as the rockets, and have much greater accuracy. Therefore, they are more useful for strikes against such protected targets as entrenched command centres. The SM-240 design is unconventional, although fairly rudimentary. The M-240 is mounted on a simple hydraulic cradle on the rear of the vehicle, which is lowered to the ground, base-plate first, for firing. The mortar fires rearwards from the vehicle. The M-240 is breech-loaded, and the vehicle incorporates a power-assisted loading system in the rear hull superstructure. This is a major advantage over the towed version of the M-240. It is not certain when this vehicle first entered service, but it is the authors' opinion that it was in about 1965. It was first spotted by

186▼

186. The SS-12 Scaleboard is an army or front-level missile, and has greater range than the Scud. It too is based on the BAZ-543 truck, but the missile is entirely enclosed in a launch canister. (US Army)

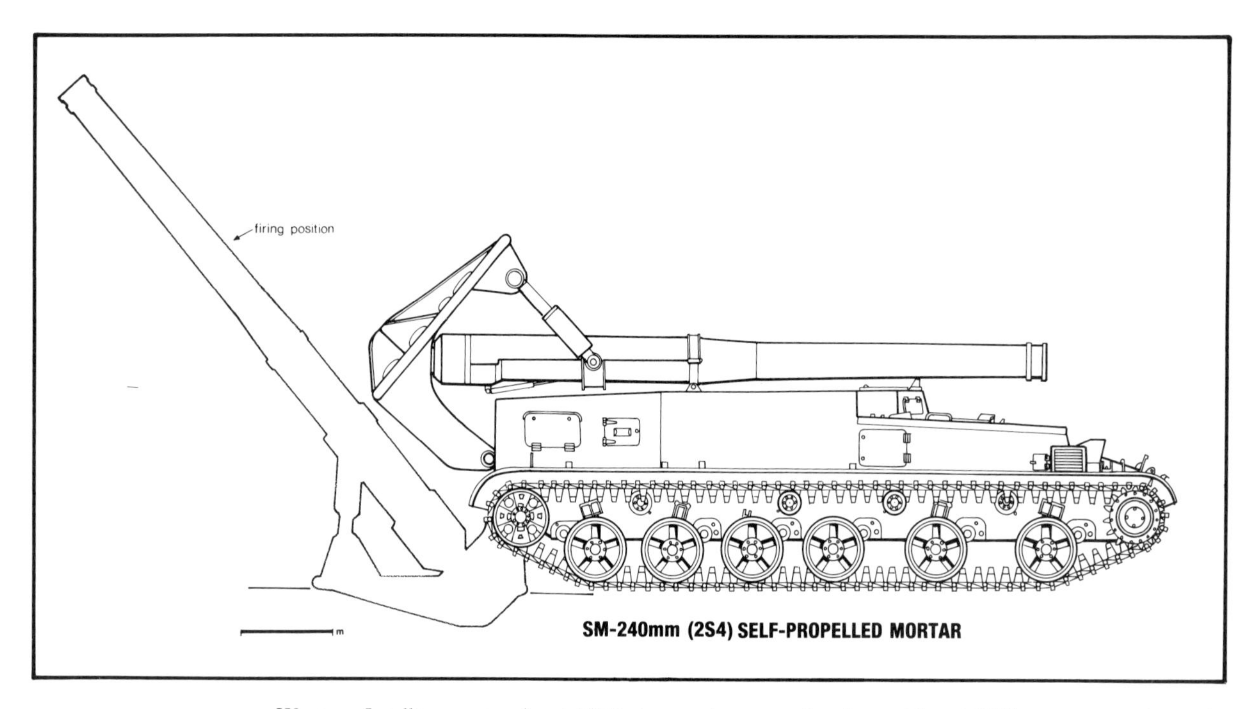

SM-240mm (2S4) SELF-PROPELLED MORTAR

Western Intelligence in about 1975, hence the STANAG designation M1975 240mm self-propelled mortar. Nor is it clear how it is deployed, but it is probably used by heavy mortar battalions in special heavy artillery regiments at army or front level. It is believed that only about 200–300 of these vehicles were fielded. No unclassified photographs of this vehicle have yet been released at the time of writing, and the accompanying scale plan here should be regarded as provisional.

Mechanized Artillery Requirements

In about 1965, the GRAU began to lay down requirements for a new generation of artillery vehicles. After two decades of distraction with the monumental task of building up the tactical nuclear forces of the Army, the artillery branch finally turned to the more mundane task of modernizing its conventional tubed artillery. The need for mechanized artillery had become more manifest by this time. NATO had been significantly improving its artillery force with, most notably, the US M109 155mm and M110 203mm self-propelled howitzers and the British Abbot self-propelled 105mm howitzer. More importantly, NATO's ability to conduct counter-battery fire was improving. With the advent of more and improved artillery location radars, Soviet artillery sites could be quickly identified and targeted. New ammunition developments, especially chemical weapons, and improved conventional munition (ICM) cargo rounds made artillery crews especially vulnerable to counter-battery fire. The Ground Forces had received several excellent towed artillery pieces in the 1960s, notably the D-30 (2A18) Sonyushka which had appeared in 1963. But towed guns took precious time to emplace, move and re-site when faced by counter-battery fire. Towed guns were not survivable on a nuclear battlefield. What was required was mobility so as to avoid counter-battery fire if possible, and armoured protection to resist it. The obvious direction was self-propelled howitzers using proven howitzer designs such as the Petrov bureau's fine D-30 122mm and D-20 152mm howitzers.

The TTT requirement for this new generation of weapons was co-ordinated between the GRAU (gun development) and the Central Auto-Tractor Directorate (TsAvTU) which was responsible for the chassis development. The configuration selected for both vehicles was the conventional self-propelled howitzer configuration pioneered by the US Army, with the gun mounted in a fully rotating turret on the hull rear. For logistical reasons the TsAvTU decided to develop the new vehicles on the basis of two common chassis. The *Gvozdika* (Carnation) light howitzer vehicle, using the 122mm D-30 gun, was to be based on a derivative of the new MT-LB artillery tractor design. The *Akatsiya* (Acacia) medium howitzer vehicle, using the D-20 152mm gun, was to be based around the same chassis already in use with the GMZ mine-laying vehicle, SA-4 Ganef/Krug air defence missile system and the SM-240.

187▲

187. The SO-152 Akatsiya (2S3) 152mm mechanized howitzer is the Soviet equivalent of the American M-109 155mm self-propelled howitzer. (US Army)
188. The SO-152 Akatsiya also serves in the German NVA as seen here.

The SO-152 Akatsiya

The 152mm self-propelled howitzer was the first to emerge, in 1972. It received the designation SO-152, but is also known by its industrial index number, 2S3, or by its project name, *Akatsiya*. It is also sometimes called the *152mm SG* in Soviet sources, which is simply an acronym for mechanized howitzer (*samokhodnaya gayubitsa*). The SO-152 uses a 4-man crew (internally), but generally an additional two crewmen would be carried on the ammunition trucks. These two loaders stand at the rear of the vehicle, and feed ammunition into the vehicle through two small rear ports. The ports feed into a conveyor system which passes the ammunition into the fighting compartment. The SO-152 has power-assisted loading because of the weight of the ammunition. This gives it a rate of fire of about three rounds a minute, and a sustained rate of about 60 rounds per hour. It can fire the normal OF-540 high-explosive-fragmentation projectile (43.5kg, 6.4kg HE) to a range of 17.3km. Its maximum range is probably about 30km when firing rocket-assisted

188▼

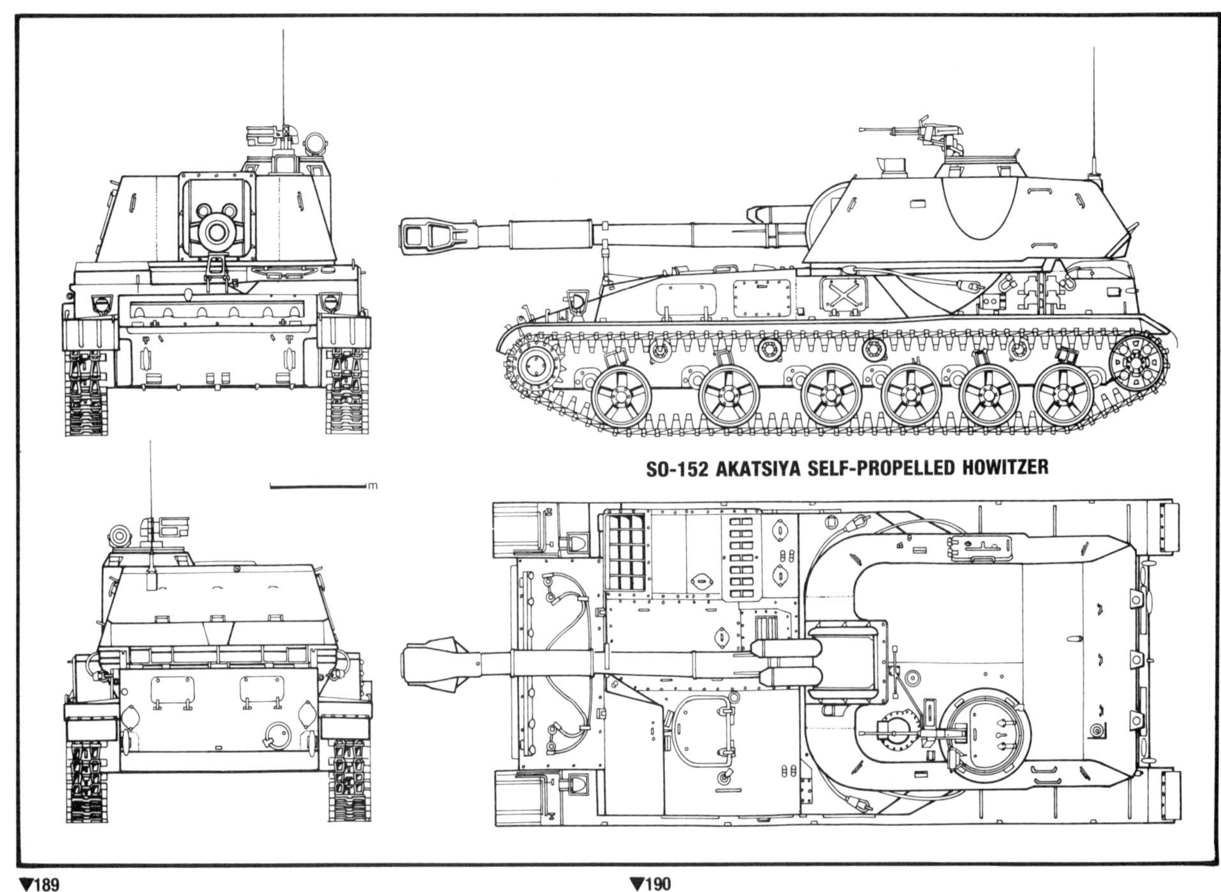

▼189

▼190

projectiles. It is capable of firing a variety of chemical rounds and also probably can fire nuclear projectiles.

The SO-152 is fairly similar in performance and characteristics to the US M109 self-propelled howitzer. The SO-152 Akatsiya was used to replace the D-1 152mm howitzer battalions in motor rifle division artillery regiments. The reconfigured regiments have a battalion of eighteen SO-152 in three 6-gun batteries. In the tank divisions, the SO-152 Akatsiya is used to replace a battalion of D-30 122mm howitzers. The SO-152 Akatsiya is also replacing some towed guns in artillery divisions and in army-level artillery regiments and brigades.

The Czechoslovak Army decided against adopting the SO-152, and opted instead for a wheeled 152mm howitzer vehicle, developed co-operatively between Tatra (chassis) and Skoda (gun system). This vehicle, called the *vzor 77 152mm samohybna houfnice DANA*, is based on a version of the Tatra 813 heavy truck. The gun is

191▲

189. Configuration of the initial production version of the SO-152 Akatsiya. The two lower, circular ports are used to feed ammunition into the vehicle.
190. Modified rear details of the standard production SO-152 Akatsiya. The circular reloading ports have been reduced in number and the other doors altered.
191. SO-122 Gvozdika (2S1) on parade following the Zapad 81 autumn exercises.

mounted in an armoured turret and has an automatic loading system. It is unquestionably one of the most unconventional self-propelled artillery vehicles since 1945. It is used by the CSLA, and has been exported to Libya.

The SO-122 Gvozdika

The SO-122 Gvozdika appeared in service about a year later than the Akatsiya. It too is known by its industrial index number 2S1, and by its Soviet acronym, 122mm SG. The basic chassis was developed at the same time as the MT-LB chassis, and shares a common power-train, engine and many other features. The gun system is derived from the D-30 (2A18) 122mm howitzer designed by F. F. Petrov's bureau. Although mounting a smaller and lighter gun than the SO-152, the SO-122 is nearly as large. The size is deceptive; the bulky hull was incorporated to provide enough buoyancy to allow the SO-122 to float. The SO-122 does not have a specialized amphibious propulsion system, but uses its tracks. When prepared for swimming, a small track cover (normally stowed on the rear of the turret) is placed over the front hull side to better direct the water flow over the tracks, and a set of swim vanes is attached behind the tracks. Covers are also placed around the engine air intakes to prevent water ingestion into the engine compartment.

As in the case of the SO-152, the 4-man SO-122 crew is usually supplemented by two additional loaders outside the vehicle during prolonged firing to assist in ammunition handling. The SO-122 fires the full range of Soviet 122mm ammunition. It can fire a typical high-explosive round such as the OF-462 (21.7kg, 3.5kg HE) to a maximum range of 15.2km. The SO-122 is being used in motor rifle and tank divisions to replace 122mm howitzers. The tank divisions were the first to receive the SO-122, and initially had a single battalion in their artillery regiments, with three batteries of six vehicles each (18 SO-122 per battalion). As production has continued, Category 1 motor rifle divisions have received up to six battalions of SO-122, two in their artillery regiment, and one in their tank regiment and each motor rifle regiment. Category 1 tank divisions have been re-equipped with up to six battalions, two in the artillery regiment, and one each in the three tank regiments and the motor rifle regiment. Total production of Soviet self-propelled guns since 1972 has been more than 10,000. The vast majority of these have been the SO-122 and

192. Interesting overhead view of the SO-122 Gvozdika (2S1).

▲192

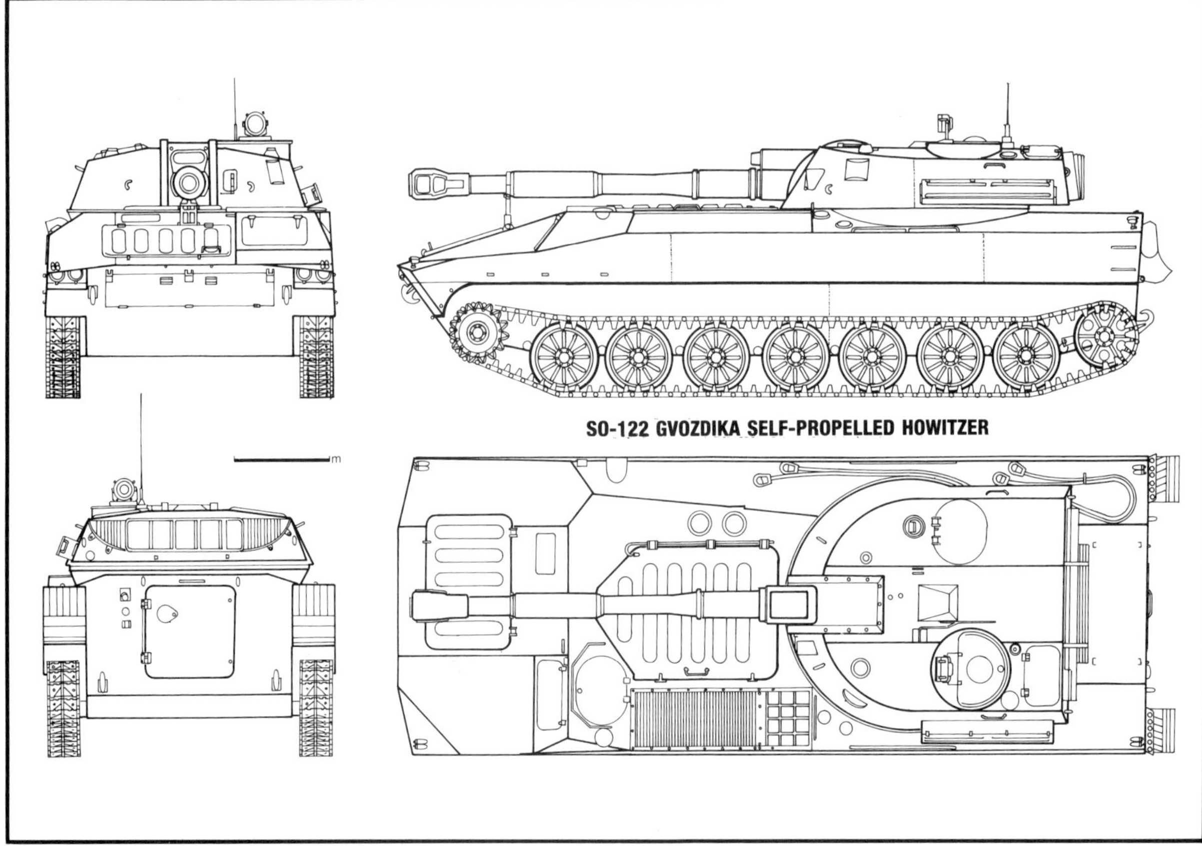

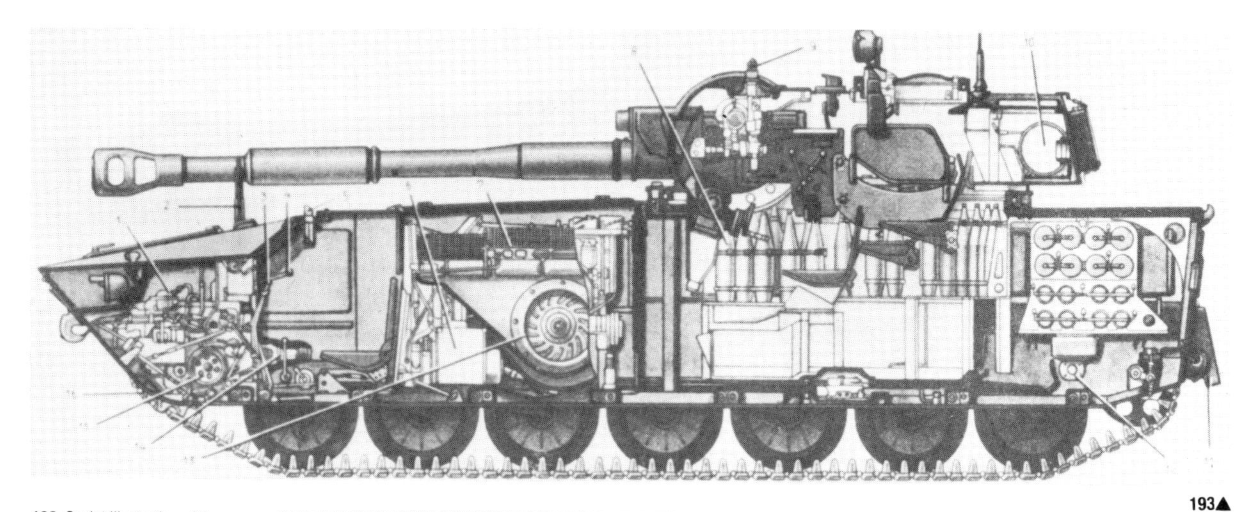

193▲

193. Soviet illustration of the internal configuration of the SO-122 Gvozdika (2S1).

194. The Czechoslovak CSLA uses the vz.77 Dana wheeled, mechanized 152mm gun, developed in co-operation between Tatra and Skoda, in lieu of the Soviet SO-152. (Eastfoto)

194▲ 195▼

195. Rear view of the vz.77 Dana, showing the unusual configuration of the vehicle. The entire centre turret traverses.

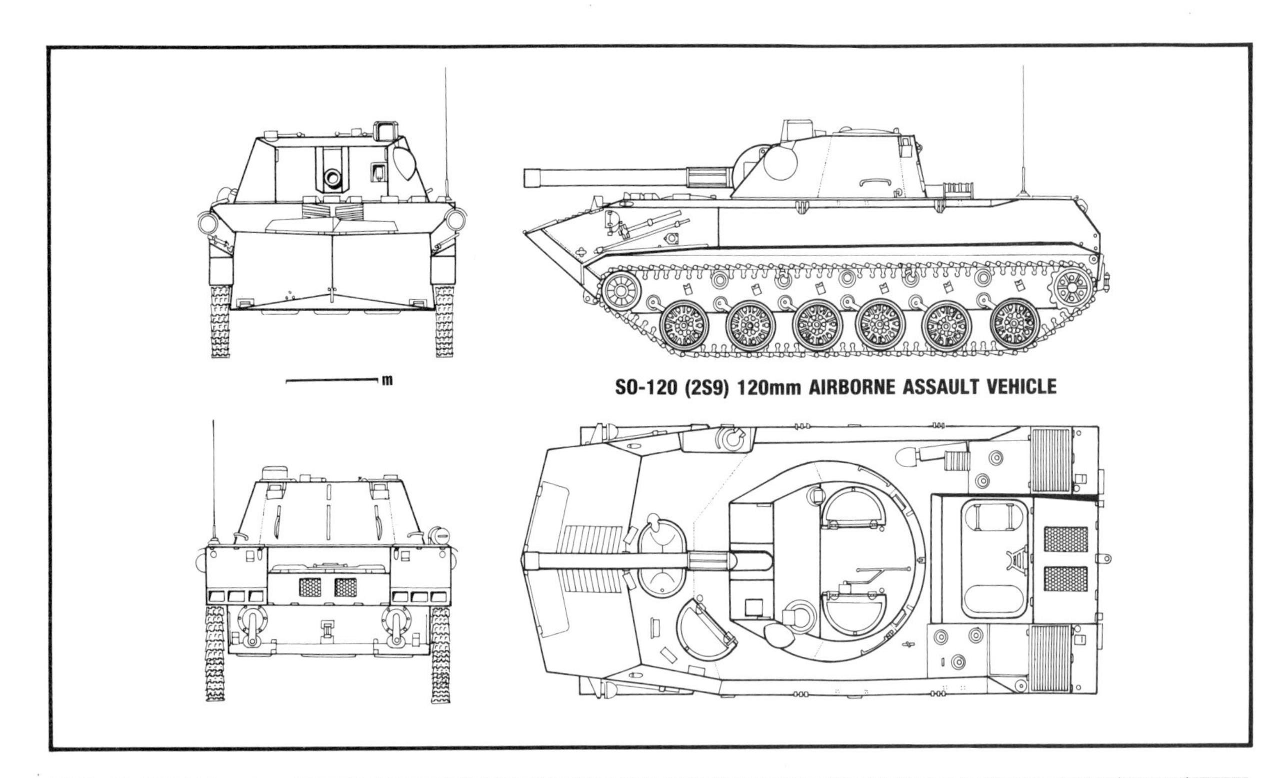

196. The SO-120 (2S9) Anona is an offshoot of the BMD airborne assault vehicle. It is armed with a hybrid gun-mortar which can be used for high-angle artillery barrages, or anti-tank use. Reportedly, there is a similar vehicle for the Ground Forces using the same turret on a BMP-2 chassis.

197. The PRP-3 is a derivative of the BMP used as an artillery reconnaissance vehicle. It is fitted with the Small Fred radar which folds down on the roof of the turret.

▲196 ▼197

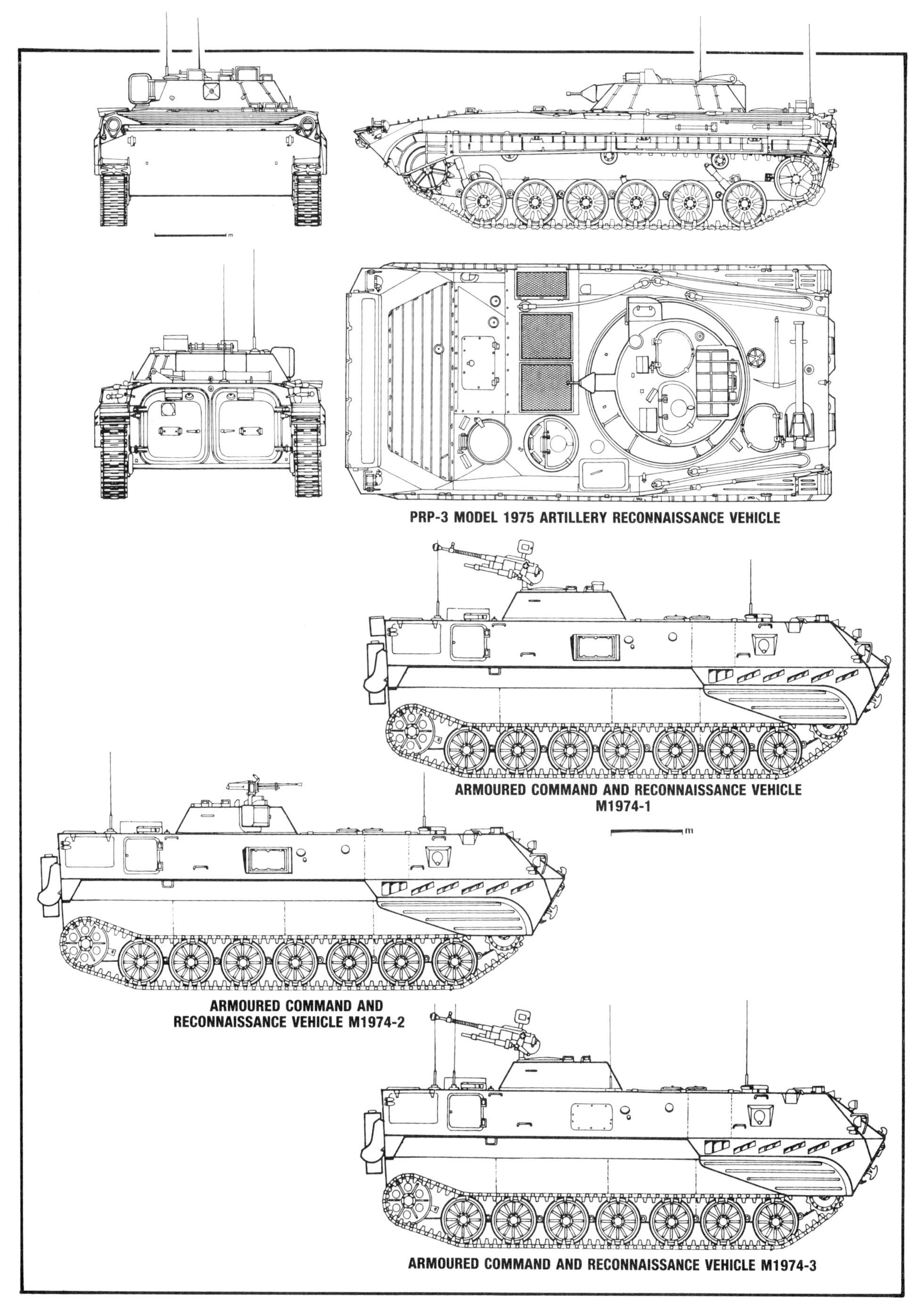

PRP-3 MODEL 1975 ARTILLERY RECONNAISSANCE VEHICLE

ARMOURED COMMAND AND RECONNAISSANCE VEHICLE M1974-1

ARMOURED COMMAND AND RECONNAISSANCE VEHICLE M1974-2

ARMOURED COMMAND AND RECONNAISSANCE VEHICLE M1974-3

198. The ACRV is an artillery command vehicle based on a modified SO-122 Gvozdika (2S1) chassis. This particular vehicle is an ACRV M1974-2 with a laser rangefinder port on the right side of the turret.
199. The SNAR-10 is an artillery radar vehicle based on a modified MT-LB chassis. It is fitted with a Big Fred radar at the rear of the superstructure.
200. The 2S5 is a new 152mm mechanized gun based on a chassis derived from that of the SO-152 Akatsiya (2S3). It is a long-range weapon; a major role being the delivery of nuclear projectiles. (US DoD)

▲198

SO-152, with the SO-122 probably being the more numerous. SO-122 production is also believed to have been undertaken in Poland.

The Armoured Command and Reconnaissance Vehicle

The original TTT for the SO-122 and SO-152 also seems to have incorporated a requirement for an associated command and control vehicle. The Soviet designation for this vehicle is not certain, though it has been referred to as KShM and TT-LB. It is usually called the ACRV M1974 (Armoured Command and Reconnaissance Vehicle) in NATO. The ACRV was also developed on the basis of the MT-LB, and the lower chassis is virtually identical with that of the SO-122. The hull is large and boxy, befitting a command vehicle where the staff has to stand to consult maps. There are three distinctly different versions of the ACRV, each tailored to particular artillery battalion staff requirements. The ACRV M1974-1 is a battery fire direction centre and there is one per SO-122 or SO-152 battery (three per battalion). During operations, the vehicle is co-located with the guns, and is crewed by the battalion's senior officer with his associated fire control and communications troops. This vehicle serves as the link between the battery and higher command elements. The ACRV M1974-2 is the battery and battalion command vehicle. There are four in each battalion, one with each battery commander and one with the battalion commander. It is used as a command and observation post. The ACRV M1974-2 is fitted with a laser rangefinder in the turret and often carries a dismountable laser rangefinder such as the DAK-1 (NATO Codename: Sage Gloss). The ACRV M1974-2 is normally located beside the command vehicle of the tank or motor unit that the battery or battalion is supporting. For example, if a battery is supporting a tank regiment, the battery ACRV M1974-2 would be beside the regimental command tank or other command vehicle. The ACRV M1974-3 is the battalion fire direction centre. It is commanded by the battalion chief of staff, and contains the battalion's electronic field artillery computer. There is only one of these per battalion, and it would be located at battalion headquarters.

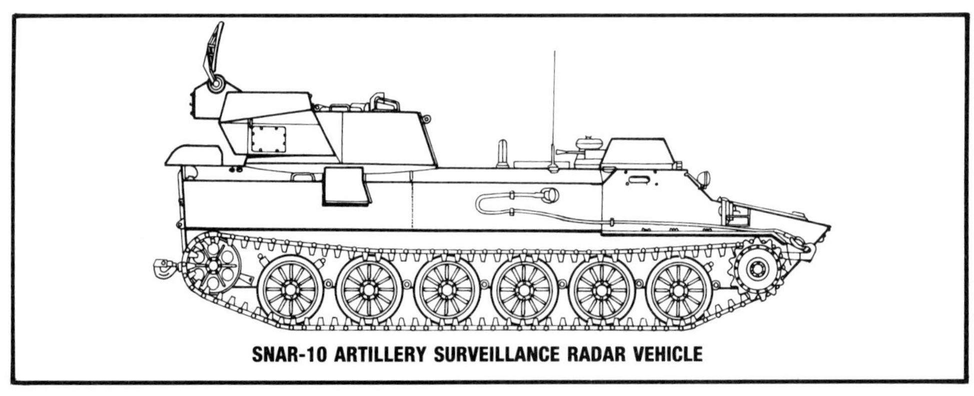

SNAR-10 ARTILLERY SURVEILLANCE RADAR VEHICLE

199▲ 200▼

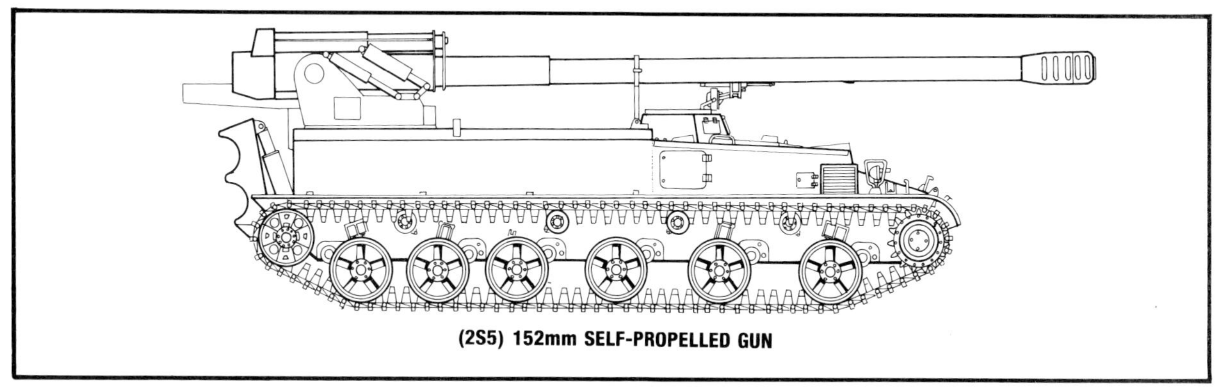

(2S5) 152mm SELF-PROPELLED GUN

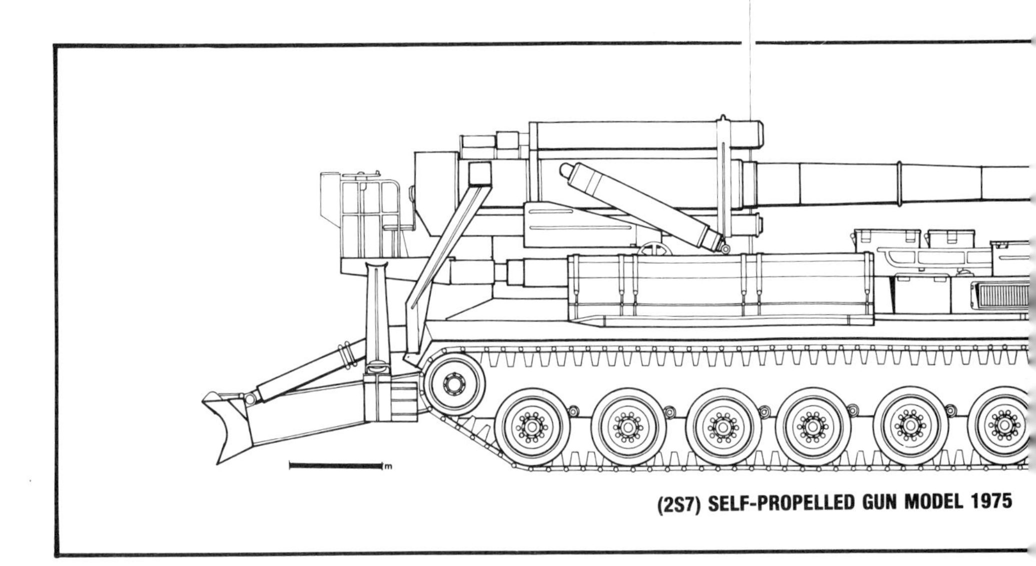

201. The SO-203 (2S7) is the largest of the new Soviet mechanized guns, and is based on a new chassis which may be related to that employed with the SA-12 air defence missile system.

202. The US DoD released this illustration, purporting to show the new 203mm self-propelled gun. It does not resemble the photos of the 2S7 at all, and may be an earlier predecessor of the 2S7, or perhaps even a self-propelled derivative of the S-23 180mm gun. (DoD)

▲201 ▼202

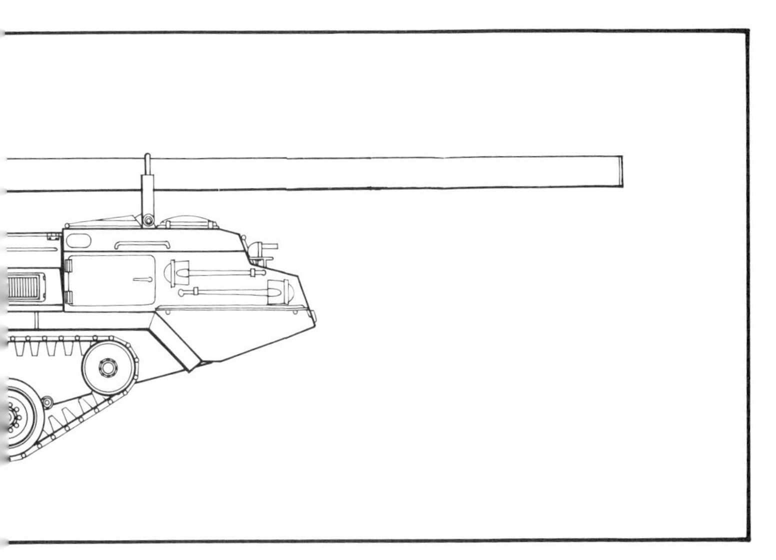

The 2S5 152mm Mechanized Gun

One of the last of the first generation mechanized artillery vehicles to appear was the 152mm self-propelled gun which was first spotted by NATO in 1981. Its Soviet designation is not known, but may be SP-152; its industrial index is 2S5. It is based on the same chassis as the SO-152, but unlike the Akatsiya, it is not fitted with a turret. A towed version of the same gun was introduced concurrently. The 2S5 was probably adopted to replace some of the towed guns in the heavy artillery brigades at army level. It is a long-range system, capable of firing nuclear projectiles as well as conventional and chemical rounds. Very few other details of the system are available.

The SO-203 (2S7) Heavy Mechanized Gun

The largest of the new self-propelled guns to emerge was the SO-203 which was first spotted by NATO in 1977. The SO-203 is a massive weapon, and perhaps the largest armoured vehicle currently in the Soviet inventory. The chassis may be related to that of the SA-X-12 Gladiator air defence missile system. Its primary role is probably long-range attack of vital rear area targets such as airfields, missile-launching sites and command posts, and it is capable of firing conventional, nuclear and chemical munitions to a range of 30km. The 203mm gun is mounted on the rear, and has power elevation and traverse, controlled from a small crow's-nest on the left rear corner of the hull. Loading is power-assisted using a power rammer fitted to the right rear of the hull. Its rate of fire is probably about two rounds per minute, with a sustainable rate of about 30 per hour. US sources place its production up to 1985 at about 400 vehicles. It is probably deployed only at front level in special high command reserve (RGK) regiments or brigades.

SOVIET MECHANIZED ARTILLERY VEHICLES

Soviet designation	SO-122	SO-152		SO-203	SM-240
Industrial index	2S1	2S3	2S5	2S7	2S4
Soviet name	Gvozdika	Akatsiya			
Crew	4+2	4+2	4+4	4+4	4+5
Weight (tonnes)	15.7	27.5	30	40	30
Length (m)	7.3	8.4	9.5	12.8	8.5
Width (m)	3.05	3.2	3.2	3.5	3.2
Height (m)	2.42	2.8	2.8	3.5	3.2
Ground clearance (cm)	46	40	40	40	40
Ground pressure (kg/cubic cm)	0.5	0.6	0.6	0.6	0.6
Gun designation	D-30S	D-20S			M-240S
Gun calibre (mm)	122	152	152	203	240
Gun type	howitzer	howitzer	gun	gun	mortar
Depression/elevation (degrees)	−3+70	−4+60	−3+65	−3+65	+45+70
Max. rate of fire (min)	5	3	4	2	1
Effective rate of fire (min)	5	2	2	1	
Ammunition stowed	40	46			
Effective range (km)	15.2	17.3	27	30	12.7
Nuclear capability	no	yes	yes	yes	yes
HE projectile weight (kg)	22	40	43.5	100.0	130.7
Engine designation	YaMZ-238N	V-59	V-59		V-59
Horsepower	240	520	520		520
Fuel stowed (litres)	550	850	850		850
Road range (km)	500	500	500		500
Max. speed (km/h)	60	60	62		62
Amphibious	yes	no	no	no	no
CBR	PAZ+PBZ	PAZ+PBZ	partial	partial	partial
Max. turret armour (mm)	15	15	–	–	–
Max. hull armour (mm)	20	20	20	15	20

Tactical Missile Modernization

Modernization of divisional tactical missile units also was initiated in the early 1970s. The first of these systems to appear was the *Tochka* (Point, US/NATO designation: SS-21 Scarab) in 1976. The Tochka was developed as a replacement for the divisional Luna-M. One of the main tactical problems with the Luna-M and R-17 is that the missiles are left unprotected on the launch rail. This leaves them exposed to the elements, and subject to damage by artillery airbursts or even smallarms fire. In the late 1960s, the GRAU experimented with enclosed Luna-M, having a metal environment shelter over the rocket, but with the advent of an improved missile, these plans were put aside in favour of a new launch vehicle. This was developed at the Likhachev Automotive Factory in Moscow, and is closely related to the Transporter-5937 vehicle used in the ZRK-SD Romb/SA-8 Gecko system. It has an elevatable missile-launcher in the central vehicle bay which can be covered by overhead doors when the missile is in transit. The new Tochka/SS-21 Scarab system is gradually replacing the Luna-M in Category 1 divisions on a one-for-one basis. As of 1985, all but two of the Soviet divisions in the Group of Soviet Forces-Germany had been re-equipped. The first country confirmed to have received the Tochka/ SS-21 outside the USSR was Syria in 1983, followed by Czechoslovakia in 1984–85.

Two other tactical rocket systems have been modernized in the past few years, though details of both systems are lacking. The designation SS-22 was originally used to refer to an im-

▲203

▲ 204

▼205

203. The SNAR-2 was a 1950s artillery surveillance radar mounted on an unarmoured AT-L tractor. It is being replaced in mechanized artillery units by the SNAR-10.
204. The ARSOM-1 was a 1950s artillery radar, mounted on a modified AT-T heavy artillery tractor chassis.
205. The SS-21 Scarab (Tochka) is the new rocket system being adopted in the Warsaw Pact to replace the FROG-7. It is based on a wheeled ZiL transporter derived from a similar vehicle used with the SA-8 Gecko (ZRK Romb) air defence missile system. The Czechoslovak CSLA was among the first Warsaw Pact countries to acquire this system.

proved version of the SS-12 Scaleboard. However, in 1985, the designation was dropped, and it is now referred to as the SS-12M Scaleboard. It was first seen by NATO in 1979, and is used to equip missile brigades at front level with 12–18 launchers per brigade. The SS-23 is a replacement for the R-17E/Scud B. It is apparently based on a modernized MAZ-543 truck with a reconfigured superstructure. As in the case of the Tochka/SS-21, the new hull permits the missile to be stored under cover during transit. For firing, the roof hatches are opened, and the launcher is elevated to a vertical position over the rear of the vehicle. The SS-23 Spider first became operational in about 1984, and is beginning to replace the R-17E/Scud B in some army-level missile brigades.

206▲ 207▼

206. Probably one of the most controversial new Soviet missiles is the SS-20 Saber (Pioner). This missile is not Ground Forces command, but is controlled by the RSVN Strategic Missile Force. (US DoD)
207. The new SS-23 Spider is intended to replace the Scud in Ground Forces rocket brigades. This is an artist's conception prepared by the US DoD in 1985. (US DoD)

SOVIET MOTORIZED BALLISTIC MISSILE/ROCKET LAUNCH VEHICLES

	FROG-1	FROG-3	FROG-7	Scud A	Scud B	Scud B	Scaleboard	Scarab	Spider
US Designation				SS-1b	SS-1c	SS-1c	SS-12	SS-21	SS-23
Soviet Designation			R-75	R-11	R-17	R-17E			
Soviet industrial number			9K21		8K11				
Soviet name	Luna	Luna 2	Luna-M					Tochka	
Derivative chassis	IS-2	PT-76	BAZ-135L4	IS-2	IS-2	MAZ-543	MAZ-543P	ZiL-5937	MAZ-543
Weight (tonnes)	36.5	14.2	23.0	38	38	29	32	10	30
Length (m)	10.7	10.5	10.75	12.5	12.6	13.58	13.0	9.1	13.2
Width (m)	3.2	3.18	2.8	3.2	3.2	3.02	3.02	2.9	3.02
Height (m)	3.32	3.05	3.66	3.32	3.32	3.7	2.6	2.13	3.2
Engine type	V-2IS	V-6	ZiL-375	V-2IS	V-2IS	D-12A	D-12A	ZiL-375	D-12A
Horsepower	520	240	360	520	520	525	525	175	525
Max. speed (km/h)	37	44	65	37	37	70	70	60	70
Missile/Rocket Characteristics									
Weight (tonnes)	3.17	2.26	2.3	4.5	6.37	6.37	9.7	3.0	
Length (m)	10.2	10.5	9.1*	10.7	11.2	11.2	12.0	6.0	
Diameter (m)	.84	.535	.55	.84	.84	.84	1.0	.85	
Warhead weight (kg)	1180	454	450	680	770	860	1000	450	
Max. range (km)	32	35	70	150	300	300**	900	120	500
Guidance	none	none	none	radio	inertial	inertial	inertial	inertial	inertial
Fuel type	solid	solid	solid	liquid	liquid	liquid	liquid	solid	solid
CEP (m)			400	800	800	800	650	240	320
Reaction time (min)	15-30	15-30	15-30	60	60	60	60	10	15

*FROG-7b=9.5m
**Scud B (KY-3 version)=550km

▲208

▲209 ▼210

208. After the Second World War the SU-100 remained in production in the USSR, and later in Czechoslovakia. This is a Czech-manufactured SU-100 which was exported to Egypt in 1956, and lost in the Sinai fighting that year.

209. The ISU-152, and the improved ISU-152K, were the principal heavy assault guns manufactured in the USSR after the Second World War. This vehicle is currently displayed in the Kiev Army Museum.

210. The ISU-122S was a stable-mate of the ISU-152, and served into the 1950s in the Soviet Ground Forces. It was also supplied to the Polish LWP as is seen here.

Assault Guns and Tank Destroyers

During the Second World War, the Red Army fielded a number of turretless assault guns which were used in the anti-tank role as well as to provide heavy, long-range fire support for tank units. In the medium assault gun range, the two principal types were the SU-85 of 1944 and the SU-100 of 1945. In the heavy range were the ISU-122, ISU-122S and ISU-152. The attractiveness of these weapons was as much due to cost advantages as tactical utility. An assault gun cost less than the turreted tank from which it was derived, but could mount a more potent gun, and often more protective armour as well. For example, the SU-100, based on the T-34-85 chassis, carried the D-10T 100mm gun instead of the 85mm gun carried on the tank version. The light SU-76M mounted a 76mm gun in place of the 45mm gun on the basic T-70M light tank. The ISU-152 mounted a 152mm howitzer in place of the 122mm gun on the basic IS-2 tank. In 1943, assault gun production constituted 17 per cent of total Soviet armoured vehicle production; in 1944 it peaked at 41 per cent, and declined to 23 per cent of total Soviet production in 1945.

Soviet assault guns are frequently misinterpreted in the West as self-propelled artillery. While this may be technically appropriate, tactically, the assault gun was developed and manned by the Soviet tank force. Assault guns were often used as surrogate tanks. The SU-76, which made up 57 per cent of Soviet wartime assault gun production, was forced on the Red Army, in spite of its tactical limitations. Its parent tank, the T-70, was virtually useless by 1943, yet the automotive factories which produced it were not capable of manufacturing medium tanks. The SU-76 was developed initially as an expedient tank destroyer to take advantage of the automotive production facilities, but remained in production since it proved useful in providing infantry units with direct fire support in lieu of unavailable medium tanks. The SU-85 and the later SU-100 proved to be excellent anti-tank vehicles. They were usually employed in the overwatch role, where their long-range firepower was an asset, while their shortcomings, such as the lack of a turret, were minimized. In an overwatch role, they would take up a static position overlooking the enemy as tank units advanced in front of them, and could counter anti-tank guns or tanks firing on the advancing Soviet tanks. The heavy ISU-122 and ISU-152 were developed for a similar role, as well as to counter German heavy tanks like the Royal Tiger which could not be dealt with by medium tanks such as the T-34-85.

In the immediate post-war years, there was still considerable interest in assault guns. Soviet design teams, primarily those under Kotin and Dukhov, were involved in a number of projects. A superheavy assault gun, designated *Zvierboi* (Animal Hunter) was considered, but dropped. An improved ISU, based on the IS-3 tank and mounting the 130mm naval gun, was developed to prototype stage but did not enter production. A follow-on to the SU-100, based on the T-44 was also developed. It mounted a 100mm D-10T gun in a fixed superstructure; unlike the SU-100, the engine was front-mounted and the fighting compartment was on the rear of the vehicle. Two assault guns were developed for motor rifle units, the SAU-57P with a 57mm anti-tank gun and a new SU-85. Neither entered production. The ASU-76 entered production in 1949; it was a light 5.8tonne vehicle armed with the LB-76S gun. Soviet sources state that it was intended for motor rifle units, but the ASU designation would imply that it was developed for airborne forces. Nothing is known of the vehicle, or the chassis on which it was based.

In spite of this activity, production remained focused on wartime designs. The SU-100 remained in production, in slightly improved form, as the SU-100M until 1953. It remained in production in Czechoslovakia until 1956. The ISU-152 remained in production, with engine and external stowage improvements, as the ISU-152K until 1955. Production of the ISU-122 halted briefly after the war, but was resumed in 1947, lasting until 1952. The SU-76 was the only major wartime assault gun to be dropped from production in 1945 because of its obvious limitations.

Post-war deployment of the assault guns followed much the same lines as wartime use. The SU-100 was used mainly by independent assault gun regiments and brigades, although it

211. The initial version of the ASU-57 used the Ch-51 gun with a peculiar multi-slatted muzzle brake as is seen here. (Sovfoto)
212. The more common production version of the ASU-57 used the improved Ch-51M with a more conventional muzzle brake. The ASU-57 was often used as an improvised troop carrier in airborne units, as seen here. (Sovfoto)

▲211 ▼212

could be found in the armoured regiment of rifle divisions as well. The SU-76 was also used in independent units, but was mainly found in 6-vehicle batteries in each rifle regiment. The ISU-122 and ISU-152 were found in independent heavy assault gun regiments and brigades. One of the few changes from the war years was the formation of heavy armoured regiments to support tank, mechanized (and later, motor rifle) divisions. A mixed formation of 46 IS-2 or IS-3 tanks and 21 ISU-122 or ISU-152 assault guns, these heavy armoured regiments provided long-range fire support to the division's medium tank regiments. This formation gradually disappeared in the late 1950s, being replaced by a homogeneous heavy tank regiment as more T-10 heavy tanks became available. Although heavy assault guns remained in use in some units well into the 1970s, by the 1960s most had been relegated to secondary roles, especially by conversion to heavy armoured recovery vehicles.

Airborne Assault Guns

In the immediate post-war years, the Astrov design bureau was assigned to develop a very light assault gun/tank destroyer for use by airborne forces. The vehicle had to be light enough to be dropped by parachutes. The design was based on the ATP-M light artillery tractor which was under development at the time, and mounted a Ch-51 57mm anti-tank gun. It appeared in 1950 as the ASU-57, and was first publicly shown in 1957. The ASU-57 was very lightly armoured, and lacked overhead armour protection. Its small size was dictated by the lack of heavy transport aircraft at the time, and it was initially carried in special aluminium containers (P-90), one under each wing of a Tu-4 (B-29 copy) bomber. Later, as transport aircraft like the An-12 were developed, its transportation method was improved. A special pallet was developed which could be dropped out the rear door of the aircraft. Parachutes slowed the fall to about 15m/sec, and near the ground a retrorocket was fired to reduce the descent to a more reasonable 5m/sec speed to prevent the vehicle smashing into the ground. A considerable number of small design changes were made throughout the ASU-57's production run, which lasted until 1962. The most noticeable was the substitution of the improved Ch-51M gun which had a more conventional muzzle brake than the slatted type used on the initial production vehicles. Details of their deployment are sketchy, but it would appear that each airborne regiment had nine ASU-57 in an anti-tank company, while airborne divisions had an anti-tank battery with a further eighteen ASU-57. The ASU-57 was used by the Soviet VDV and was also supplied to the Egyptian Army in small numbers.

As the Soviet Airborne Force (VDV) grew, so to did its air transport force. The availability of newer transport aircraft such as the AN-12 made it possible to carry larger, better armoured and better armed vehicles than the puny ASU-57. As a result, in the early 1950s, the Astrov bureau was assigned the task of developing a more adequate anti-tank vehicle than the ASU-57 which would be airlifted rather than air-dropped. This was based on a heavily modified version of the PT-76 scout tank chassis, and was armed

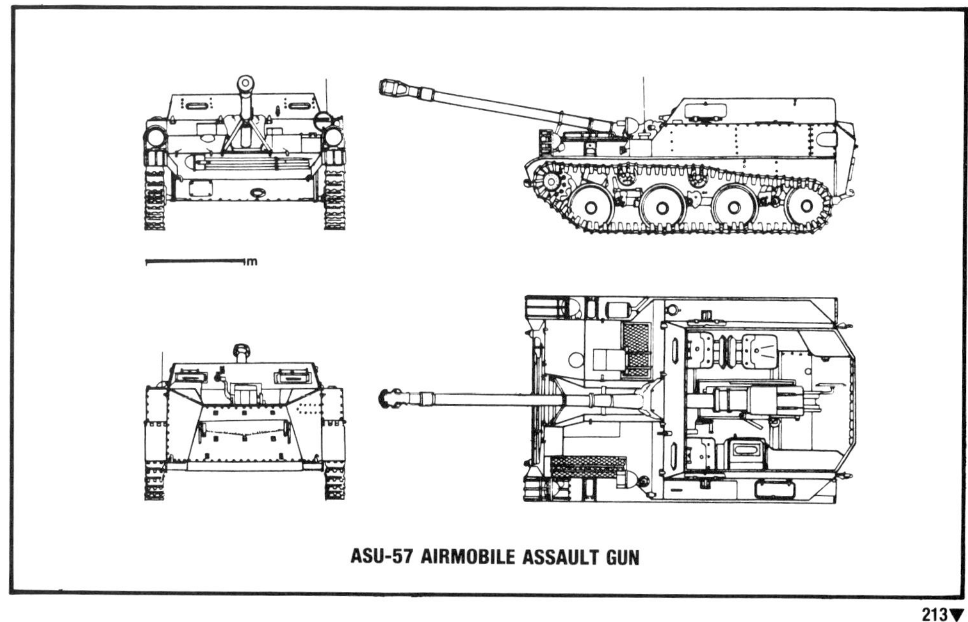

ASU-57 AIRMOBILE ASSAULT GUN

213▼

213. ASU-57 were initially carried in these peculiar underwing containers, with one slung under each wing of a Tu-4 heavy bomber.

▲214 ▼215

214. Interior of an ASU-57 showing its tiny size and the vulnerability of its crew to any form of hostile fire. (Zaloga)
215. A gun-less command version of the ASU-57 was used in Soviet VDV airborne units in the 1950s. The space freed by deleting the gun was filled with radios.

216▲

216. Once larger transport aircraft became available, the ASU-57 was dropped using parachutes and a load pallet like the one seen here.
217. The ASU-85 was used in the VDV as a tank destroyer throughout the late 1970s, but is now being replaced by the dual-purpose SO-120.
218. During the 1970s, some ASU-85 were modernized, including the addition of this 12.7mm DShK machine-gun position. (Sovfoto)

217▲ 218▼

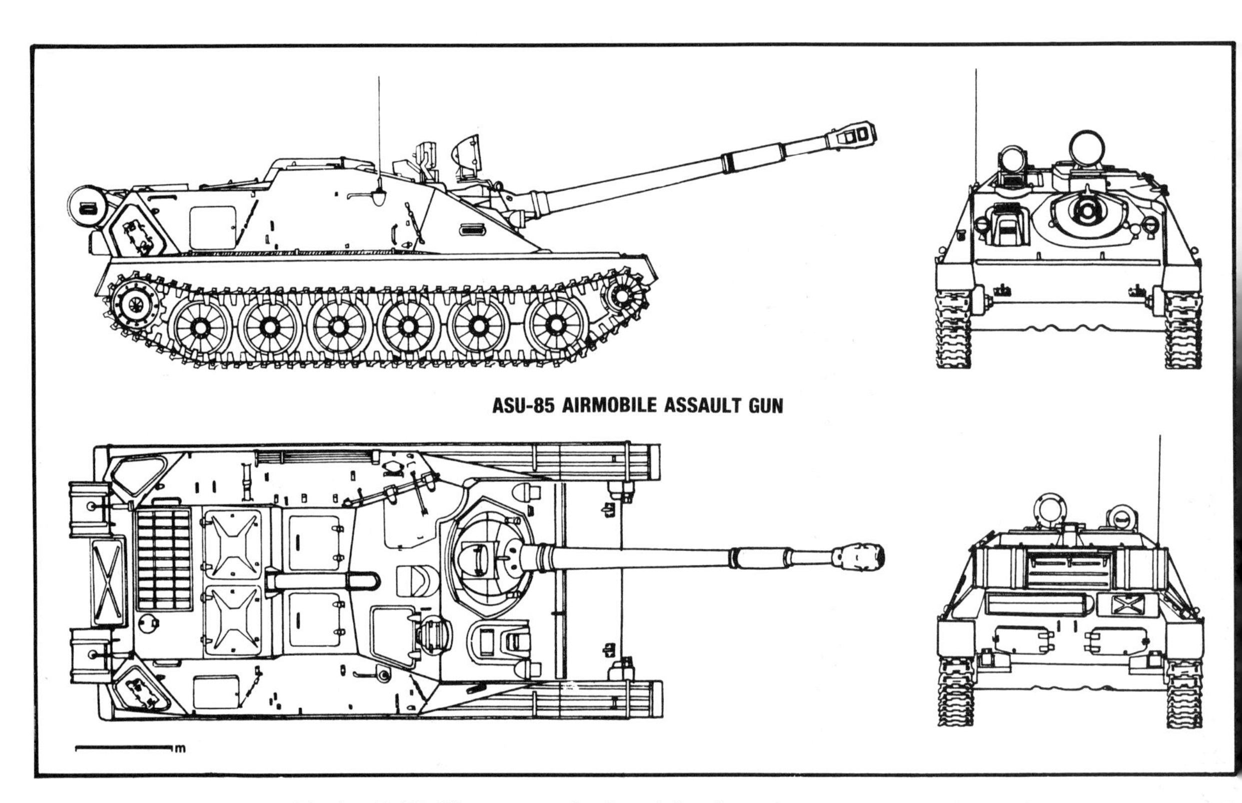

with the D-70 85mm gun, developed by the Petrov bureau. It appeared in 1960 as the ASU-85 and remained in production until 1966–67 in modest numbers. The ASU-85 was very thinly armoured, offering protection only against small arms fire and light machine-guns. It equipped special assault gun battalions in each of the eight airborne divisions, with 31 ASU-85 per battalion. Its utility was somewhat circumscribed by its size, since it could only be used to support airborne operations if an airstrip could be seized and held in order for the vehicles to be flown in. By the mid 1960s, plans were under way to field a new airborne assault vehicle, the BMD, which substantially undercut the need for the ASU-85 and halted its further development. The ASU-85 was used by the Soviet VDV and was also supplied to the Polish LWP where it was used by the 7th Pomeranian Airborne Division. Astrov's ASU-85 chassis design served as the basis for the later ZSU-23-4 and the launch and radar vehicles for the SA-6 Gainful (ZRK-SD Kub) air defence missile system.

The IT-122 Tank Destroyer

Although it might seem that assault gun development in the 1950s concentrated on their airborne applications, this was not the case. Extensive work was done on designs to succeed the wartime generation of such vehicles as the SU-100 and ISU-152, but few details are known. Soviet sources indicate that two new assault guns, the SU-100P and SU-122, were developed in the 1950s but, again, few details are known. There were also efforts to develop unconventional tank destroyers. These had rear-mounted turrets, and heavier armour, but few details are known. The SU-122 may have been the precursor of, or an earlier designation of, the IT-122, developed in 1949 as a successor to the SU-100 which ended production in the USSR in 1953. The IT-122 mated the T-54A hull with the new D-49S gun developed by the Petrov design bureau. The design was conventional in most respects, and resembled the wartime SU-100 design. The most novel feature was the incorporation of an optical rangefinder in the commander's cupola in the right front corner of the superstructure. This feature gave greater long-range accuracy than was possible using stadiametric sights. The IT-122 was a clear reflection of wartime assault gun design trends that emphasized the utility of uparmed, turretless tank derivatives to offer long-range fire support for medium tanks. It may also have been prompted by the advent of heavy tanks in NATO like the British Conqueror and the US M103. Even the gun on the T-10 heavy tank would have had a hard time dealing with these monsters, but the improved D-49S of the IT-122 offered a counterbalance to the increase in NATO tank armour thickness. The deployment of the IT-122 remains a mystery. It probably entered

219▲

219. This is one of the few photographs of the enigmatic IT-122 tank destroyer. Note that the cupola to the left of the machine-gun position is fitted with an optical rangefinder to assist in long-range engagement of hostile tanks.
220. Artist's impression of the IT-130 assault gun.

service in the mid-1950s in independent tank destroyer regiments or brigades, and may have been used in tank and motor rifle divisions' heavy armoured regiment in lieu of the older and less effective ISU-122 and ISU-152. Viktor Suvorov indicates that in later years it was issued on the basis of one battery per motor rifle regiment. In the early 1970s, General Potapov, later head of the Soviet Armoured Forces, suggested adding a platoon of four IT-122 to each T-54 or T-55 tank battalion. Apparently this was not carried out. It is a very mysterious vehicle, and has seldom been seen.

Even more enigmatic is the IT-130 tank destroyer, a successor to the IT-122. It consisted of a modified T-62 tank with a fixed superstructure very similar to that of the IT-122, but mounting a 130mm M-76T gun. There is reason to believe that in place of the short, cupola-mounted rangefinder of the IT-122, the IT-130 mounted a more sophisticated optical rangefinder with a wider base. Photographs of this vehicle have never appeared, but a converted IT-130 being used as an armoured recovery vehicle has shown up in Red Square parades since 1977. The IT-130 probably entered service in thc early 1960s to support the new T-62 tank. It may have been designed to deal with newer NATO designs, such as the heavily armoured Chieftain tank, in long-range engagements. Beyond the IT-130, nothing further is known of Soviet assault guns. It is not known

220▼

▲221

whether an assault gun derivative of the T-64 or T-72 has ever been developed, but given the Soviet predilection for conventional assault guns as stop-gap insurance for NATO advances in armour technology, it is likely that such vehicles has been developed and perhaps even deployed. There have been reports of a 100mm assault gun, capable of firing 100mm guided anti-tank missiles as well as conventional ammunition, but details are lacking.

SOVIET ASSAULT GUNS

	ASU-57	ASU-85	IT-122
Crew	3	4	4
Weight (tonnes)	3.3	15.5	30
Length (cm)	500	844	1102
Width (cm)	210	297	327
Height (cm)	120	194	235
Ground clearance (cm)	20	42	42
Ground pressure (kg/cubic cm)	0.35	0.44	0.75
Gun designation	Ch-51M	D-70	D-49S
Gun calibre (mm)	57	85	122
Depression/elevation (degrees)	−5+12	−4+15	−4+20
Max. rate of fire (min)	6-10	6-8	4
Ranging method	stadia	stadia	coincidence
Ammunition stowed	30	45	40
Coaxial gun	–	PKT	KPVT
Gun calibre (mm)	–	7.62	14.5
Ammunition stowed	–	200	500
Engine designation	M-20E	V-6R	V-55V
Horsepower	55	240	580
Fuel stowed (litres)	140	250	900
Road range (km)	250	360	500
Max. speed (km/h)	45	45	50
Max. frontal armour (mm)	6	40	150
Side armour (mm)	6	15	120
Top armour (mm)	none	7	30

Wheeled Tank Destroyers

In the early 1950s, the Soviet Ground Forces began considering alternatives to conventional assault guns, especially in the anti-tank role. The design bureau under Boris Shavyrin had been assigned to develop lightweight anti-tank weapons, and these had included the B-10 82mm and B-11 107mm recoilless rifles. Whether these were adapted to light armoured vehicles to create lightweight tank destroyers has not been confirmed, but it is likely. Both Shavyrin's and Nikolai Makarov's bureaux were also assigned the task of examining the possibility of guided anti-tank missiles. In 1945, the Red Army had captured examples of the German X-7 *Rotkappchen* anti-tank missile which was guided either by a trailing wire, or could be command-guided by radio in other versions. The Soviet design bureaux began to develop improved versions of the X-7, with the first known version appearing in about 1955 as the PUR-61 (3M6) *Shmel* (Bumblebee/NATO Codename: AT-1 Snapper). The Shmel was a relatively large missile for this role, and was not suitable for use from a man-portable launcher. Instead, two wheeled launchers were developed. The 2P26 'Baby Carriage' consisted of four Shmel launch rails mounted on the rear of a modified GAZ-69 light truck. The missile operator had a small joystick control and could guide the missile either from a launch station on the truck, or from a short distance away using a portable control and wire reel. The main advantage of this system was that it was very cheap; the main disadvantage was that it had no armoured cover, and was very

221. All that has been seen of the elusive IT-130 tank destroyer is this armoured recovery vehicle based on a defanged version of the assault gun. (US Army)
222. The first known Soviet missile tank destroyer was the 2P26 based on the GAZ-69 jeep. It was popularly called the 'baby-carriage' in Warsaw Pact service because of the folding canvas cover over the rear launch section. It was armed with four 3M6 Shmel (AT-1 Snapper) missiles.
223. The armoured counterpart of the 2P26 was the 2P27 based on the BRDM-1. It carried only three 3M6 Shmel missiles, and is not known to have had any reloads carried on board. When not in use, the missile-launcher folded into the rear compartment and was completely enclosed under armoured covers.
224. A 2P27 of the Hungarian Army on display. (Chris Foss)

222▲

223▲ 224▼

▲225

225. Closeup of the launchers on a 2P32 Falanga tank destroyer. (Sovfoto)

226. A counterpart of the 3M6 Shmel was the improved Falanga (AT-2 Swatter) missile. This was mounted on a similar 2P32 launcher, but four missiles could be carried. This photograph suggests that early tank destroyer units had mixed equipment as the vehicle in the foreground is a 2P27 with 3M6 Shmel missiles.

likely to attract hostile attention after the missiles were launched because of the visibility of the back-blast. This led to the development of a corresponding armoured version, the 2P27, mounted on a modified BRDM-1 chassis. The 2P26 and 2P27 anti-tank missile-launchers entered service in the late 1950s. They were intended to supplement more conventional anti-tank weapons such as the T-12 100mm anti-tank gun. While the accuracy of conventional guns dropped dramatically at ranges beyond 1,500m, the accuracy of the Shmel was much better out as far as 2,500m.

Nevertheless, the Shmel was still fairly primitive. It used manual command-to-line-of-sight (MCLOS) guidance which required a very experienced operator to obtain the desired level of accuracy. The missile was very slow, and took 30 seconds to fly to its maximum range of 2,500m (compared to about three seconds for an anti-tank gun round). During this 30 seconds, tanks could take evasive action, or try to suppress the missile by firing on the gunner. The missile was so large that only three could be carried in the BRDM-1/2P27. Rate of fire was also extremely slow since only one missile at a time could be controlled from each launch vehicle.

The Shmel was followed in 1960 by an improved type, the PUR-62 *Falanga* (NATO Codename: AT-2 Swatter). The Falanga offered

226▼

several advantages over the Shmel: it was almost twice as fast, and had greater range. It was also smaller, and a 2P32/BRDM-1 could carry four launchers instead of three. Quite surprisingly, the Falanga was followed barely one year later by the PUR-64 (9M14) Malyutka (NATO Codename AT-3 Sagger). The Malyutka was much smaller than either the Shmel or Falanga, and was shorter ranged. Like the Shmel and Falanga, it used MCLOS guidance, but employed a trailing wire command link instead of the radio command systems used by the earlier missiles. This made it cheaper and more suitable for use in a man-portable version. It would seem that it was adopted to supplement the more powerful and longer ranged Falanga. A major advantage was that its smaller size permitted reload rounds to be carried on the armoured launch vehicle. For example, the 2P32/BRDM-1 launch vehicle carried six rounds on the launch rails and eight more rounds in the hull. This was more than three times the available stowage compared to the BRDM-1 with the Falanga.

The new wheeled tank destroyers were usually deployed in anti-tank batteries attached to motor rifle regiments. Each battery had three platoons with three launch vehicles and a command BRDM each. The batteries' armoured vehicles totalled nine BRDM tank destroyers and four BRDM-V command vehicles. These batteries

▲227 ▼228

227. Side view of the Falanga (AT-2 Swatter) missile and its launch assembly on a BRDM-1/2P32.
228. On the heels of the Falanga came the smaller, shorter-ranged 9M14 Malyutka in 1964. These were carried on a BRDM-1 launcher, but because of the small size of the missile, reload missiles could be carried in the launch vehicle. These Malyutka tank destroyers are on parade in Bucharest with the Romanian ASR.

were supplemented by anti-tank platoons at motor rifle battalion level, each platoon having two recoilless rifles or SPG-9, and four man-portable Malyutka 'suitcase' launchers. These platoons were usually transported on BTR armoured vehicles. The success of the small Malyutka missile also led to its widespread dispersion as a supplementary weapon on armoured vehicles. It was adopted as a standard, supplementary weapon on the BMP-1, BMD-1, and on some versions of the OT-64 SKOT. Some attention was also paid to its adoption as a supplementary weapon on tanks. In the early 1970s, some T-62 had a container added at the rear of the turret, believed to contain a single Malyutka missile. This notion paralleled French attempts to mount the SS-11 anti-tank guided-missile on tanks. The concept does not appear to have been regarded as a success by the Soviet Army, probably due to the awkwardness of integrating guided-missile controls into the already complicated fire control scheme of a tank. In the late 1960s, the BRDM-1 launch vehicles were supplemented with new launch vehicles based on the improved BRDM-2. The first of these to appear was fitted with the improved Falanga M (AT-2B Swatter B) missile, but this type was relatively short-lived. The more common tank destroyer version of the BRDM-2 carried a sextuple 9M14M Malyutka M (AT-3 Sagger) launcher.

229. Interesting view of a German NVA 2P27 Shmel tank destroyer with its missile racks folded inside the launch vehicle.
230. The German NVA converted some of its older BTR-40 transporters to tank destroyers armed with the 9M14 Malyutka (AT-3 Sagger) missile.

229▲ 230▼

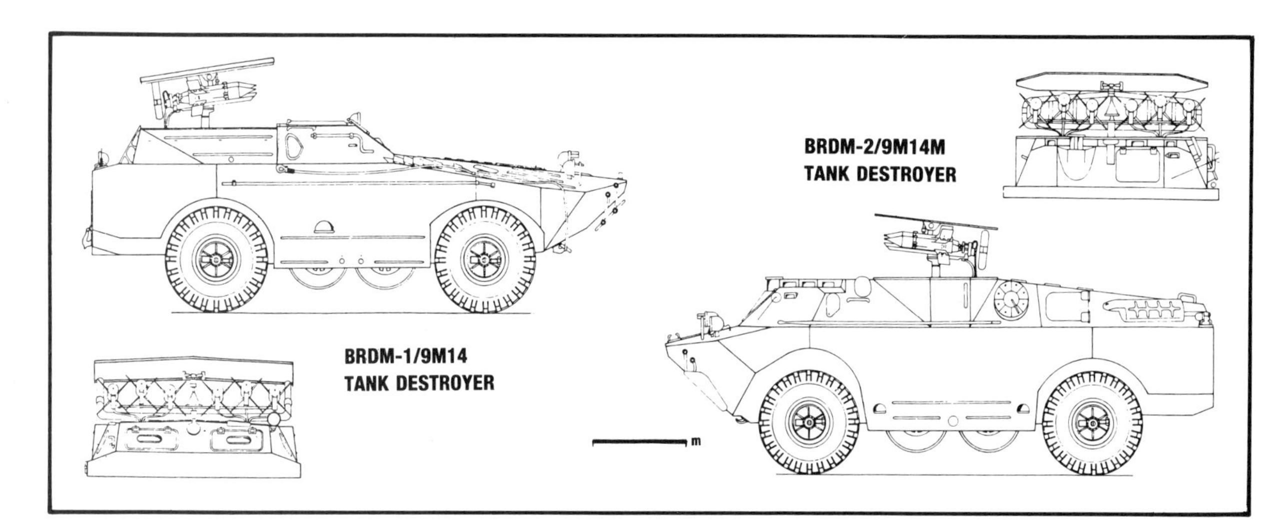

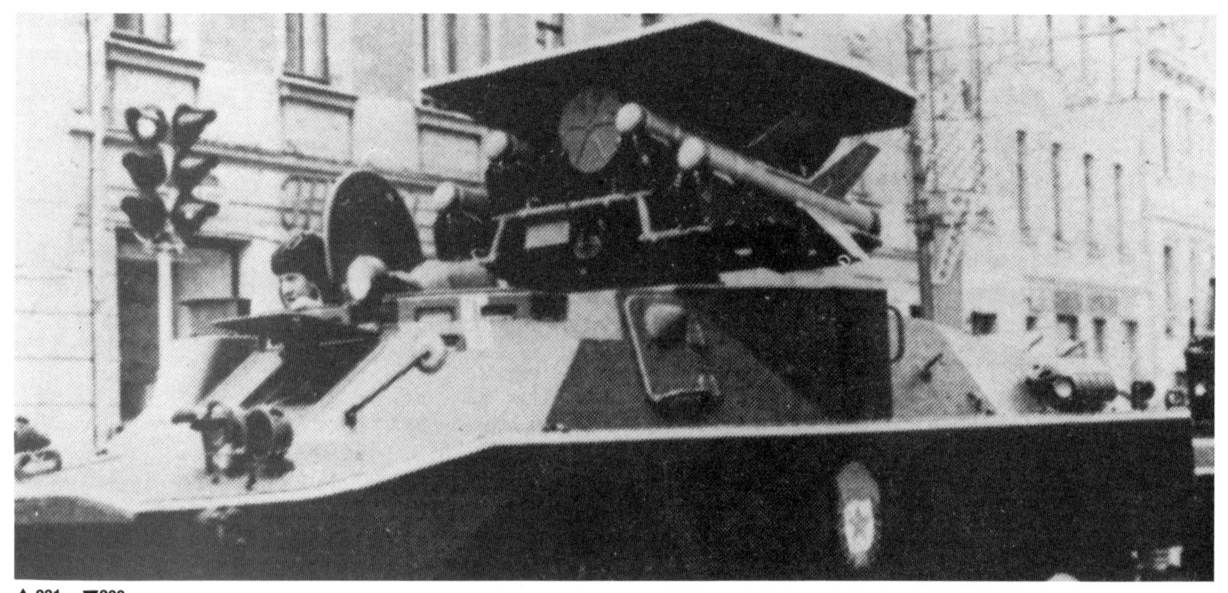

▲231 ▼232

231. With the advent of the newer BRDM-2 scout vehicle, production of wheeled missile tank destroyers shifted to this chassis. This is the BRDM-2 configured to fire the improved AT-2b Swatter A (Falanga M) missile. The dish in the centre of the launch array may be a radio antenna used in the missile's command guidance system.
232. View showing the similarity of the BRDM-2/Falanga M tank destroyer and the BRDM-2/Malyutka M tank destroyer using the 9M14M missile.
233. A German NVA BRDM-2/Malyutka M (9M14M) missile tank destroyer with the launch assembly folded down. The gunner's sight is located opposite the driver's port.

233▲

This became the single most common wheeled tank destroyer in Soviet Ground Forces service, eventually numbering more than 3,000 vehicles.

The effectiveness of this first generation of anti-tank missiles is the subject of some controversy. The US Army suggested that they had a probability of a hit (Ph) of between 67 and 90 per cent at ranges over 2,000m, and a probability of kill (Pk), if the tank was hit, of about 65 per cent. These were idealized estimates which assumed a highly trained crew, lack of enemy countermeasures and other factors which were extremely unlikely in the real world. To become proficient, a Malyutka operator had to fire at least 2,300 simulated rounds on a missile trainer, and regularly had to fire 50–60 simulated rounds per week on a trainer. Beyond these technical skills, an operator had to have a particularly stout heart when actually using such weapons in combat, as they took about 30 seconds from launch to target impact, with the operator vulnerable to enemy suppressive fire during the time of the launch-hit interlude. They were first used during the 1967 war when the Egyptian Army used a number of 2P26 Baby Carriages without much success. They were also used in the 1970 War of Attrition. The advent of the Malyutka missile changed their prospects since it could be deployed in much larger numbers. The man-portable Malyutka was used in Vietnam from 1972 with some success, and the use of both man-portable and vehicle-launched Malyutka in the 1973 Arab-Israeli war came as a shock to many observers. The Press interpreted Egyptian successes with the Malyutka against Israeli tank formations in the opening days of the war as a signal of the demise of the tank, akin to the demise of the armoured knight with the advent of the longbow at Crécy. More sober observers felt that the initial Israeli tank losses were due as much to Israeli over-confidence and poor tank-infantry co-operation. During the later phases of the war, the successes of the Malyutka teams disappeared as Israeli tankers came to understand their vulnerability to counter-action during the launch-hit interlude. What the 1973 war demonstrated was that the actual probability of hit of one of these missiles was dramatically lower than the idealized figures of 65–90 per cent suggested by the US Army, and generally averaged 25 per cent or less (often as low as 2 per cent). In 1969 the Soviet Ground Forces began to receive an improved version of the Malyutka missile, called AT-3C Sagger C by NATO, which had semi-automatic command-to-line-of-sight (SACLOS) guidance. This second-generation system offers much better hit probability than the first generation MCLOS. If

▲234 ▼235

236▲

234. A BRDM-2/Malyutka M (9M14M) tank destroyer with the missile launch array in raised position. The Malyutka missile (AT-3 Sagger) proved deadly in the 1973 war with Israel if used in volume by well-trained crews. (Chris Foss)
235. The BRDM-2/Malyutka (9M14M) tank destroyer with the missile launcher folded down inside the hull. This is a late production vehicle with the mushroom vent covers over the air intakes.
236. Rear view of an Afghan Army BRDM-2/Malyutka tank destroyer. This is the initial production type of the BRDM-2 tank destroyer which has the same slatted grill doors over the central air intakes as the intermediate production model of the normal BRDM-2 scout car.

US experience is comparable, SACLOS offers hit probability of about 50 per cent versus about 25 per cent for the earlier MCLOS systems. Sagger C did not see action in the Middle East during the war of 1973.

Experience with the first generation of guided anti-tank missiles had convinced the Soviet Ground Forces of the need for more sophisticated SACLOS guidance. The improved AT-3C Sagger C version of the Malyutka was only an interim step in this direction. Two new missiles were under development, the short-ranged 9M111 *Fagot* (Bassoon; NATO Codename AT-4 Spigot) and the long-range 9M66 (NATO Codename: AT-5 Spandrel). These two missiles paralleled the Euromissile Milan and HOT; they are fielded in launch tube containers which offer better environmental protection. The 9M111 Fagot was intended as a replacement for the 9M14M Malyutka man-portable launcher, and also replaced the 9M14M on later production BMP-1 and BMD-1. The 9M66 was intended to be a vehicle-launched missile. It was fitted on dedicated tank destroyers, like the BRDM-3, and as a supplementary weapon on newer armoured infantry fighting vehicles, such as the BMP-2. The BRDM-3 has launch rails for five missiles on its roof launcher which can be retracted into the hull for reloading under armour cover. It is believed that the BRDM-3 carries ten reload rounds. Some BRDM-3 have been seen with a mixture of three 9M111 Fagot in the centre launch positions, and two 9M66 missiles on the outer launch rails. The new missiles began to appear in 1973 (9M111 Fagot) and 1974 (9M66), and replaced the earlier missile-launchers in Category 1 units.

While the BRDM-3/9M66 tank destroyer was under development, the Ground Forces were also developing a tracked tank destroyer, designated IT-1. Apparently at least two versions of this vehicle were tested operationally. One was an ordinary T-62 tank with its gun removed and the launchers placed on the rear turret roof. The other version had its turret replaced by a low superstructure. This later type was accepted for service. The missile associated with the IT-1 was named Drakon, but there is uncertainty as to whether this was the 9M66 (AT-5 Spandrel) or an unknown missile. The IT-1 became operational in 1968, apparently before the BRDM-3, and was deployed in independent tank destroyer battalions on a scale of one per army. Few other details are known. In the 1970s, a T-72-derived tank destroyer was developed as the IT-2, but even less is known of this vehicle.

237. The BRDM-3/9M66 (AT-5 Spandrel) tank destroyer carries five launch rails, plus an estimated 10 reload missiles in the hull. (Sovfoto)
238. Closeup of the AT-5 Spandrel launcher on the BRDM-3/9M66 tank destroyer. This launch assembly folds back inside the hull for travel or during reloading. (US Army)

▲237 ▼238

SOVIET WHEELED MISSILE TANK DESTROYERS

Chassis type	BRDM-1	BRDM-1	BRDM-1	BRDM-2	BRDM-2	BRDM-3
Soviet missile name	Shmel	Falanga	Malyutka	Falanga M	Malyutka M	
Soviet designation	PUR-61	PUR-62	PUR-64	PUR-62	PUR-64	
Soviet index number	3M6		9M14		9M14M	9M66
Soviet launcher number	2P27	2P32				
US missile number	AT-1A	AT-2A	AT-3	AT-2B	AT-3C	AT-5
NATO system name	Snapper	Swatter A	Sagger	Swatter B	Sagger C	Spandrel
No. of missile rails	3	4	6	4	6	5
No. of missile reloads	0	0	8	0	8	10
Missile guidance*	MCLOS	MCLOS	MCLOS	MCLOS	SACLOS	SACLOS
Guidance command link	radio	radio	wire	radio	wire	wire
Date of introduction	1957	1960	1961	1966	1969	1974
Missile length (cm)	114	116	86	116	86	125
Span diameter (cm)	75	65	45	65	45	45
Missile weight (kg)	24.2	16	11.3	17	11.3	22
Missile speed (m/sec)	90	150	120	150	150	185
Minimum range (m)	500	500	500	500	500	100
Maximum range (m)	2500	3500	3000	3500	3000	4000
Flight time to max range (sec)	30	17	25	23	21	20
Warhead weight (kg)	5.3	5.4	2.5	5.4	2.5	3.0
Warhead diameter (mm)	140	140	120	140	120	125
Armour penetration (mm/0 deg)	300	500	410	500	410	600

*MCLOS=Manual command to line of sight guidance
SACLOS=Semi-automatic command to line of sight guidance

239. Detailed view of the AT-5 Spandrel launcher. The bulged door immediately below the rear of the launcher opens to permit the launch assembly to be folded into the hull during travel. (US Army)

239▲

The Future of Soviet Tank Destroyers

In the late 1960s, NATO armies began the first experiments with laminate armour using ceramic panels and other novel non-steel materials. These new types of armour were developed to counter the growing profusion of anti-tank rockets and missiles, all of which use shaped charge (HEAT) warheads. The Soviets, also working on similar configurations, adopted a ceramic plate system for the T-72, somewhat akin to the system developed in the USA in the 1960s for the T-95 tank. The most successful of these systems was developed in Britain, and became known after the location of its development centre at Chobham. Improved versions of this Chobham armour were incorporated into the generation of tanks developed by NATO countries in the 1970s, notably the German Leopard II, the American M1 and the British Challenger. The new armour significantly degrades the performance of shaped-charge warheads, and the fronts of these new tanks are virtually impervious to the shaped-charge warheads of the 1960s and 1970s generation of missiles and rockets. Besides these new forms of passive armour, the USA and Israel were also involved in the development of active armour which uses arrays of thin sheets of plastic explosives to break up the high-pressure jet formed by shaped-charge warheads on impact before they can penetrate the main armour. The Israelis first deployed their version of this armour, called Blazer reactive armour, in the 1982 war in Lebanon.

These new types of armour have serious implications for Soviet anti-tank vehicles. They seriously undermine the utility of specialized tank destroyers using anti-tank missiles, since all these missiles use shaped-charge warheads. On the other hand, its development may breathe new life into gun-based tank destroyers, since the new armour does not offer a significant improvement in protection against traditional kinetic energy penetrators which can be fired from guns. The Soviets have long favoured anti-tank guns, and it would not be surprising to see new tank destroyers or assault guns supplementing missile tank destroyers. Alternatively, the Soviets may emulate NATO armies, and deploy new anti-tank missiles with larger, improved warheads, to defeat the new armour, or novel missile guidance systems, such as top attack systems, which strike in places where the new armour is not fitted.

▲240 ▼241

Reconnaissance Vehicles

240. The PT-76 was the standard scout tank of Soviet mechanized units into the 1970s when it began to be replaced by the BRM. This is an early version with the D-56T gun and its multi-slatted muzzle brake. (Sovfoto)
241. The PT-76B was the standard tank of the Soviet Navy's Naval Infantry Force for many years until supplemented with T-55 (and recently, T-72M). The white and pale-blue flag is the ensign of the Naval Infantry. (Sovfoto)

During the Second World War, reconnaissance vehicles took over many of the roles formerly undertaken by the cavalry. Although the primary role of reconnaissance vehicles was nominally scouting for tank and mechanized units, such vehicles performed a much wider range of tasks than their name would suggest. They were often used to provide flank security for mechanized units, or to mop-up pockets of resistance behind the front. The Red Army used two main classes of vehicle in the reconnaissance role: light tanks, and armoured cars. Light tanks were used to perform more demanding missions, such as scouting in advance of a mechanized unit, or providing flank security. The armoured cars and armoured transporters were used for less demanding roles such as liaison between commanders, mopping-up, or scouting in less contested areas. The light tanks included domestic designs such as the T-60 and T-70, and Lend-Lease designs such as the British Valentine. Armoured cars and transporters included the BA-64B armoured car as well as a number of Lend-Lease types, especially the American M3A1 scout car and the British Universal Carrier.

The wartime generation of scout vehicles was not highly regarded. Many of the designs had been selected as much for their low cost and ease of production as for their combat utility. The BA-64B was very poorly armed and lacked mobility. The T-70 suffered from a very poor engine configuration and was not well armed. In 1944, work began on two new scout vehicles: a light tank called the K-90 and a wheeled scout vehicle based on the GAZ-63 light truck. However, neither project had much priority, and both were delayed until after the war.

The PT-76 Scout Tank

One of the main drawbacks of the T-70 light tank and its Lend-Lease counterparts like the Valentine, was that they lacked amphibious capability; rivers inhibited their ability to perform their main mission of scouting. Soviet tank designers has realized the importance of this feature in their pre-war scout tank designs such as the T-37, T-38 and T-40, but wartime pressures led to this feature being dropped after the war's outbreak because of the added cost and design complexity of amphibious tanks. The new design requirement for the K-90 light tank reverted to the pre-war preferences. The K-90 project was led by an unidentified colonel whose last name began with the letter 'K', hence the unusual K-90 designation instead of the expected T-90. In about 1947, the Ministry of Transport Machine Building decided to give the K-90 project greater priority, redesignating it 'Project 740', and decided to develop it competitively, adding three more design teams, headed by L. Troyanov, N. Astrov and N. Shashmurin. From the outset, it was anticipated that the basic K-90 chassis would be used to develop a variety of other light armoured vehicles including armoured transporters and armoured utility vehicles. The designs were all fairly similar; two of them using a conventional propeller for water propulsion. Shashmurin, at that time working in Kotin's bureau at the Kirov Factory in Leningrad, was the winner, with a design that featured a hydrojet system developed by N. Zhukovskiy and N. Konovalov. It was accepted in 1950 as the PT-76 (Amphibious Tank-76mm Gun), and entered production in 1951. Unclassified sources have attributed PT-76 production to the Kirov Factory in Leningrad and the Volgograd Tractor Factory.

The PT-76 was a fairly unconventional tank in many respects. No NATO army had an amphibious scout tank. The US Army, for example, was adopting the M-41 Walker Bulldog at this time. The PT-76 was unusually large for a light tank of this period, due mainly to the buoyancy requirements for its swimming capability. The hydrojet system allowed the PT-76 to cross rivers whose stream speeds were no greater than about 8km/h. It had a water speed of about 10km/h. The engine was simply a T-54 engine sliced in half, with six cylinders instead of twelve. The PT-76 was armed with the new D-56T gun developed by Petrov's design bureau. The PT-76 chassis served as the basis for a variety of other armoured vehicles including the BTR-50 armoured transporter, the Luna nuclear missile launch vehicle, the Penguin Arctic research vehicle, and the ASU-85 airborne assault gun.

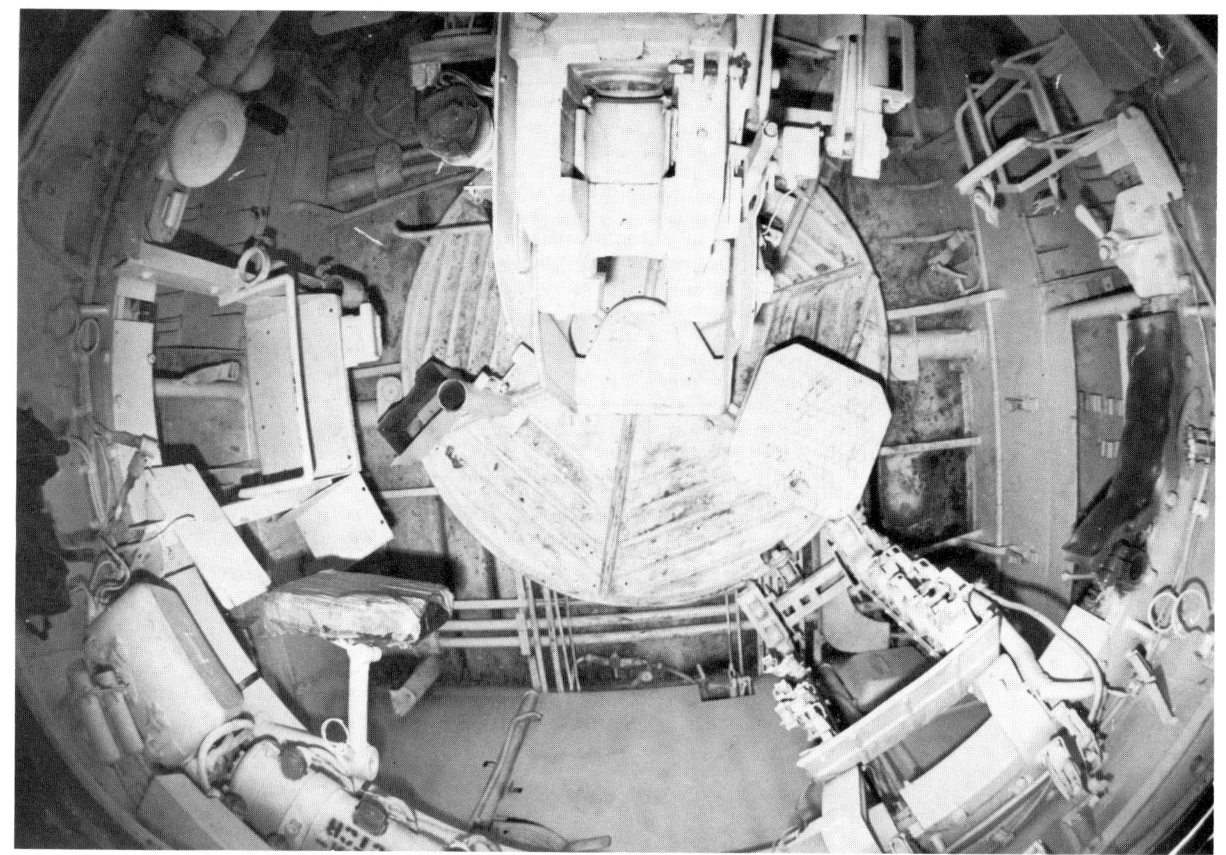

▲242

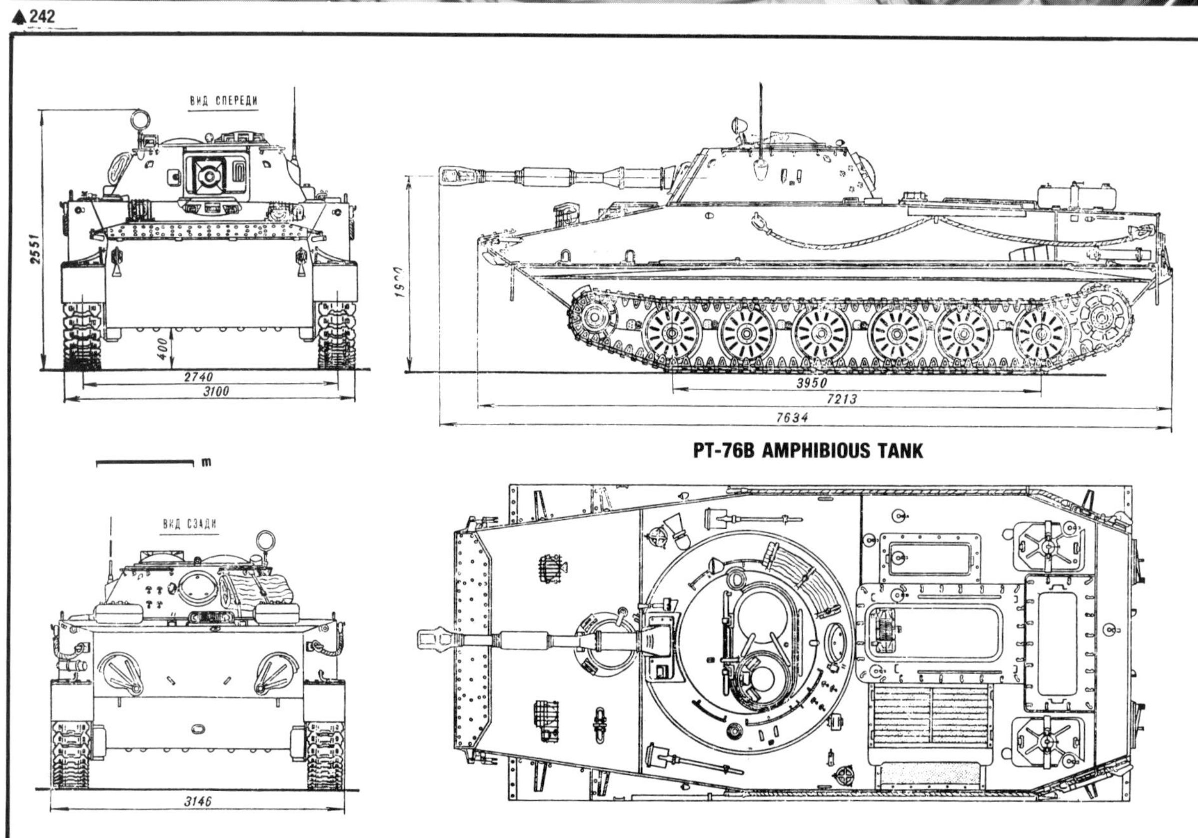
ВИД СПЕРЕДИ
2551
400
2740
3100
3950
7213
7634
PT-76B AMPHIBIOUS TANK
m
ВИД СЗАДИ
3146

242. View from above of the very spacious interior of the PT-76B. Once filled with ammunition it would be less roomy, but still a great deal better than Soviet medium or heavy tanks. (Zaloga)

243. The BTR-40 was a cross between a troop carrier and a scout vehicle, and was used in both roles. This vehicle was used by the Polish LWP in the 1950s.

Indirectly it also spawned a later generation of light vehicles including the ZSU-23-4 Shilka air defence gun vehicle.

On the initial production model the D-56T gun had a multi-baffle muzzle brake, but this was soon followed on the standard production model by the D-56TM gun which had a more conventional muzzle brake. In the late 1950s, the PT-76 underwent significant internal redesign in keeping with the general trend in the Ground Forces to reconfigure equipment for suitability on a nuclear battlefield. This led to the PT-76B which had a filtration system installed, and was fitted with a new stabilized gun system, the D-56TS. The PT-76 was used in both tank and motor rifle divisions. Each tank and motor rifle regiment was allocated a reconnaissance company with five PT-76 and three armoured transporters (usually the BTR-50). Besides these regimental scout units, each division had a separate reconnaissance company with an additional five PT-76. In the 1960s, the establishment was reduced in strength to only three PT-76 per company.

Production of the PT-76 continued until 1967 (or 1969 according to some estimates); by 1967 it was obsolete. It was a very large and conspicuous target and it was not well armed. It is still in service in dwindling numbers, and is being supplanted by a derivative of the BMP, the BRM. A total of about 7,000 PT-76 were built, of which about 2,000 were eventually exported. The PT-76 was a popular export item in the 1960s and 1970s, being cheap and easy to maintain. The People's Republic of China began to manufacture a PT-76 derivative, the Type 60 light tank, in 1966, followed shortly afterwards by the heavily reconfigured Type 63 light tank which has remained in production to this day.

The BTR-40 Sorokovke

During the Second World War, the primary armoured scout car of the Red Army was the BA-64b, developed by V. A. Grachev's design bureau at the Gorkiy Automotive Factory (GAZ). It was in production from 1943 to 1946, and remained in use in the Soviet Army until the late 1950s. In 1944, work began on a new vehicle based on the GAZ-63 light truck which had been developed by P. I. Muzyukin. The main difference was the accommodation for a larger crew. There had been attempts to increase the size of the BA-64b by deleting the turret (the BA-64d), but there was still not adequate room for a crew plus a full radio unit and other equipment, and the programme petered out from a lack of interest. In 1947 it was revived as

243▼

244. Driver's station in a BTR-40. (Charles Perkins)
245. A BTR-40V in use with an Afghan airborne unit.
246. The BTR-40A was a fire support counterpart of the larger BTR-152A, and is seen here in use with Pathet Lao troops at the time of the Vietnam War.

▲244 ▼245

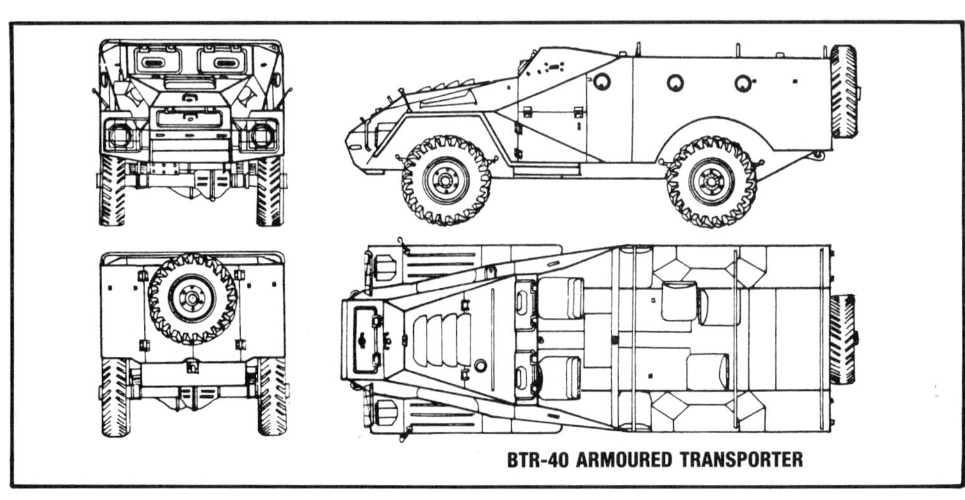

246▲

zavodskoe izdeliye 141, and a new design bureau under V. A. Dedkov was set up at GAZ to carry out its development. The '141' was intended to carry a squad of eight men. This differed markedly from the BA-64b which carried only two. The change in configuration was due to Red Army experience with the Lend-Lease American M3A1 Scout Car, which was widely used as scout vehicle, command vehicle and armoured transporter. A total of 3,340 of these had been supplied to the Red Army, rivalling the BA-64b in numbers, and had proved to be more useful in a wider range of roles.

The actual design of the new vehicle was undertaken by V. K. Rubtsov. The TTT called for the design of two complementary vehicles: a basic armoured transporter, and a fire support vehicle armed with twin 14.5mm Vladimirov heavy machine-guns on a ZPU-2 mounting. This paralleled the requirement presented to Fitterman's design bureau at ZiS for the larger BTR-152 armoured transporter which was also developed in two versions. The first prototypes of the '141' were completed at the end of 1947. The prototypes had a 'coffin' hull, similar to that of the BA-64b, with sharply angled sides. Although the angling offered better ballistic protection than vertical sides, it reduced the internal volume of the vehicle drastically and made it difficult to meet the seating requirement. It also complicated the siting of the ZPU-2 in the fire support version. The initial designs were rejected, and the '141' was sent back to the designers for reconfiguration. The redesigned vehicles had a simple, boxy rear end, very similar to that on the M3A1 Scout Car. These were resubmitted for state trials in 1949 and were accepted for series production which began at GAZ in 1950. They were also accepted after the subsequent Ground Forces operational trials, and received the designation BTR-40 for the basic armoured transporter, and BTR-40A for the fire support version with the ZPU-2 twin 14.5mm heavy machine-gun mount. The Dedkov design bureau received a state prize for the design in 1950, and would later become the premier Soviet wheeled armoured vehicle design bureau in the decade that followed.

The BTR-40 was not purely a scout vehicle. It was classified as an armoured transporter, like its larger counterpart, the BTR-152. It was intended for roles where the large seating capacity of the BTR-152 was not needed. It was used to transport heavy weapons teams in motor rifle units, to conduct scouting operations, to tow anti-tank guns and to carry communications and

▲247 ▼248

247. The old and the new. Bugle call from the rear of a spanking new BTR-40 during summer exercises somewhere in the Soviet Union in the 1950s. Even as recently as this the Soviet Army was still dependent on the horse in many roles.
248. A Soviet scout patrol in the early 1960s with a BRDM-1 in the lead, followed by a PT-76.

249▲

249. In 1957, the BTR-40B appeared with an armoured roof. Behind it is a BTR-152K, also with an armoured roof.

command units. In many respects, it was a general-purpose armoured utility vehicle, and its roles overlapped those of the BTR-152 in some areas. It was known popularly as the 'Sorokovke', the diminutive form of the Russian word for 'forty'. In 1956, the modernized BTR-40V appeared, which incorporated the central tyre-pressure regulation system first used on the BTR-152V. In 1957 it was succeeded by the BTR-40B which had an armoured roof in order to offer some protection in a nuclear contaminated environment. Production continued until 1960 (1958 according to US estimates), when it was supplanted by the BRDM. Total BTR-40 production was about half that of the BTR-152, about 8,500 vehicles. It was exported to the other armies of the Warsaw Pact, but was not extensively exported elsewhere. It remained in service until the 1960s, often being relegated to support roles, particularly as an armoured command vehicle and with combat engineer troops. Many were rebuilt with armoured roofs for the command role. In 1969 a rail scout version, the BTR-40zhd, was produced, which used a unique convertible suspension to ride on railway lines. This was used for railway patrolling, and to support armoured trains. Some BTR-40 were later reconfigured as chemical/radiological scout vehicles with flag-warning emplacers at the rear, designated BTR-40RKh. The East German NVA rebuilt some of their BTR-40 as launch vehicles for the 9M14M Malyutka anti-tank missile, but this does not appear to have been standard outside the NVA.

The BRDM Scout Vehicle

Experience with the BTR-40 led the Soviet Ground Forces to alter their concept of a wheeled scout vehicle. The BTR-40 had too large a troop compartment for a practicable scout vehicle, and it was too small for many other roles. Its main drawback in the scouting role was that it was not amphibious. It was decided that the next generation of wheeled armoured vehicles would include an armoured transporter for infantry requirements (BTR-60) and other roles, and a scout vehicle better suited to the reconnaissance role. In 1954, Dedkov's design bureau at GAZ was issued a TTT for the *zavodskoe izdeliye 40P*, sometimes also called the BTR-40P. The 40P design used a hydrojet propulsion system derived

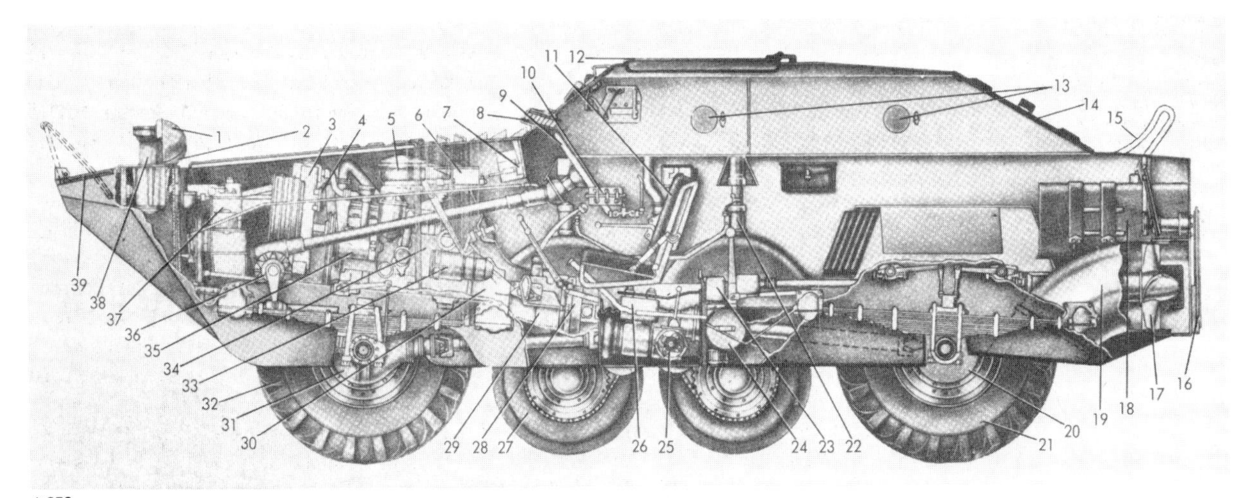

▲250

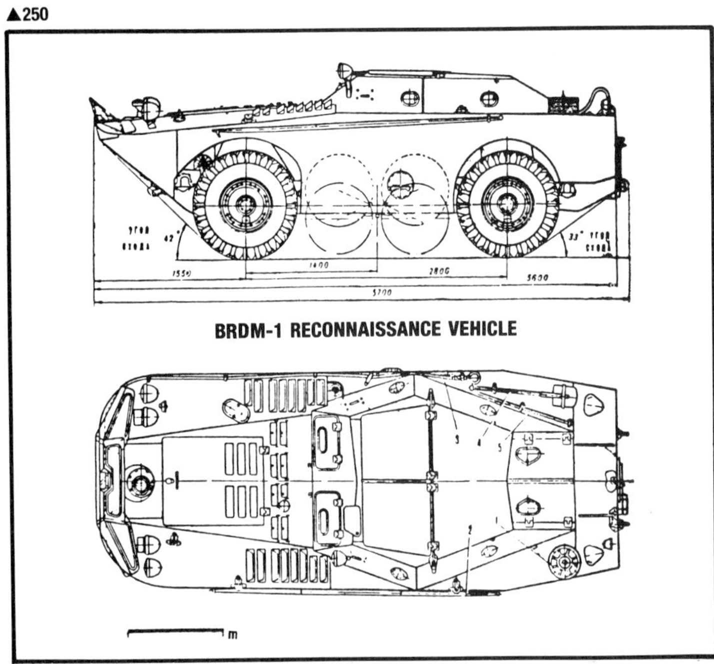

from that on the PT-76. To improve cross-country performance, the vehicle used the central tyre-pressure regulation system of the BTR-40V, and also incorporated a novel retractable auxiliary wheel system. In rough terrain, four small wheels (two per side) could be lowered using a chain drive. This reduced ground pressure, increased traction and helped surmount obstacles. The first prototypes were delivered in February 1956 for state trials in the Black Sea. The trials were successful, and initial production began in 1957. After Ground Forces' operational trials in 1957, the 40P was accepted as the BRDM (*bronirovannaya razvedivatelnaya dozornaya mashina*: armoured scout patrol vehicle). The original version of the BRDM had an open roof and was armed with an SGMB machine-gun. This was not entirely satisfactory, so in 1958 an improved version with an armoured roof and a PKT machine-gun was developed. This was designated BRDM-1, and became the standard production version of the series. The

▼251

250. Interior layout of the BRDM-1 reconnaissance vehicle.
251. Rear view of a Polish BRDM-1 showing the cover for the rear hydrojet water propulsion system.
252. The BRDM-1 was exported in modest quantities; this vehicle is serving with the Indonesian Marines.

BRDM-1 could carry up to five men, though four was the more common complement. The new BRDM-1 reflected the tactical trends of the time with their accent on nuclear fighting capability. Besides being used as a conventional scout vehicle, the BRDM-1 normally carried a DP radiac to identify nuclear contamination, and a PKhR-54 chemical detector to identify chemical warfare agents. The BRDM-1 was widely distributed in scout companies throughout motor rifle and tank divisions of the period. For example, in a tank division in 1966, the reconnaissance battalion had twelve BRDM-1; the tank regiments each had seven and the motor rifle regiments each had ten. A command version fitted with additional radios and antennas was also built. This was designated BRDM-V or BRDM-1V. Besides the basic BRDM-1 scout vehicle, missile-armed tank destroyer versions were also built such as the 2P27. These are covered on pages 155-73.

In the mid-1960s, a dedicated nuclear/chemical scout version of the BRDM-1 was developed, the BRDM-1RKh. This vehicle was fitted with a more comprehensive selection of detection devices than the normal BRDM-1, including a DP-3B nuclear area survey meter, a DP-5A radiac meter, a KPO-1 biological warfare sampling kit, a PPKhR vehicular chemical detector and a VPKhR portable chemical detector. The vehicle was also fitted with a variety of alarms and signal systems for warning nearby troops of chemical or radiological contamination. The most prominent of these devices was a pair of 20-warning flag emplacers mounted at the rear of the vehicle. These emplacers had a small explosive squib at the top of each warning flag. On detecting a contaminated area, the squib could be electrically fired from inside the vehicle, firing the flag into the ground. Other warning systems included both a GSP-1M or GSP-11 nerve gas alarm and a radiation alarm. The vehicles also normally carried 40mm SKhT signal cartridges for flare pistols. These are 'sound stars' which when fired launch two red signal stars to a height of 200 metres, and emit a loud whistle for twelve seconds. The BRDM-1RKh was widely distributed throughout the motor rifle and tank divisions, normally consisting of four per tank and motor rifle regiment, four per divisional reconnaissance battalion and nine in the chemical defence battalion for a total of 29 per division.

BRDM-1 production lasted from 1958 to 1968, and totalled about 10,000 vehicles. Of these, about 1,500 were exported. The main shortcoming of the BRDM was that it was poorly armed. It normally carried only a single SGMB 7.62mm machine-gun which had to be mounted externally. Some were re-armed with a 12.7mm DShK heavy machine-gun and two SGMB 7.62mm machine-guns. These had no protection for the gunner, and were awkward to use if in a contaminated area. What was clearly required was a turreted machine-gun. The BRDM-1 was not suitable for mounting a turret, however, because of the rear troop compartment, and a turret would have added excessive weight to the rear of the vehicle, compromising its buoyancy in water. Instead, in the early 1960s, work began on a reconfigured BRDM-1 with a central troop compartment and a turret; this emerged in 1966 as the BRDM-2.

The BRDM-2 Scout Vehicle

Design of the *zavodskoe izdeliye 41* began in about 1962 by the Dedkov design bureau at GAZ. The

252▼

▲253 ▼254

255▲

253. The BRDM-2 shared much in common with the BRDM-1, but had the crew compartment shifted into the centre of the vehicle to permit the addition of a turret KPVT 14.5mm heavy machine-gun.

254. This BRDM-2 has the interesting dual supplementary wheels locked down. These wheels prevented the BRDM from bellying onto terrain obstructions, and reduced ground pressure to permit the vehicle to ride on soft soil or snow. (Michael Green)

255. An interesting overhead view of some Polish BRDM-2. These are of the initial production type with the rhomboid-shaped air intake doors behind the turret.

BRDM-2 was a clear evolutionary outgrowth of the BRDM-1. The engine was shifted to the rear to permit the troop compartment to be located more centrally, and a more powerful, 140hp GAZ-41, engine was used in place of the 90hp GAZ-40P. A new turret was added, which was identical with the turret being developed by the Dedkov bureau for the BTR-60PB, armed with a 14.5mm KPVT heavy machine-gun. The BRDM-2 is also fitted with a TNA-2 land navigation system and normally carries the R-123 tank radio. Full-scale production of the BRDM-2 began in 1968 at GAZ. The BRDM-2 was initially misidentified as the BTR-40P2, probably due to the use of the term SPW-40P2 for the BRDM-2 by the East German NVA. As was the case with the BRDM-1, a number of variants were developed. The BRDM-2RKh is a direct counterpart of the BRDM-1RKh, and carries many of the same sensors and alarms. Two versions of the BRDM-2RKh were fielded. The initial version, the BRDM-2RKha, was fitted with the same 14.5mm KPVT heavy machine-gun as the normal BRDM-2. The improved BRDM-2RKhb had a 7.62mm PKT machine-gun substituted for the KPVT, and the additional space permitted more sensing equipment to be fitted. There are a variety of command and radio versions of the BRDM-2, varying in small details such as generators and radio antennas. These are usually called BRDM-2U by NATO. The most common type is turretless, and has an added generator in a rectangular metal container in lieu of the turret. Another turretless command and control version has the generators mounted over the rear of the vehicle, and yet another has no additional external generators but is fitted with a simple hatch in place of the turret.

The BRDM-2 was manufactured from 1966 to the late 1970s, and there was some production variation during this period. The original production vehicle had two simple hatches over the air intake entrance behind the turret. This was followed in the late 1960s by a slightly improved air intake with a slatted grill. Finally, in the 1970s, this was supplanted by a new design having six oval mushroom covers over the air intake which prevented water from seeping into the engine compartment. This last version is shown on the scale plan of the SA-9 Gaskin air defence missile vehicle. Total BRDM-2 production probably amounted to about 19,000 vehicles of all types. About half the total production was of the specialized types such as the BRDM-2RKh, BRDM-2U and BRDM-2 tank destroyers (see Chapter 6). The BRDM-2 has proven to be a very popular export item, being

▲256

▲257 ▼258

256. These Romanian BRDM-2 are of the intermediate production type, with the slatted grill air intake doors behind the turret.

257. The command version of the BRDM-2, the BRDM-2U, comes in a variety of configurations. This German NVA vehicle is typical, with long whip aerial masts added on each side of the hull, and the turret deleted.

258. The BRDM-2RKhb is armed with only a single PKT machine-gun in place of the usual 14.5mm KPVT heavy machine-gun and coaxial PKT. This view of several vehicles undergoing CBR decontamination shows the revised armament and the small sensor port on the revised mantlet.

259. The TAB-C is a Romanian equivalent of the BRDM-2, derived from a shortened copy of the BTR-70. It is not clear if this is an original Soviet design that did not enter production in the USSR, or if it is purely a local Romanian design.
260. A good view of a BRDM-2RKh with the flag emplacers in place and fully loaded. When not in use, the emplacer assembly folds forward and is usually covered by a canvas cover.
261. A German NVA chemical defence crew preparing the launching squibs on a flag emplacer at the rear of a BRDM-2RKh.

259▲

260▲ 261▼

cheap and relatively easy for a Third World army to maintain. About 4,500 BRDM-2 were exported up to 1985.

The Hungarian FUG Scout Vehicle

During the war, Hungary had a modest armoured vehicle production capability, mainly turning out derivatives of foreign designs such as the Toldi (a light tank based on the Swedish L-60) and the Turan (a medium tank based on a Czechoslovak design). However, Hungary did develop an indigenous armoured car design, the Csaba. The Hungarian armoured vehicle industry languished after the war, but in the late 1950s, the Hungarian Army approached the Military Industrial Commission of COMECON, and won approval to begin design of a scout

▲262 ▼263

264▲

262. The FUG is a Hungarian equivalent of the BRDM-1, and is widely used outside of the Soviet Union in the Warsaw Pact countries including Poland, Hungary, Bulgaria, Czechoslovakia and East Germany.
263. The FUG-US or VS-FUG is a direct counterpart of the BRDM-1RKh, and is fitted with a similar flag dispensing system at the rear.
264. Following their purchase of the FUG, the Czechoslovak CSLA modified some of their FUG as the OT-65 with a small turret taken from the OT-62 TOPAS, armed with a PKT machine-gun and an 82mm Tarasnice recoilless rifle.

vehicle corresponding to the Soviet BRDM. Permission was granted, and the vehicle was designated D-442. Its design was something of a precursor of the BRDM-2. The chassis was heavily based on the BRDM-1 design, but like the later BRDM-2, the engine was shifted to the rear. The D-442 used the locally produced Csepel D-414.44 100hp diesel engine instead of the 90hp petrol engine of the BRDM-1. State trials of the D-442 were successful, and production began in 1963 as the FUG (*Felderito Uszo Gepkocsi*). The FUG carried a scout unit of four men plus the driver. As with the BRDM, the main armament was an SGMB 7.62mm machine-gun which normally was externally mounted. Besides the basic scout vehicle, a chemical/nuclear scout vehicle, corresponding to the BRDM-1RKh, was also manufactured, designated VS-FUG or FUG-US. In 1964, the Hungarians began to market the FUG to other Warsaw Pact countries as an alternative to the BRDM. It was purchased by the Polish LWP, Czechoslovak CSLA and the Bulgarian BNA. It was favoured over the BRDM because of its diesel engine and improved design features. The Czechoslovak CSLA was not entirely happy with its limited armament, and on receiving the first vehicles in 1965, developed a modification kit to enable them to be fitted with the turret developed for the OT-62 TOPAS with the Tarasnice recoilless rifle. These modified vehicles are designated OT-65 in the CSLA. Production continued from 1963 to 1969 and probably amounted to about 3,000 vehicles.

In the late 1960s, development of an improved FUG was undertaken. As with the BRDM-1, the main shortcoming was the poor armament configuration. A simple cast turret was developed, at first armed with a 23mm gun and later with other weapons. Prototypes, mounted on a modified FUG, began operational trials in 1966 as the FUG-2, but were not accepted. Design work continued, including the incorporation of the uprated Raba-MAN D-2156 engine, with a new welded turret including a 14.5mm KPVT heavy machine-gun and a 7.62mm PKT coaxial machine-gun. Other design changes included the addition of side doors to improve access and exit. This vehicle received the factory designation D-944. It was submitted for state trials and was accepted by the Hungarian Army in 1970 as the PSzH-IV (*Panceloskonalony Szallito Harcjarmu*), replacing the FUG in production. It is frequently misidentified as the FUG-70. The PSzH was not as successful in the export market as its predecessor, the FUG, and was only exported to the Czechoslovak CSLA (as the OT-66 or OT vz. 66), the East German Frontier

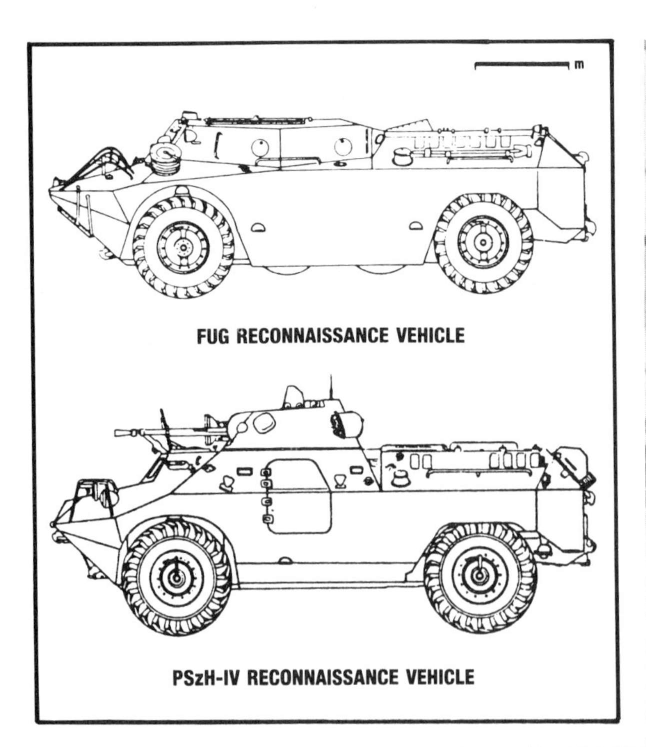
m
FUG RECONNAISSANCE VEHICLE
PSzH-IV RECONNAISSANCE VEHICLE

▲265 ▼266

267▲

265. The FUG was superseded in Hungary by the PSzH-IV, armed with a 14.5mm heavy machine-gun and a coaxial 7.62mm PKT machine-gun. Although frequently misidentified as a troop transporter, the PSzH-IV is a scout vehicle and a direct counterpart of the BRDM-2.
266. A CSLA OT-65 in temporary summer camouflage paint.
267. The East German SK-1 was a small vehicle patterned on the BA-64b. It was used mainly by East German security and militia forces, not by the regular NVA.
268. The Czechoslovak CSLA toyed with this Tatra 805 light armoured car in the 1950s, but rejected it for Army service. It bears considerable resemblance to the wartime Soviet BA-64.

Troops and MfS security forces. Total production was about 3,500 vehicles and probably ended in the late 1970s. It would appear that some vehicles were fitted with a unique RPG-7 launcher on the turret roof, linked to the main gun barrel. The launchers elevate and depress with the main gun, and can be fired from inside the vehicle to give it a measure of anti-armour protection. A turretless command version was also built in small numbers.

Czechoslovakia has also been involved in the development of armoured scout vehicles. In the late 1950s, Tatra developed an experimental four-wheeled scout vehicle designated Tatra T805, which resembled a modernized, turretless BA-64. It was not accepted. In the 1980s, the Czechs were reportedly working on a large, wheeled scout vehicle, but there are few details.

Romania has also been involved in armoured scout vehicle development. In the late 1970s, the Romanian Army (ASR) authorized licensed production of the Soviet BTR-70 armoured infantry transporter. The Romanians developed a local derivative of this vehicle, called TAB-C, which appears to be a shrunken version of the troop carrier for use as a scout vehicle. Unlike the eight-wheeled infantry transporter, the TAB-C has only four wheels.

268▼

▲269 ▼270

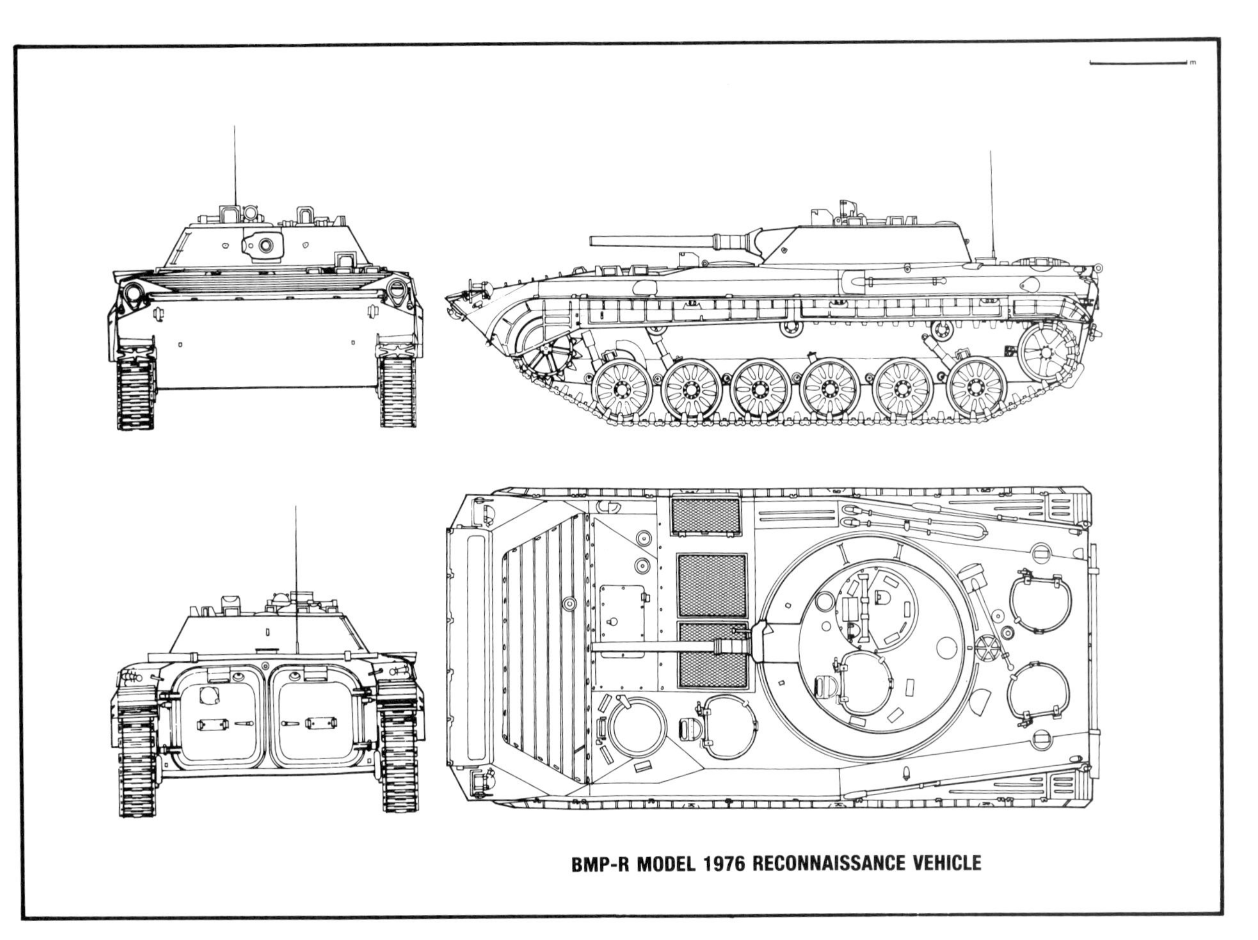

269. The PSzH-IV also serves with East German Border Guard and internal security units.
270. The BMR is a derivative of the BMP-1 infantry vehicle, fitted with a larger turret, and equipped with more extensive communication equipment. It has been replacing the PT-76 since the 1970s. (US Army)

The BRM Scout Vehicle

With termination of PT-76 production in 1967–69, the Ground Forces issued a requirement for a replacement vehicle. Rather than develop a new vehicle, it was decided to develop a derivative of the BMP-1 infantry fighting vehicle. This emerged in the early 1970s as the BRM (*bronirovannaya razvedivatelnaya mashina*), also sometimes called the BMP-R. The BRM differed from the normal infantry version in being fitted with a much larger turret for a 2-man crew. The crew of the BRM is six, including two scout troops in the rear compartment. It carries a larger number of radios than the normal BMP, and has a folding, telescoping antenna mounted over the rear doors to improve transmission. The vehicle is armed with the same 2A28 gun as the BMP-1, and the initial BRM also carried the 9M14M Malyutka missile-launcher over the gun tube. However, this anti-tank missile launcher was deleted from the standard production models, as is shown on the accompanying scale plan. Shortly after the development of the basic BRM, an improved version was developed with a small battlefield surveillance radar, given the NATO codename Tall Mike. The antenna for this radar is fitted on the upper rear of the turret, somewhat akin to the PRP-3. This version is designated BRM-1.

Originally, the BRM was issued on a very modest scale, with only a single BRM and three normal BMP to each reconnaissance company in the tank and motor rifle regiments, and three BRM in the divisional reconnaissance battalions of each division. In the early 1980s, however, the reconnaissance battalions in the Category 1 divisions began to be reorganized. Each reorganized battalion now has three BRM-1 and twelve BRM scout vehicles. There is a single BRM-1 at battalion HQ, and the other BRM-1 are used by the commanders of the two tracked scout companies. Each scout company has two platoon of threee BRM each, and a platoon of medium tanks. In addition, the battalion has a wheeled scout company with two platoons of BRDM-2, totalling twelve BRDM-2 and one BRDM-2U in the company, an electronics Intelligence company with truck-mounted equipment, and a separate chemical defence platoon with four RKhM. This expansion and modernization of the reconnaissance battalions also extends to regimental scout companies as more BRM become available. The modernized reconnais-

271. Rear view of the RKhM showing the flag emplacing system in folded position with a canvas cover over it.
272. The RKhM is a derivative of the SO-122 Gvozdika self-propelled howitzer chassis, specially designed as a radiological/chemical scout vehicle to replace the BRDM-2RKh in tank units.

▲271 ▼272

sance companies in tank and some motor rifle regiments include one BRM-1, three BRM, three RKhM and four BRDM-2.

Artillery Reconnaissance Vehicles

In the 1950s, the Soviet Ground Forces fielded a variety of battlefield surveillance radars on tracked vehicles such as the SNAR-1 on the M-2 or Ya-11 tractor (Long Trough), and the SNAR-2 on the AT-L tractor (Pork Trough); and counter-battery radar vehicles such as the ARSOM-1 on the AT-T (Track Dish) and ARSOM-2 on the AT-LM (Small Yaw) for use by artillery units to locate enemy artillery and mortar batteries. In the early 1970s, it was decided to develop armoured radar vehicles which could accompany the new mechanized artillery units with SO-122 and SO-152 self-propelled howitzers. Two artillery reconnaissance vehicles were envisaged: a battlefield surveillance and ranging vehicle based on the BMP, and a battlefield target acquisition vehicle on the MT-LB. The BMP-based vehicle, designated PRP-3 (*Podvizhniy razvedivatelniy punkt-3*: Mobile Reconnaissance Post-3, NATO Codename: Small Fred, also called BMP-SON), was based on the BRM version. Like the BRM, it was fitted with a large, 2-man turret. The turret carries a folding surveillance radar antenna on the rear of the roof, and on the right turret side is an electro-optical sensor array including a night vision device and a laser rangefinder. The radar has an effective range of about 20km. The PRP-3 carries a 5-man crew, and extensive communications equipment. The PRP-3 was first seen in 1975, but had probably entered service a few years before that. There is one PRP-3 in the artillery battalions of selected tank and motor rifle regiments, especially those equipped with self-propelled howitzers. Also, each divisional artillery regiment has one in each battalion, plus an additional vehicle in the target acquisition battery. This would give a division a total of eight PRP-3.

The target acquisition vehicle based on the MT-LB is designated SNAR-10 (*Stanitsiya nazemnoi artilleriy radiolokatsionnaya-10*: Artillery radar ground station-10; NATO Codename: Big Fred). The chasis of the SNAR-10 is

273▲

273. The SNAR-10 is an artillery radar scout vehicle based on the MT-LB. Details of this and other artillery scout vehicles can be found in the chapter on artillery vehicles.

basically similar to the normal MT-LB, but a turret-like superstructure has been added on the rear to house a large surveillance and target acquisition radar. A large folding antenna is fitted at the rear of the turret, and the radar has an effective range of about 20km. The vehicle has a crew of three, but can carry additional troops if necessary. The SNAR-10 entered service in about 1974, and is a fairly rare vehicle. There is only a single SNAR-10 in each divisional artillery regiment, attached to the target acquisition battery. It is used to locate hostile mortars and artillery and to help direct counter-battery fire.

The RKhM Chemical Scout Vehicle

As part of the general modernization of scouting vehicles, in the late 1970s, the Ground Forces requested the development of a specialized chemical/nuclear scout vehicle to supplement the BRDM-2RKh. The main requirement was that the vehicle be tracked to enable it to operate in bad terrain. The new vehicle was based on the hull of the SO-122 (2S1) Gvozdika self-propelled howitzer. In lieu of the turret, a small superstructure was added, surmounted by the 7.62mm PKT machine-gun turret from the MT-LB. The RKhM carries the same type of flag-emplacers as the BRDM-2RKh, but incorporates a modernized and expanded nuclear and chemical sensor suite. The RKhM is deployed in the reconnaissance battalions in the tank and motor rifle divisions, with a platoon of four vehicles in each battalion. It will probably replace the BRDM-2RKh in the chemical defence battalions of tank divisions.

New Wheeled Scout Vehicles

In the late 1970s, the Soviet Ground Forces began deploying a new wheeled scout vehicle which may eventually supplant the BRDM-2. Apparently it is a six-wheeled vehicle designated BTR-72 or BTR-74. A Soviet article on contemporary wheeled armoured vehicles would suggest that this vehicle may form the basis for a family of vehicles, including a scout vehicle, armed with a 30mm cannon like the BMP-2, and a wheeled infantry fighting vehicle to replace the BTR-70, armed with a 14.5mm KPVT turret. Other suggested derivatives of the family include a turretless armoured ambulance(SM), a radar surveillance vehicle (RLS) and an anti-tank guided-missile launch vehicle (UPTUR).

▲274 ▼275

274. The IRM engineer reconnaissance vehicle is used by combat engineer troops to conduct minefield reconnaissance, and other scouting chores. It is not yet clear if the IRM and IPR are identical vehicles, or two related vehicles with different sensors for different scouting roles.

275. The IPR is a highly specialized combat engineer scout vehicle designed to assist engineer scout teams in preparing for river-crossing operations. The vehicle is fully amphibious, or can be submerged to scout along river beds. This model shows most of its system in folded travelling position.

WARSAW PACT ARMOURED RECONNAISSANCE VEHICLES

	BTR-40	BRDM-1	FUG	BRDM-2	PSzH-IV	PT-76B	BRM	RKhM
Crew	2+8	4	5	4	4	3	6	4
Weight (combat loaded, tonnes)	5.3	5.6	6.1	7.0	7.5	14	14.5	15
Length (cm)	500	560	579	575	579	763	675	730
Width (cm)	190	225	250	235	250	314	294	304
Height (cm)	183	229	190	231	250	226	208	220
Ground clearance (cm)	28	31	30	35	30	37	39	46
Ground pressure (kg/cubic cm)	3.5	2.5	2.5	2.7	2.7	0.5	0.59	0.5
Armour (mm)								
Turret front	–	–	–	7	14	17	23	7
Turret sides	–	–	–	7	7	16	19	7
Hull bow (max.)	15	11	13	14	12	14	19	7
Hull sides (max.)	9	7	7	7	7	14	18	7
Hull rear	7	7	7	7	7	7	16	7
Main armament	SGM	SGMB	SGMB	KPVT	KPVT	D-56TS	2A28	PKT
Gun calibre (mm)	7.62	7.62	7.62	14.5	14.5	76.2	73	7.62
Depression/elevation (degrees)	−15+60	−15+60	−15+60	−5+30	−5+30	−4+31	−4+33	−5+30
Ammunition stowed	1000	1500	1500	500	500	40	39	2000
Coaxial armament	–	–	–	PKT	PKT	SGMT	PKT	–
Gun calibre (mm)	–	–	–	7.62	7.62	7.62	7.62	–
Ammunition stowed	–	–	–	2000	2000	1000	2000	–
Driver's night vision	no	active IR	active IR	active IR	active IR	active IR	passive II	passive II
Gunner's night vision	no	no	no	no	no	no	passive II	no
Engine designation	GAZ-40	GAZ-40P	D-414.44	GAZ-41	D-2156	V-6	5D20	YaMZ-238V
Engine type	petrol	petrol	diesel	petrol	diesel	diesel	diesel	diesel
Horsepower	78	90	100	140	100	240	300	240
Fuel stowed (litres)	122	150	150	290	200	380	460	550
Road range (km)	480	500	500	750	700	400	500	500
Max. speed (km/h)	79	80	80	95	80	44	80	60
Amphibious propulsion	no	hydrojet	hydrojet	hydrojet	hydrojet	hydrojet	track	track
CBR protection	no	partial	no	PAZ	no	partial	PAZ+PBZ	PAZ+PBZ
Radio	10RT-12	R-113	R-113	R-123	R-123	R-113/20	R-123M, R-130, R-107	R-123M, R-130, R-107

The IPR/IRM Engineer Reconnaissance Vehicle

The Soviet Ground Forces attach considerable importance to the proper reconnaissance of rivers prior to crossing. Since deep wading may be necessary, detailed information as to depth and water speed, and the nature of the riverbed must be secured. In the late 1960s and early 1970s, Soviet engineer reconnaissance units were equipped with the AR-2 river reconnaissance system. This was an amphibious sled fitted with sensors, towed behind an amphibious vehicle, usually a BTR-50PK. The sled used simple mechanical devices to test river depth. In the 1980s, a new amphibious engineer vehicle entered service, designated the IPR. Very little is known of this vehicle, but it would seem to be fully amphibious, using directable propellers, and fully submersible. It is fitted with a variety of unexplained sensors, probes and tubing. The chassis seems to have been derived from the BMP. It would appear that the vehicle was developed as a specialized reconnaissance vehicle for combat engineer scout groups (IRG) and scout patrols (IRD) to replace the primitive AR-2 system. The vehicle could check the suitability of river beds for fording, for tanks using OPVT snorkels in deep wading, or for bridging operations. While operating in the amphibious mode, the IPR could use its probes to check bed conditions and flow rates. It is probably fitted with an acoustic echograph for depth-sounding. In its submerged mode, it could make more detailed examination of the river bed, check for obstructions, and perhaps mark the bottom for future deep wading. The IPR could also be used to help establish a small engineer bridgehead prior to other operations such as bridging. There are probably only a few IPR in each divisional engineer battalion. Another version of this vehicle is the IRM (*Inzhenernaya razvedivatelnaya mashina*, Engineer reconnaissance vehicle). It appears to differ from the IPR in the types of sensors carried. The IPR is used mainly for river scouting, while the IRM is fitted for minefield scouting and other land reconnaissance.

276. The IPR with its snorkel fully erected, and ready for river-bed scouting. This would be done before sending tanks across in a deep wading operation to prevent the tanks from getting mired underwater due to obstructions or soft soil conditions.

▲277

▲278 ▼279

277. The ZSU-37 was the first Soviet post-war mobile air defence gun to enter production, but it was not very successful because of slow turret traverse and inadequate gun rate of fire.

278. The ZSU-57-2 was the first successful Soviet post-war mobile air defence gun system. The vehicle here carries the white and blue anchor insignia of the Polish 7th Naval Assault Brigade.

279. The ZSU-57-2 was used in small numbers by the North Vietnamese Army, like this vehicle knocked out in the fighting at An Loc in 1972. (US Army)

Air Defence Vehicles

The threat posed by attack aircraft to mechanized ground formations has increased considerably since the Second World War. The German Luftwaffe estimated that it had accouted for about 6–9 per cent of the Soviet tanks destroyed on the Eastern Front, though these figures are probably exaggerated. During the fighting in Normandy and Brittany in 1944, Allied fighter-bombers accounted for 19 per cent of the German armoured vehicles destroyed, according to later ground surveys. During the fighting in Korea in 1950, US fighter bombers destroyed 43 per cent of the armoured vehicles knocked out by UN forces. During the 1967 Sinai fighting, Israeli aircraft were credited with destroying at least 23 per cent of the Egyptian tanks found destroyed after the fighting. Tanks are very difficult targets for aircraft, but unarmoured elements of ground armies, especially truck supply columns, are very vulnerable.

During the war Soviet interest in air defence vehicles was modest. At the beginning, the Red Army was equipped with the 4M system, a quad 7.62mm Maxim machine-gun mount on the rear of a truck. Eventually, a variety of truck-mounted gun systems was fielded and there was some work on armoured vehicle-mounted air defence systems. In 1943 and 1944, the Astrov KB developed a number of experimental air defence vehicles by mounting machine-guns on light tank chassis. In 1944, a new version of the 37mm anti-aircraft gun, the V-47, was mounted on modified SU-76 chassis, resulting in the ZSU-37. In 1945, the twin-barrelled naval 2M8 25mm gun system was adapted to a similar vehicle, resulting in the ZSU-25. These two vehicles were built in very small numbers for operational trials, but neither became standardized to any extent. The main problem with both designs was that turret traverse was too slow to track most low-flying aircraft.

In the late 1940s, some attention was paid to less elaborate vehicles, notably the fire support variations of the BTR-152 and BTR-40, the BTR-152A, BTR-152D, BTR-152E and BTR-40A. These vehicles mounted the twin- or quad-barrelled 14.5mm KPV heavy machine-gun in a ZPU-2 or ZPU-4 mounting. They were intended to provide general long-range fire support to their motor rifle battalions, and were not configured solely for anti-aircraft use. Their fire controls were simple mechanical computing, reflex optical sights, and gun traverse was slow and manual. Although the basic KPV machine-gun was quite lethal against aircraft of the period, the system was not very effective against jet fighter-bombers of the period unless used in massive concentrations. Rather than rely on small numbers of mechanized air defence guns, *PVO-Voiska* (Air Defence Force-Army) doctrine in the late 1940s and early 1950s put its faith in conventional towed anti-aircraft guns.

In 1950, the Ground Forces began to field new air defence regiments with the tank, mechanized and rifle divisions, equipped with the new S-60 57mm air defence gun and its associated SON-9 (Fire Can) radar fire controls. This was the first division-level, radar-directed air defence gun in Soviet service, and it considerably enhanced the anti-aircraft fire power of the divisions receiving it. The main drawback of the S-60 system was that it took considerable time (25–30min) to fully deploy the guns, PUAZO-6/60 predictors, generators, cables, and their associated fire control radars. In this configuration, it was useful for the protection of relatively static sites such as command centres or major communication and transport lines such as bridges, but it was not very practical for the defence of fast-moving armoured columns. As a result, the PVO-Voiska requested a self-propelled version using a new twin-barrelled derivative of the S-60, the S-68 Model 1952 57mm gun. This emerged in about 1955 as the ZSU-57-2.

The ZSU-57-2 used a lightened version of the T-54 tank chassis. Hull armour was reduced to a level sufficient to defeat heavy machine-guns, and because of the weight reduction, the suspension was modified by deleting a single road wheel on each side. The S-68 gun system was mounted in a large, boxy turret. The two guns have a maximum rate of fire each of 240rpm (a practical rate of 140rpm), and the vehicle stows 316 rounds (with 264 rounds in ready clips). The original version of the ZSU-57-2 used optical sights without a range-finder, but the later model was fitted with a more

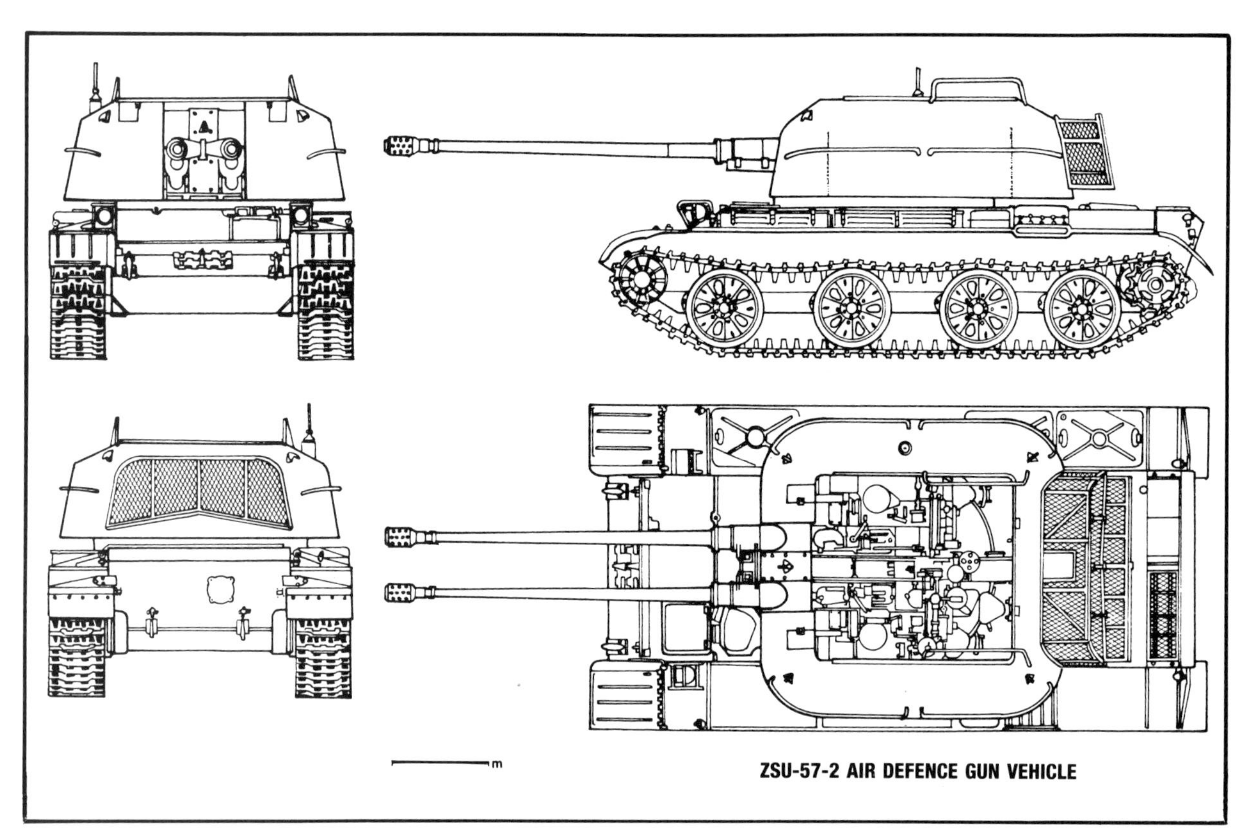

280. The Czechoslovak CSLA adopted a locally designed air defence vehicle in lieu of the ZSU-57-2, based on an armoured version of the Praga V3S truck. It is designated *vz.59 protiletadlovy dvojkanon 30mm.* (US Army)
281. Closeup of the vz.53/59 twin 30mm gun system on the *vz.59 protiletadlovy dvojkanon 30mm.*

sophisticated sight. This model is identifiable by the two small ports in the forward upper portion of the turret front. The ZSU-57-2 could also be used in a secondary role against ground targets.

The ZSU-57-2 was issued on a basis of one battery of four–six vehicles per tank or mechanized regiment. Beginning in 1960, the ZSU-57-2 was also made available to some of the Warsaw Pact armies. It saw combat in 1967 and 1973 in the Middle East wars, and was used on a limited scale during the Vietnam War. The main drawback of the ZSU-57-2 was its lack of a surveillance or fire control radar. Rangefinding depended on the use of a mechanical computing sight with an optical reflex sight. It was dependent on visual target identification, or in some circumstances could be cued by the divisional air defence surveillance radars via 10RT-2b or R-113 radio link. Even supposing that the crew could identify a target at the outer effective tactical anti-aircraft range of the gun system (4km), a hostile aircraft travelling at 725km/h (450mph) would be within the lethal envelope of the ZSU-57-2 for only 40 seconds of which 5 seconds would be required for projectile flight. This is a very short time in which to acquire, identify, track, range, engage, and fire on a target using such a simple system. Since it is a daylight, clear-weather system, its utility is very circumscribed. In a Central European environment, about a third of winter and autumn mornings are foggy and another third of days (on average) have cloud ceilings below 750m (2,450ft). Even during optimal summer months, 15 per cent of the days have cloud cover under 1,000m (3,250ft). A US Army study of the vulnerability of attack helicopters to air defence guns concluded that the ZSU-57-2 was only effective at relatively short ranges. The study indicated that a ZSU-57-2 firing a single burst had a probability of kill (Pk) of 48 per cent at 1km, 14 per cent at 1.8km and only 2 per cent at 3km.

Khrushchev Era Modernization Plans

By the late 1950s, the Soviet Ground Forces had begun to take more interest in modernizing the PVO-Voiska air defence force. This was in part due to the personal experiences of many Soviet officers who had endured three years' of Luftwaffe air supremacy in 1941–43. Soviet officers had also witnessed the success of US aircraft in smashing the North Korean armoured invasion of 1950. The Khrushchev administration was clearly infatuated with missile technology, and fostered development of missile systems to meet defence needs. In the late 1950s, the PVO-Voiska issued TTT's (Tactical-Technical Requirements) for a family of new air defence

280▲ 281▼

systems. A new 23mm gun system was authorized in a towed form to replace the ZPU-2 and ZPU-4, and in a self-propelled form to supplement and eventually replace the ZSU-57-2 at regimental level. A new low-altitude mobile missile-launcher was authorized to replace the ZPU-2 and ZPU-4 used in the anti-aircraft batteries and battalions of tank and mechanized regiments. A medium-altitude air defence missile-launcher was authorized to replace the S-60 57mm gun in divisional air defence regiments. And finally, a medium–high-altitude missile-launcher was authorized to re-equip the gun batteries of corps and army-level air defence brigades using weapons like the KS-19 100mm anti-aircraft gun.

The ZSU-23-4 Shilka

The clear limitations of the ZSU-57-2 reduced Ground Forces' interest in this approach to air defence. The ZSU-57-2 was never built in numbers large enough to equip all Soviet tank regiments. Instead, in about 1958, a TTT was issued to the Astrov KB to develop a weapon with all-weather capability. Astrov selected a variation of the ASU-85 assault gun which his bureau had developed for the VDV as the basis for the *Shilka* (Awl) requirement. In place of the S-68 gun, the PVO-Voiska selected the new

▲282 ▼283

284▲

282. One of the earlier versions of the ZSU-23-4 Shilka, before the heavily reconfigured ZSU-23-4V1 appeared.
283. Another of the early ZSU-23-4 derivatives with the gun system near full elevation.
284. The ZSU-23-4V1 had a heavily redesigned turret with prominent additions on the side as is evident in this view of several Egyptian vehicles. (C. Foss)

water-cooled AZP-23 quadruple 23mm gun which was also being developed as a twin towed gun (ZU-23, with the related ZAP-23 air-cooled guns). The main advantage of the AZP-23 was that it had a rate of fire fourteen times higher than that of the S-68, giving it a greater practical hit probability; and it had much less recoil than the S-68 which would have been a problem on a light chassis as envisaged for the Shilka. The main disadvantage of the AZP-23 was that it had a shorter effective range than the S-68 (2.5km v. 4km). This, however, was viewed as a reasonable trade off, since the probability of a hit at ranges above 3km were quite low in any event due to fire control shortcomings on the ZSU-57-2.

The fire controls of the Shilka were considerably more elaborate than those of the ZSU-57-2. The heart of the system was a Gun Dish acquisition and tracking J-band (14.6–15.6 GHz) radar linked to an analog linear prediction computer. The radar had a maximum surveillance range of 20km, a maximum tracking range of 18km, and was backed up by conventional optical speedring periscopic sights. The engagement sequence in the Shilka operates as follows: the 3-man turret crew consists of the commander, range radar operator and height radar operator. The two radar operators have the vehicle radar switched to surveillance or sector scan mode to acquire the target. When a target is spotted, the radar is switched to automatic tracking mode, and it is interrogated with an IFF (identification-friend-foe). If the aircraft is a Soviet type with the Odds Rods IFF system, the sequence comes to a halt. If there is no response to interrogation, the sequence continues. The range and height data is fed into the computer and a gun lead is provided.

The guns can then be fired, usually in a 1-second, 60-round burst which unleashes 11.4kg (25lb) of projectiles and high-explosive against the target. A US Army study indicated that the ZSU-23-4 has a much higher probability of a kill against aircraft than the ZSU-57-2, whether used in a radar-controlled mode or with optical controls. The firing cycle takes about six seconds from initial target acquisition to radar track lock-on, but US tests of captured ZSU-23-4 Shilkas supplied by Israel found that the time from acquisition to actual firing took 20–30 seconds for an average crew. A typical jet fighter-bomber, travelling at 725km/h (450mph) would traverse the 5km lethal zone of the Shilka in only 25 seconds, and even a slow target such as a helicopter at 290km/h (180mph) could traverse the lethal zone of the Shilka in about a minute. To be effective, a Shilka crew must be well drilled, and acquire and identify targets very promptly in order to have sufficient time to track and fire.

285. One of the more distinctive external features of the ZSU-23-4M was the large rhomboid air cooling cover added on the right side of the turret opposite the vehicle commander's cupola.
286. The late production ZSU-23-4M had a digital ballistic computer added as well as other improvements. (US Army)
287. In 1985, the first poor photographs of a modernized ZSU-23-4M appeared, showing it with IFF antennas added on the cover of the gun dish radar antenna.

SOVIET AIR DEFENCE GUN VEHICLES

	ZSU-57-2	ZSU-23-4V1
Crew	6	4
Weight (tonnes)	28.1	20.5
Length (m)	8.48	6.49
Width (m)	3.27	3.08
Height (m)	2.75	2.63
Ground clearance (cm)	43	35
Ground pressure (kg/cubic cm)	0.63	0.52
Gun	S-68	AZP-23
Number of guns per vehicle	2	4
Gun calibre (mm)	57	23
Max. effective range (optical sights, km)	4	2
Max. effective range (radar, km)	–	3
System reaction time (sec)	5	7
Burst (rounds per sec)	4	60
Initial muzzle vel. (m/s)	1000	930
Max. turret slew rate (degrees per second, elevation/traverse)	20/30	45/80
Tracking rate (degrees per second, elevation/ traverse)	20/30	20/30
Depression/elevation (degree)	−3+85	−4+85
Ammunition stowed	316	2000*
Max. rate of fire (rpm)	480	4000
Turret traverse (degrees)	30	45
Guidance radar	no	Gun Dish
Radar frequency	no	J band
Radar range	no	20km
Max. vehicle armour (mm)	14	9.4
Engine type	V-54	V-6R
Horsepower	520	280
Fuel stowage (litres)	640	250
Max. road range (km)	400	260
Max. speed (Km/h)	50	44
CBR protection	no	PAZ+PBZ
Radio	R-113	R-123

*Initial ZSU-23-4 versions carried only 1000 rounds

The ZSU-23-4 undertook operational trials in about 1964 and entered service in about 1966. The early ZSU-23-4 Shilkas were plagued with fire-control problems, mainly connected with the onboard electronics. A major source of the difficulties was the density of vacuum tubes and other relatively dated eletronic components which gave off considerable heat. Various attempts were made to improve heat dissipation, but problems continued to plague the ZSU-23-4 Shilka throughout the next decade. The troubles were made manifest in the many small modifications carried out. The accompanying drawings show the evolutionary development of the Shilka. The many alterations to the turret venting systems are very noticeable. Very few details of the evolution of the onboard electronics are available. A tactical offshoot of the electronics problems was that the Shilka crews had to restrict the amount of time using the radar in the surveillance mode. The Shilka turret was substantially redesigned in an endeavour to solve some of these problems. This version emerged in about 1972 as the ZSU-23-4V1.

The ZSU-23-4 was first used operationally in 1973 in the Middle East. It was found to be a lethal system when used in combination with other Soviet air defence systems, especially the SA-6 Gainful missile. It has been credited with more than 31 of the 103 Israeli aircraft lost, or about a third of the casualties. Although the ZSU-23-4 has clear performance limitations, notably a very short range which reduces

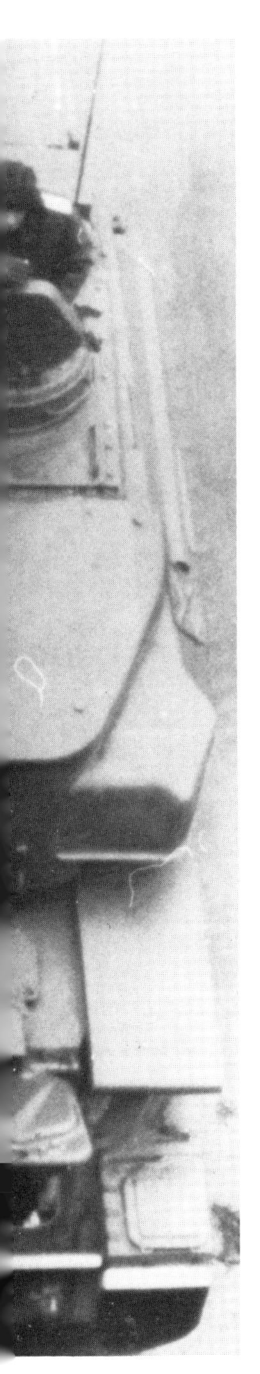

◀285 ▲286 ▼287

reaction time to a very short engagement envelope, it complements other Soviet systems to form an interlocking defence system. The SA-6 Gainful has performance shortcomings at low altitude, and so aircraft approaching at very low altitude to avoid Gainful, ended up in the deadly embrace of the Shilka.

The Soviets continued to improve the Shilka; a heavily redesigned version, the ZSU-23-4M, appeared in 1977. This version has additional cooling improvements to the turret, and probably incorporates a digital computer in place of the earlier analog system. A major emphasis was placed on systems to prevent jamming of the radar. This proved farsighted, as NATO became very familiar with the performance shortcomings and jamming possibilities of the earlier ZSU-23-4V1 model after several fell into Israeli hands in 1973. In the late 1970s, further improvements were made to the ZSU-23-4M, notably in the area of its IFF system. Production of the ZSU-23-4 lasted until 1983, and was undertaken in Czechoslovakia as well. According to US sources total ZSU-23-4 production for the PVO-Voiska

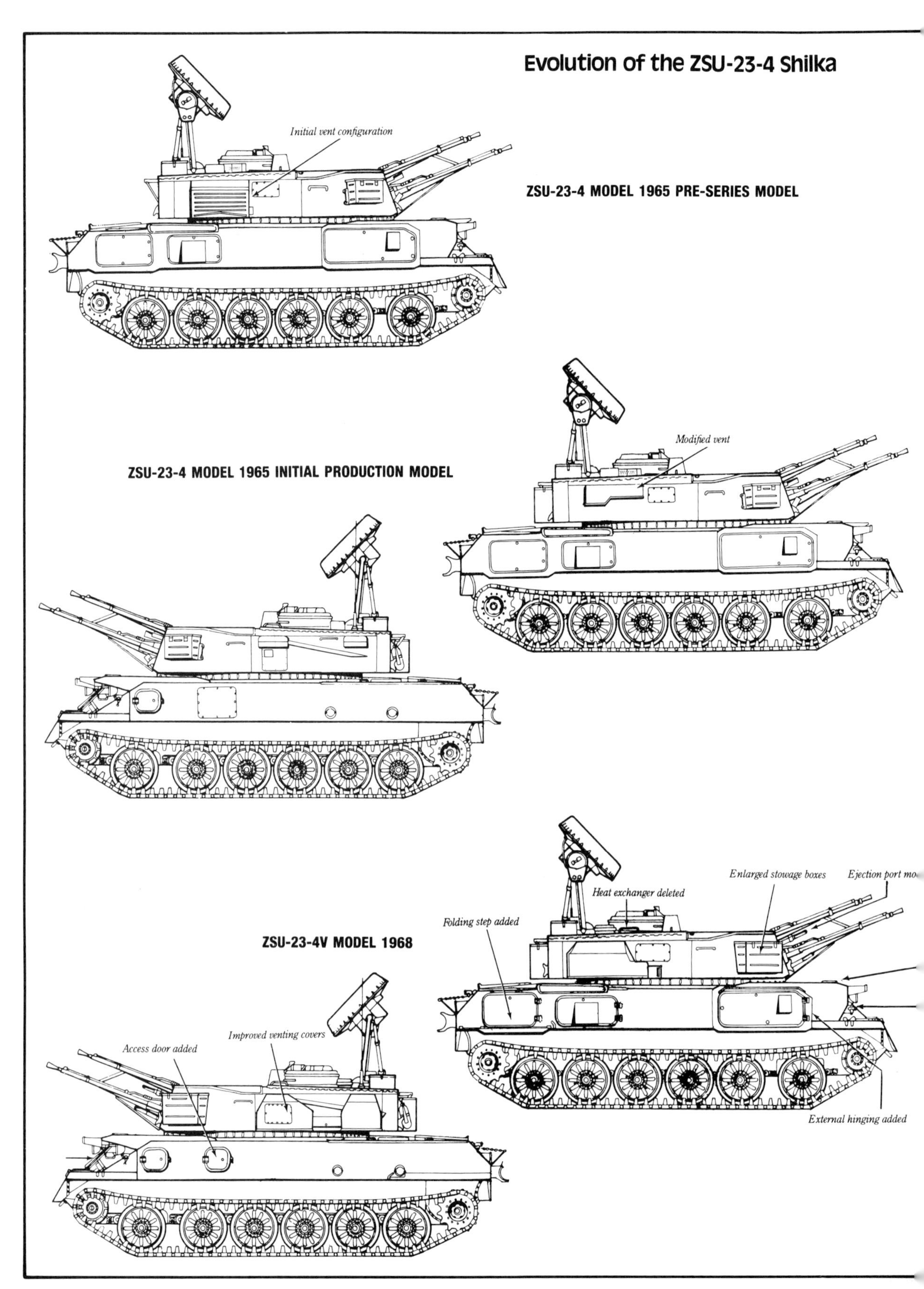
Evolution of the ZSU-23-4 Shilka
Initial vent configuration
ZSU-23-4 MODEL 1965 PRE-SERIES MODEL
Modified vent
ZSU-23-4 MODEL 1965 INITIAL PRODUCTION MODEL
Enlarged stowage boxes
Heat exchanger deleted
Folding step added
ZSU-23-4V MODEL 1968
External hinging added
Improved venting covers
Access door added

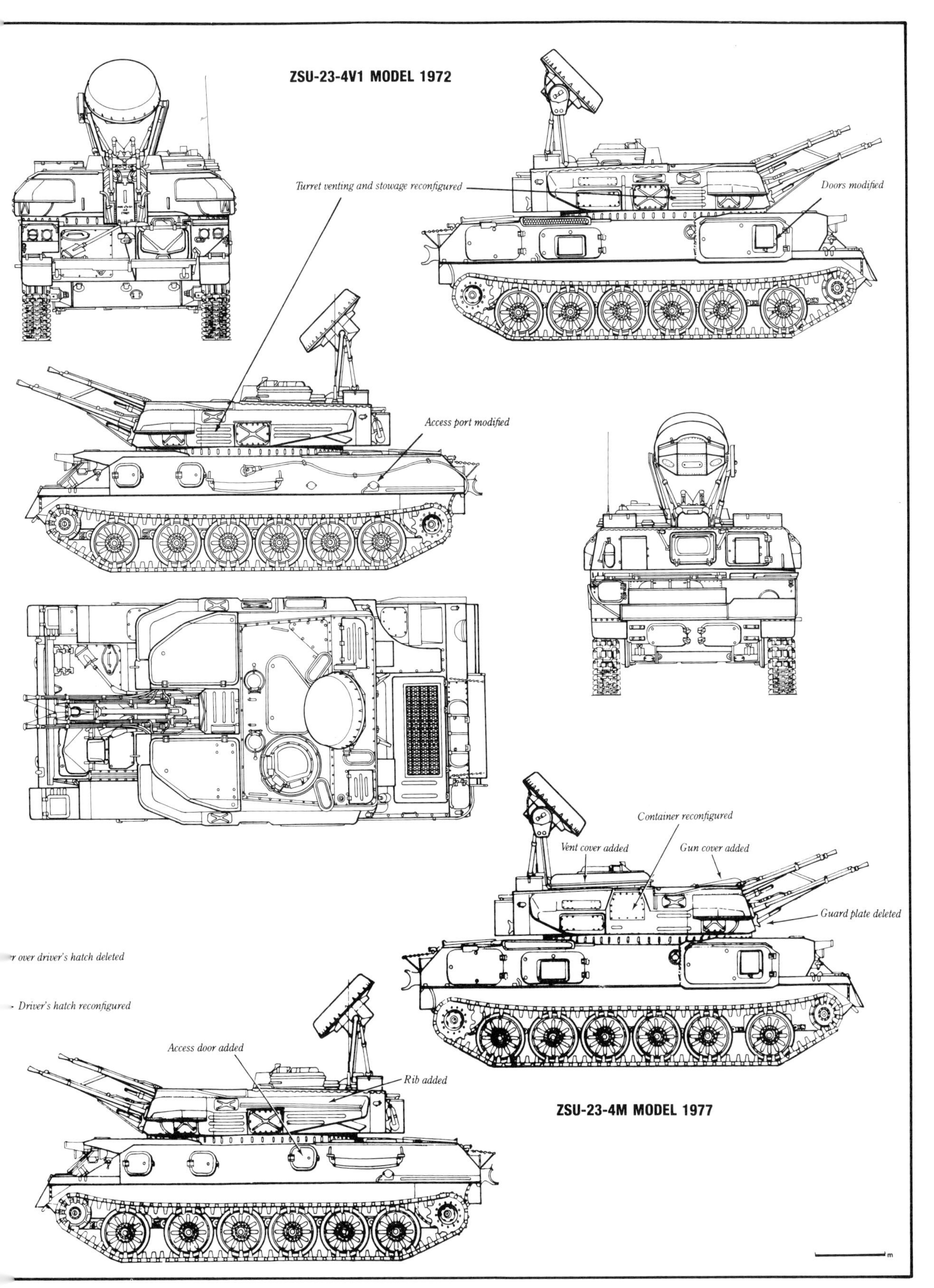
ZSU-23-4V1 MODEL 1972
Turret venting and stowage reconfigured
Doors modified
Access port modified
Container reconfigured
Vent cover added
Gun cover added
Guard plate deleted
r over driver's hatch deleted
Driver's hatch reconfigured
Access door added
Rib added
ZSU-23-4M MODEL 1977
m

288. The ZRK Strela 1 (SA-9 Gaskin) consists of four launch canisters and a launching assembly mounted on a modified BRDM-2 light armoured vehicle. Two reload canisters can be carried externally on the side reloading platforms. (US Army)

▲288

was about 4,500 and probably amounted to about 6,500 including export production.

The ZSU-23-4 is deployed in air defence batteries in the tank and motor rifle regiments of the Soviet Ground Forces. These batteries have a platoon of four Shilka, supported by another platoon with four SA-9 Gaskin or SA-13 Gopher launch vehicles. Normally the ZSU-23-4 operate in pairs, about 200 metres apart. The platoon is usually deployed about 400 metres behind the two lead battalions of the regiment with the four vehicles spaced 150–250m apart.

The effectiveness of the ZSU-23-4 declined in the 1970s because countermeasures had been developed. Aircraft especially vulnerable to gun systems like this, notably attack helicopters, can be fitted with radar warning receivers which pick up the emissions of the Gun Dish radar. If alerted in time, a helicopter crew can avoid the lethal envelope of the Shilka. There are tactical countermeasures as well. Shilkas can be engaged by attack helicopters firing long-range anti-tank missiles like TOW or HOT from ranges outside the effective range of the Shilka's gun.

The SA-9 Gaskin

The Shilka was not developed in isolation, but was tied to PVO-Voiska plans to develop a complementary missile system for regimental air defence. At about the same time as the Shilka was being developed, another design bureau had been issued a TTT for a low-altitude air defence missile system, the ZRK-BD Strela 1, better known by its US/NATO codename: SA-9 Gaskin. The TTT called for a short-range, low-altitude, infra-red guided system capable of being launched from a light armoured vehicle. Very little is known about Soviet work in this field prior to the SA-9. There were several programmes to develop low-altitude air defence missiles, including one called OSO and another named Ryabchik (Thrush), but apparently, none of these became operational. The attraction of infra-red guided systems is that they are relatively cheap, and since they are fire-and-forget, they do not have to be accompanied with a complicated and expensive radar fire-control system. In the Soviet view, gun and missile systems are complementary; guns are more effective at short ranges, and are less expensive to operate than missiles. At longer ranges, missiles have better performance than guns, and can offer better kill probabilities in many circumstances (though usually for a high cost). The Strela 1 was designed for a maximum effective slant range of about 8km. The original version of the Strela 1 missile (the ZUR 9M31) used an uncooled IR seeker, thereby limiting its engagement to circumstances where the radiant heat of a jet tailpipe was evident. At a later date improved, cooled seekers were introduced on the 9M31M, and these provide a greater variety of lock-on aspects to the missile.

While in development, the Gaskin system was apparently mounted on a modified BTR-60PB, the launcher replacing the normal turret. However, for service use, the smaller BRDM-2 was selected as the launch vehicle. The SA-9 Gaskin was introduced in 1968, about three years after

289. Interesting overhead view of the launch canisters on the SA-9 Gaskin. The initial production type of the SA-9 used the same slatted grill air intakes as the intermediate model of the normal BRDM-2 scout car. (US Army)
290. A number of SA-9 Gaskin are fitted with the 'Hat Box' passive electronic detectors. These are seen on the hull front corners, over the rear engine deck, and under the launch array.

289▲

the Shilka. It is deployed in the air defence batteries of tank and motor rifle regiments with a platoon of four Gaskin and a platoon of four Shilkas. The Gaskins are usually found 2–3km further to the rear than the Shilkas because of their greater range. They are often employed to protect the regimental artillery battalion and command post.

The SA-9 Gaskin launch vehicle is undoubtedly the simplest air defence missile vehicle system in the Soviet Ground Forces. The launch turret is traversed manually by the launch operator. The basic version of the Gaskin launcher has no fire-control system worth noting. The crew can be alerted to an incoming target by divisional air defence's regimental target aquisition battery radar teams via the air defence battery headquarters. Target acquisition is visual through the launch turret window and launch sight. On acquiring a target, the operator swings the launch assembly into the proper direction using his feet, bore-sights the missile using a simple optical sight, and selects a missile from the console. This opens the canister door and the missile seeker signals target lock-on by an audio signal. The seeker is uncaged and the missile is launched.

A second version of the SA-9 Gaskin system had the 'Hat Box' passive warning system added. Hat Box consists of four multi-faceted detector

290▼

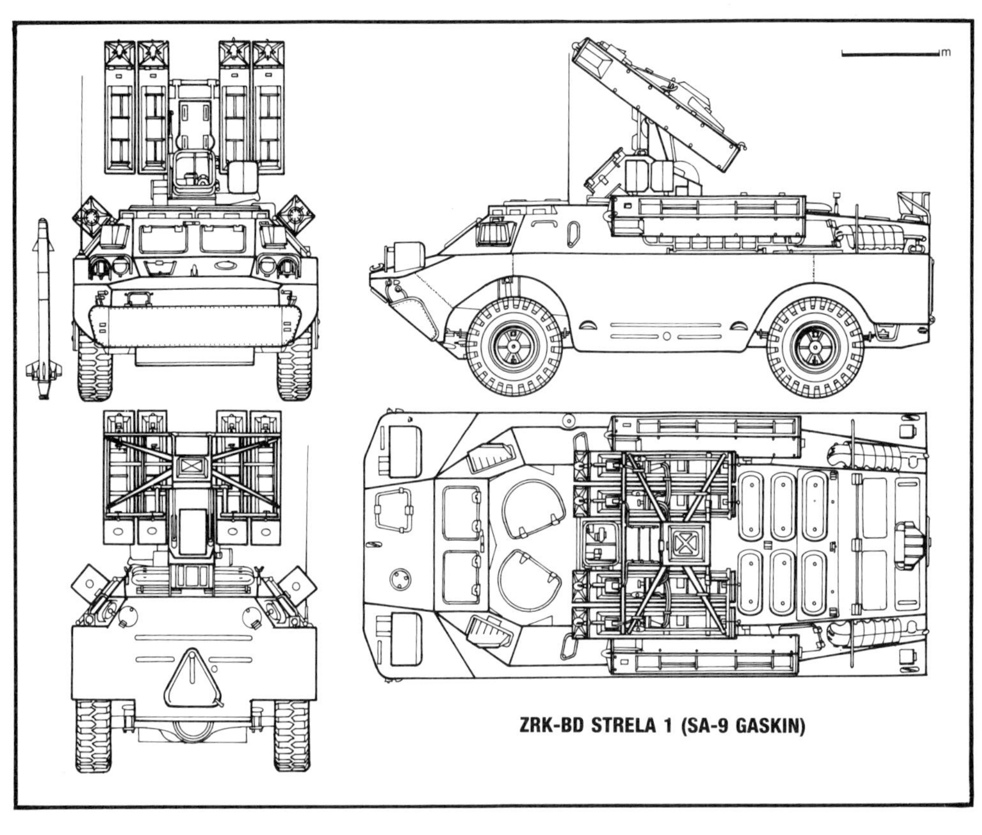

ZRK-BD STRELA 1 (SA-9 GASKIN)

panels, one on each side of the hull front, one on the turret, and one on the hull rear. These are passive radio frequency detection devices which pick up emissions from aircraft radar, TACAN, radio altimeters or other systems. Hat Box gives the Gaskin crew rough approximations of a potential target, such as the direction of approach. The scale plan here shows an SA-9 Gaskin with the Hat Box system. Normally only a single SA-9 Gaskin in each platoon is equipped with Hat Box. It appears that some versions of the BTR-60PU-12 command vehicles associated with the Gaskin launch vehicles have also been fitted with a simple data-link system which would be tied to divisional air-alert systems, such as the early warning radars associated with the division's air defence regiment.

The US Defense Intelligence Agency estimated that 640 SA-9 Gaskin were deployed with the Soviet Ground Forces in 1984. It has been widely exported, probably totalling about 850 systems. It has seen combat in Lebanon in 1982, and in the fighting between Angola and South Africa. Like many first-generation infra-red guided missiles, its effectiveness has been degraded by the advent of infra-red countermeasure systems such as helicopter exhaust deflectors, 'hot brick' systems and IR flare-dispensers. The SA-9 Gaskin is being replaced in Category 1 divisions by the SA-13 Gopher.

The SA-4 Ganef

The first mobile air defence system to be deployed by the PVO-SV was the ZRK-SD *Krug* (Circle; US/NATO codename: SA-4 Ganef). Development of the Krug system began in the mid-1950s. The aim was to develop a medium–high-altitude system which, eventually, would replace gun systems such as the radar-directed KS-19 100mm gun in air defence divisions and air defence brigades, and the cumbersome V-75 (SA-2 Guideline) air defence missile-launchers in field army use. The requirement called for the launchers to be mounted on a tracked chassis. An entirely new type of tracked chassis was developed for this requirement, which later served as the basis for a variety of other armoured vehicles including the GMZ minelayer and the SO-152 self-propelled howitzer.

The system was based around the ZUR 3M8 missile, a very large weapon using four solid wrap-around boosters and a kerosene ramjet sustainer propulsion system. Each Krug SPU (launch vehicle) carries two missiles, the left-hand missile being elevated slightly above the right-hand one. The Krug SPU has no fire controls of its own. The associated engagement radar system, the SSNR Krug (NATO codename: Pat Hand), is mounted on a separate vehicle, also based on the same vehicle chassis as the launcher. The SSNR Krug incorporates an H-band (6.44–6.68 GHz) target tracking and illumination radar.

The ZRK-SD Krug was first publicly shown in 1964, but the system had serious technical problems, and modification programmes delayed its operational deployment until 1969. The pre-series SPU shown in 1964 had sloped chassis sides. The initial production type, shown in Moscow in 1966, had vertical superstructure sides. Finally, in the late 1960s, the standard production type was introduced, and this version is shown in the accompanying scale plans.

The Krug was deployed in dedicated air defence brigades. These brigades are assigned on a basis of one per combined arms army or tank army and two per front. The brigade has three battalions, each with three launcher batteries. A launcher battery consists of three SPU Krug launch vehicles, one SSNR Krug (Pat Hand) engagement radar vehicle and three Ural-375 TZM transloader and support vehicles. The SSRTs (Long Track) is an E-band (2.6 GHz) target acquisition radar mounted on a lengthened AT-T heavy tractor. It has a maximum range in excess of 150km, and is used for surveillance, early warning and target acquisition, and is located with the battalion headquarters. It is tied by data-link to a Thin Skin truck-mounted height-finding radar and another Long Track at brigade headquarters. Once the target is within range, it is handed over to the SSNR Krug (Pat Hand) radar vehicle. This system employs a continuous wave (CW) illumination guidance system, somewhat akin to the system used with the US Navy Talos air defence missile. The main tracking beam of the SSNR Krug monitors the target aircraft. When a missile is launched from one of the accompanying SPU Krug launch vehicles, it emits a signal from a small transponder mounted on one of the rear tail fins. This signal assists the SSNR Krug system to gather the missile into the proper approach trajectory by means of command guidance. Once on the proper trajectory and in its final approach, the four interferometer antennas on the leading edge of the four forward fins pick up and home in, the CW radar illumination being reflected off the target aircraft. The missile warhead is quite large, about 135kg, and it is proximity-fuzed or command detonated. The system has an effective slant range of 80–100km and a maximum altitude of 25km. It would appear that the battery deploys in a diamond formation, with the three

291. The initial production version of the ZRK-Krug (SA-4 Ganef) SPU launch vehicle was distinctive for its sloped superstructure sides. (Sovfoto)

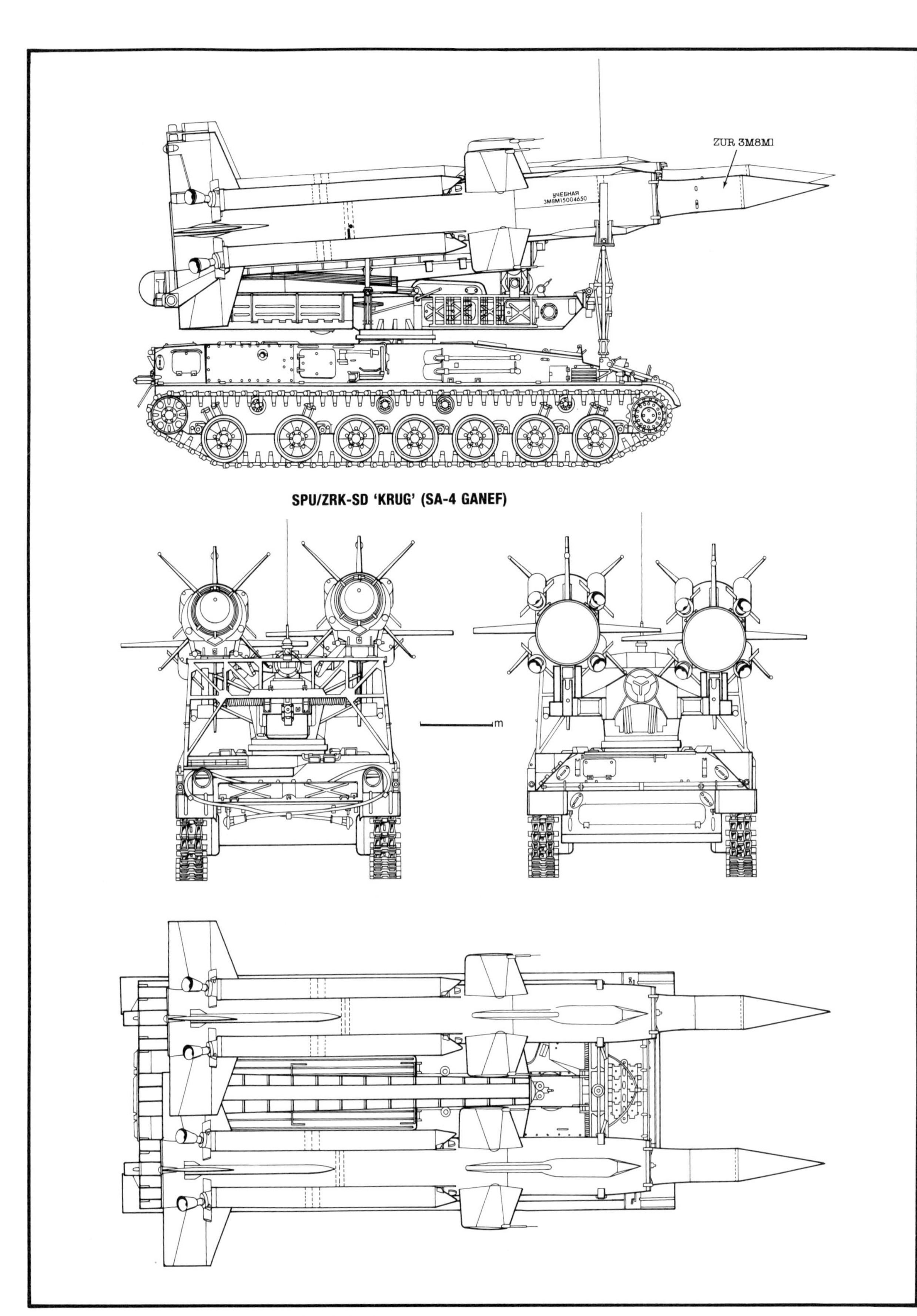
ZUR 3M8M1
УЧЕБНАЯ
3M8M15004650
SPU/ZRK-SD 'KRUG' (SA-4 GANEF)
m

292. The first version of the Krug SPU to be built in any numbers was this type, first displayed in 1965. It had vertical superstructure sides and improvements to the launcher assembly. (Sovfoto)
293. Interesting overhead view of a ZRK-Krug SPU, of the intermediate production type.

292▲ 293▼

SPU launch vehicles forming the forward elements, and the Pat Hand SSNR engagement radar vehicle at the rear. Apparently the Pat Hand SSNR can only engage a single target at a time, which significantly reduces the battery firing rate, since a single missile may take up to two minutes to reach the outer limits of its operational range.

A number of variations of the ZUR 3M8 missile appeared, including the 3M8M1 and the improved 3M8M2 short-nosed version (called Ganef Mod 1 in NATO). The short-nosed version (about 0.5m shorter in the nose section) was developed to improve missile performance in the dead zone over the launch battery. It has a shorter effective range (50km), but trades this off for improved vertical performance, reducing the dead zone. Photographic evidence suggests that many batteries intermix the long- and short-nosed versions, in order to benefit from their respective advantages.

Although mounted on a mobile launcher, the ZRK-SD Krug system is not a true mobile air defence system in the current sense of the word. The launcher vehicle cannot fire missiles on the move, and indeed, the launch battery probably takes at least fifteen minutes to deploy from road march. After the six battery missiles have been expended, the reloading procedure is quite lengthy, probably taking about 10–15 minutes to transfer a missile from the TZM transloader vehicle to the launcher. Since the transloader carries only a single missile, it would have to return to the brigade resupply point. It is not

294. The TZM transloader vehicle for the Krug (SA-4 Ganef) system is based on the Ural 375 truck.

295. The definitive version of the ZRK-Krug SPU launch vehicle. This view is interesting in that the vehicle in the foreground is armed with the initial long-nosed version of the Ganef missile, while one of the vehicles in the background is armed with the short-nosed type. Also, close inspection of the wooded area to the extreme left of the picture will reveal the antennas of the seldom seen Pat Hand engagement radar vehicle. (Sovfoto)

▲294 ▼295

296. A poor, albeit very rare, photograph of the 'Pat Hand' engagement radar vehicle. It is based on the same chassis as the launch vehicle, and is fitted with a massive radar assembly.

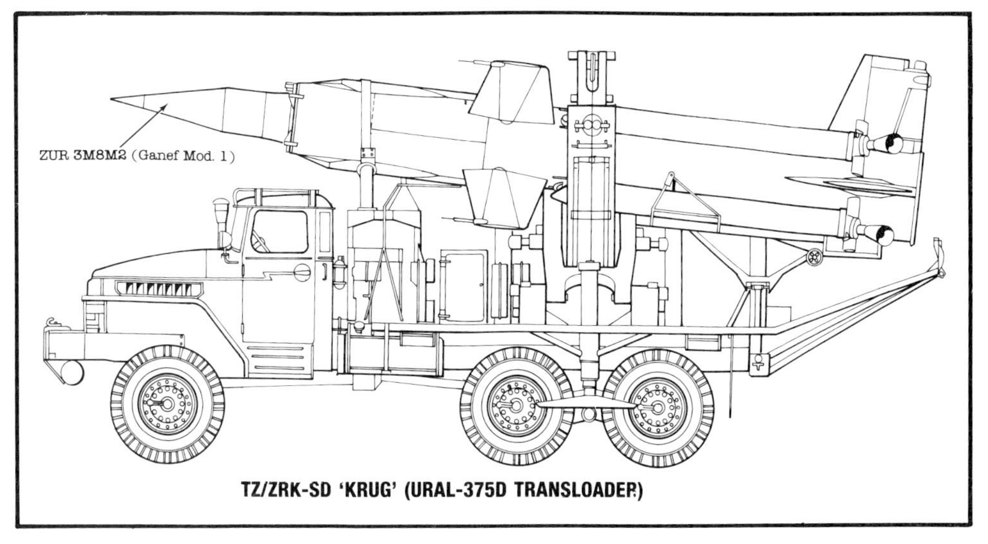

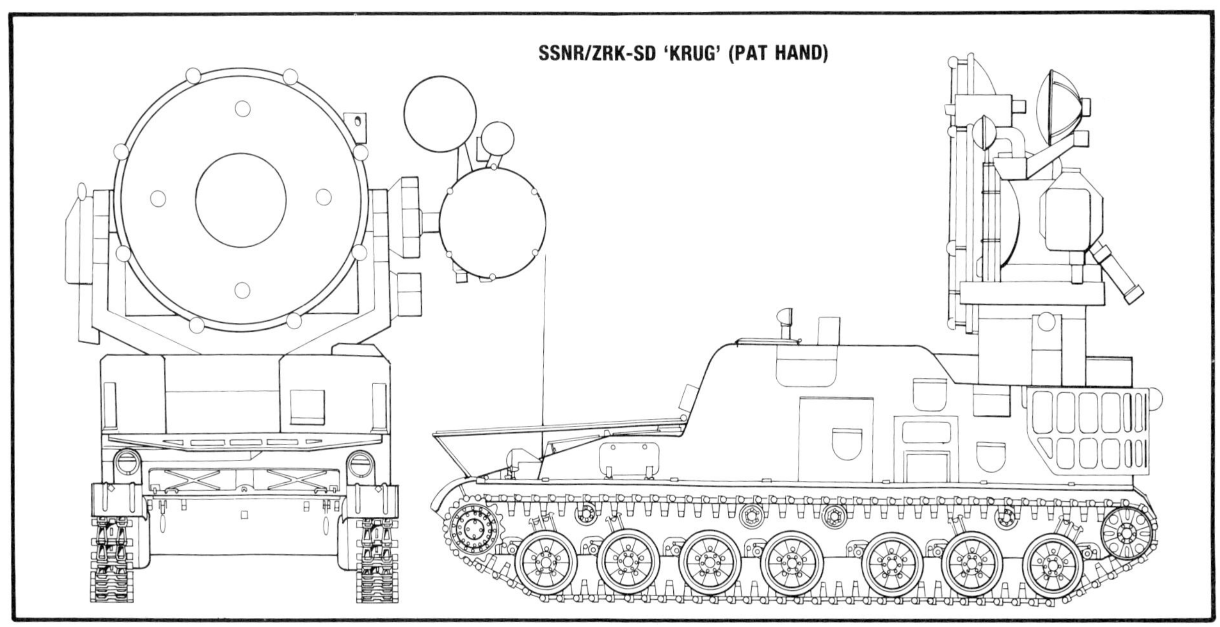

296▼

▲297

297. At brigade level, additional missiles are carried on these semi-trailers. These are then loaded onto the TZM transloader vehicles for transport to the launch vehicles in the field and eventual loading on the missile launch racks.

clear whether such a system offers any advantages over trailer-mounted systems such as the American Hawk battery.

The SA-4 Ganef was supplied to the German NVA and Czechoslovak CSLA, and possibly to Hungary and Bulgaria, but it was not exported outside the Warsaw Pact. (There have been unconfirmed reports that Libya has obtained some.) This is probably because of the sophistication and complexity of the system and its attendant high cost. The US DIA estimated that there were 1,375 SA-4 Ganef launchers deployed with the Soviet Ground Forces in 1984, which would imply that about 450 SSNR Pat Hand radar vehicles and 50 Krug brigades were deployed. A further 125 launchers serve with the other armies of the Warsaw Pact. A small number of Soviet SA-4 Ganef launchers were sent to Egypt in 1970–72, but they remained in Soviet hands and were withdrawn when relations between Egypt and the USSR cooled. Therefore, there is no historical combat evidence regarding the efficacy of the ZRK-SD Krug system. The Krug relies on a dated guidance system which would probably be very susceptible to modern electronic countermeasures despite constant attempts to improve its electronic countermeasures and counter–countermeasures features. The missile itself is large and not particularly agile. Not surprisingly, it is on the verge of replacement by the newer SA-12 Gladiator system.

The SA-6 Gainful

Development of a divisional air defence missile system, codenamed *Kub*, began in 1959 by OKB-134 in Tushino under I. I. Toropov at about the same time as the Krug system. The divisional system, called ZRK-SD Kub (Cube), was intended to supplement and then replace the S-60 57mm radar-directed guns in divisional air defence regiments. The basic tactical conception of the Kub was very similar to that of the Krug; a firing battery would consist of four launch vehicles (SPU), directed by a single engagement radar vehicle (SSNR). Development of the Kub vehicle was undertaken by Astrov's KB, and was derived from the ASU-85 assault-gun chassis (as was the ZSU-23-4). Technically, the missile selected for the Kub project was more sophisticated than that selected for the Krug. The Kub, designated ZUR 3M9 (later 9M9), was an unconventional solid rocket/ramjet, with an integrally cast solid rocket engine (in lieu of the solid rocket boosters on the Krug). This booster motor propels the missile to supersonic speed, exhausting its fuel. At this point the booster rocket nozzle falls away, to be replaced by a jet nozzle immediately in front of it. The high-speed air is forced into the combustion chamber through four intakes on the missile body, where it oxidizes solid fuel pumped into the combustion chamber by a solid-fuel gas generator. This integral rocket-ramjet propulsion unit has two major advantages: it offers excellent maximum speed (840m/s, 3,025km/h, Mach 2.5), but on the other hand, the system is very simple, reducing both unit cost and maintenance. A US evaluation of the ZUR 9M9 missile concluded that it cost 40 per cent less than a comparable liquid fuel rocket engine, and that maintenance was probably two to three times lower. On the negative side, such missiles loose oxidative efficiency at higher altitudes, and the propulsion must remain at a constant rate and so cannot be

298. The ZRK-Kub air defence missile system is mounted on a chassis developed alongside the ZSU-23-4 Shilka by the Astrov design bureau. This vehicle belongs to the German NVA.
299. A Soviet ZRK-Kub (SA-6 Gainful) in 1985. The small can on the right front corner of the superstructure is the data link which ties in the SPU launch vehicle to the Straight Flush engagement radar vehicle. (Sovfoto)
300. Although the missiles are shown pointing forward during this parade in East Germany, in travel the missiles are usually locked down pointing rearward.

298▲

299▲ 300▼

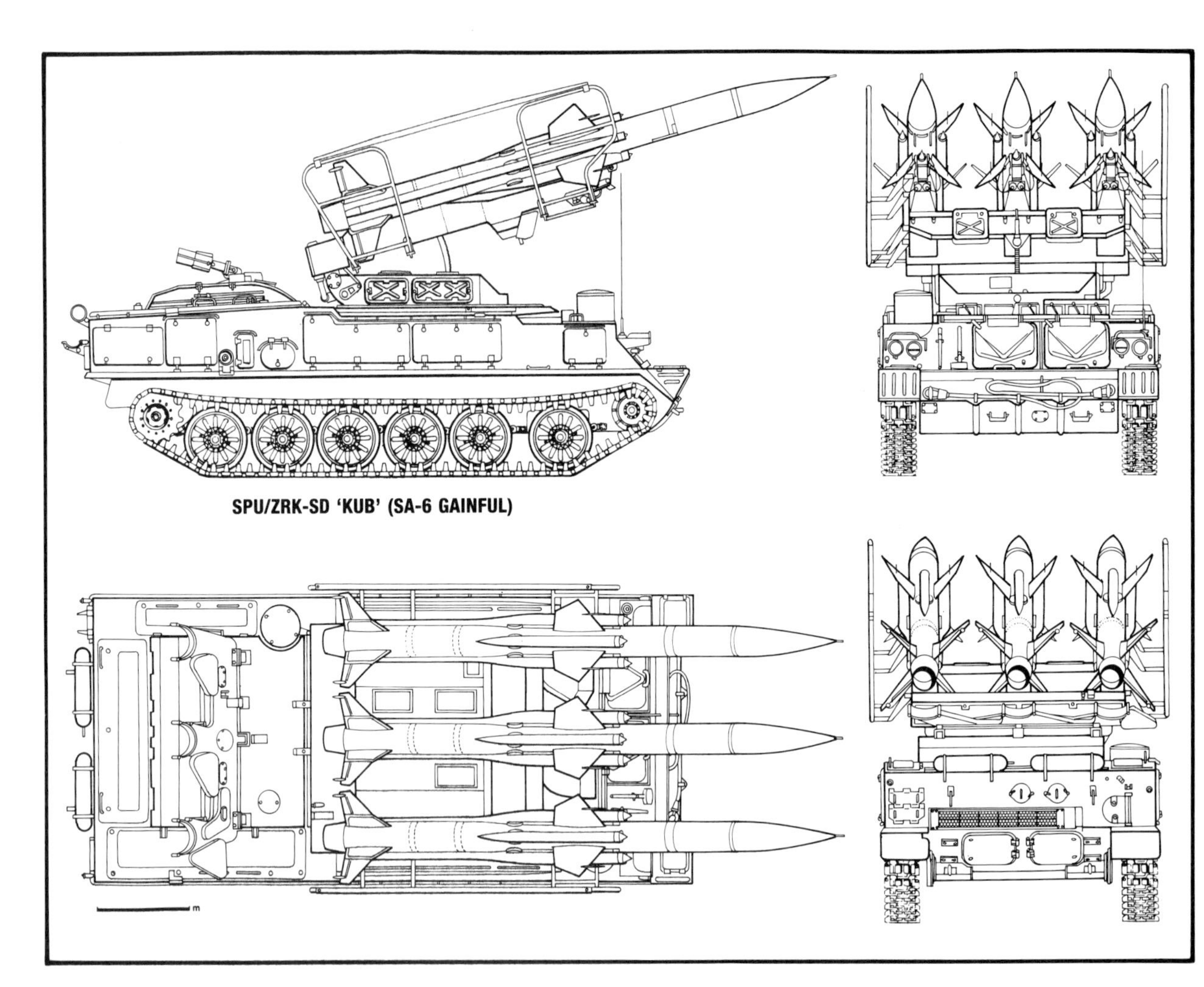

301. The TZM transloader vehicle for the ZRK Kub/SA-6 Gainful is based on the Ural 375 truck and can carry three reload missiles.

modulated for speed and altitude at other points in the flight profile. The ZUR 9M9 design shows the Soviet willingness to sacrifice performance and flexibility at some points in the mission envelope for simplicity and lower cost.

Development of the Kub proved to be protracted and complicated. The main subcontractor, OKB-15 in Zhukovskiy, had serious delays in developing the radar guidance system and its chief designer was relieved in 1961. Further political troubles plagued the programme, with I. I. Toropov being replaced by A. L. Lyapin as the head of OKB-134 in 1963.

The ZRK-SD Kub launch vehicle was first displayed in Moscow in 1967, three years after the ZRK-SD Krug. It received the US/NATO codename SA-6 Gainful. Like many of the early Soviet mechanized air defence missile systems, it was plagued by a significant number of technical problems, and did not become operational in any significant numbers until 1970. The Kub is deployed in air defence regiments of the tank and motor rifle divisions. Each of the regiments has five firing batteries, with four SPU launch vehicles, and one SSNR engagement radar vehicle (NATO codename: Straight Flush) per battery. The regiment has a single Thin Skin height-finding radar vehicle and two Long Track long-range acquisition radar vehicles

The normal disposition of the regiment places three batteries along the divisional sector, about 5km behind the battleline during offensive operations. The two remaining batteries are kept about 10km farther behind to cover gaps in the forward batteries. A battery can be deployed in a number of ways, but is normally found in a diamond-shaped pattern with the SPU launch vehicles at the corners of the diamond, 100–200m apart, and the Straight Flush SSNR in the centre. A common variant is a shallow 'V' formation with four SPU in the 'V' about 100m apart and the Straight Flush SSNR behind the 'V'. The battery is supported by two ZiL-131 TZM transloader vehicles each of which carries three missiles. At regimental level, there are a further fifteen truck/semi-trailer missile canister transporters and five more ZiL-131 TZM transloaders.

The battery is commanded from the Straight Flush SSNR and is connected by a cable or data-link between the five principal vehicles. The data-link antenna can be seen on the SPU launch vehicles on the right forward corner of the hull. The Straight Flush SSNR receives early warning and target assignment from the regimental Long Track and Thin Skin radars. In a low-threat environment, the Straight Flush would probably be shut off in order to maintain electronic silence, and would rely on other early warning and surveillance radars. The system takes about three minutes to become operational from a dormant condition, assuming that the radar antennas are erected (they are folded down during road march for protection). The upper dish antenna is conical scanning, and pivots independently of the lower antenna. It is used for

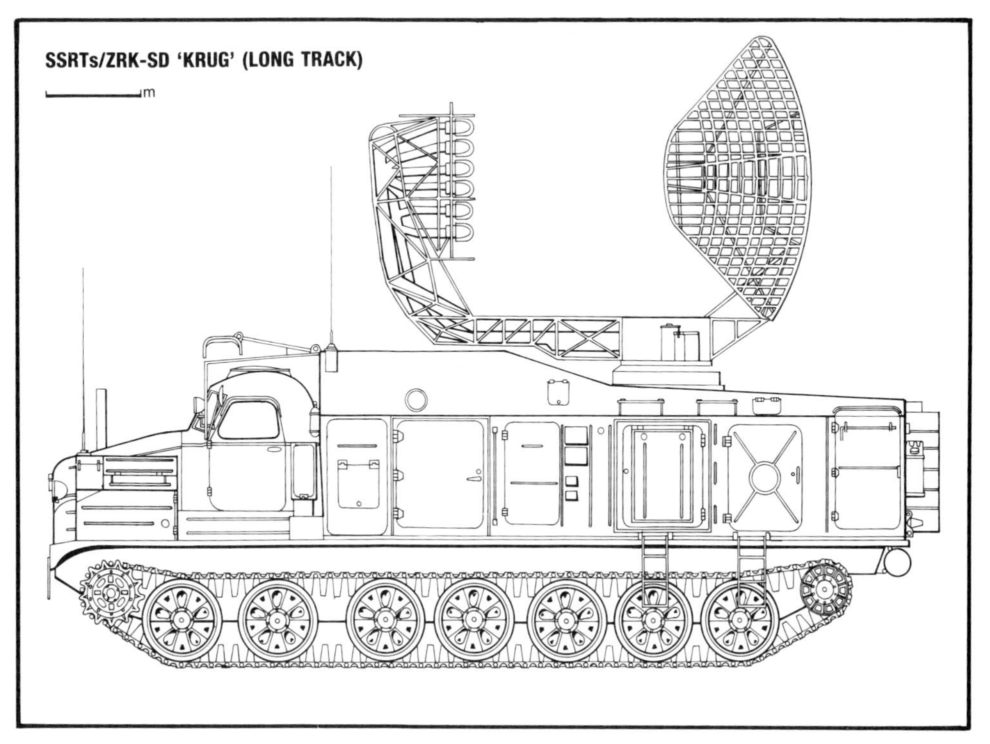

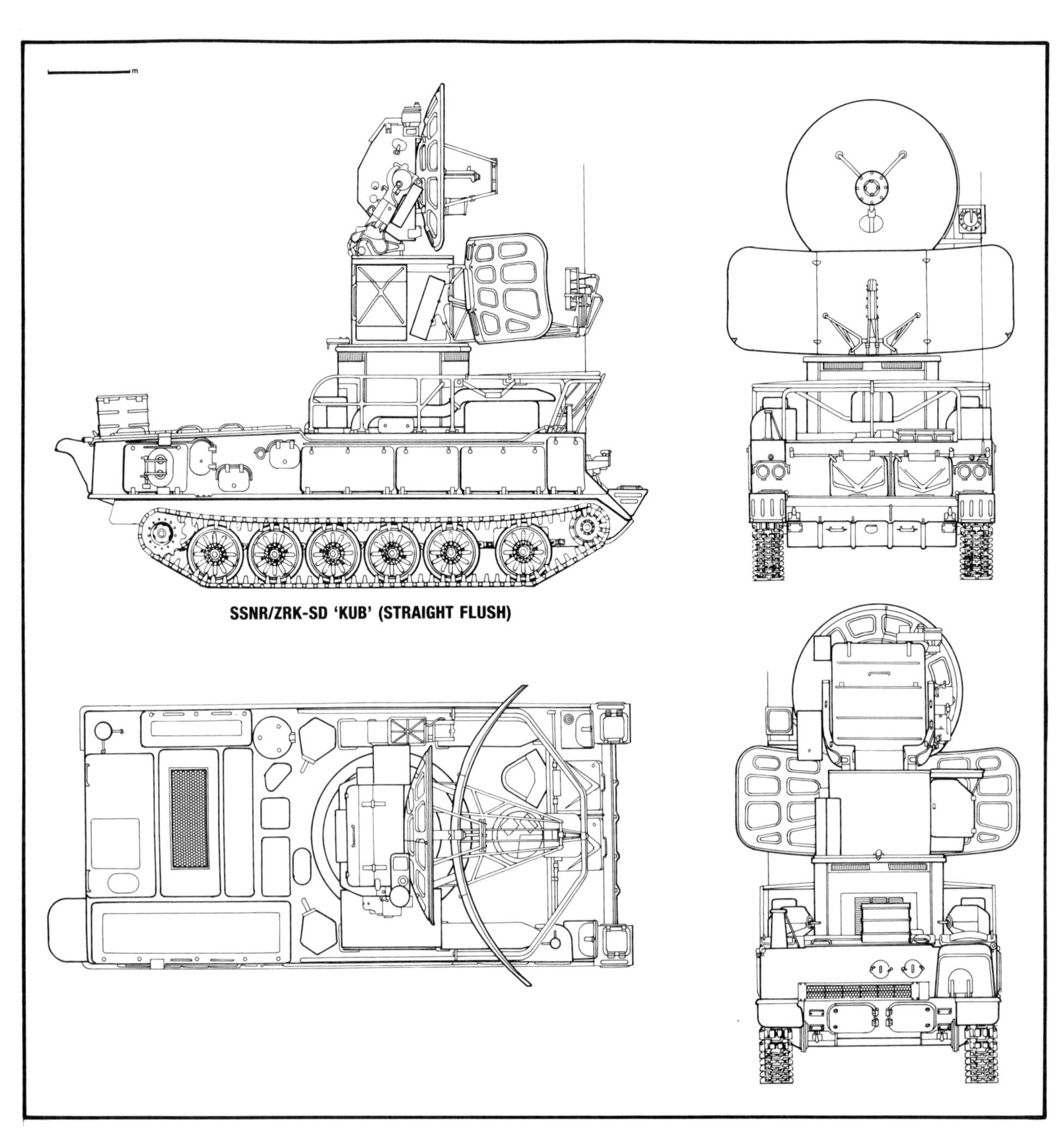

SSNR/ZRK-SD 'KUB' (STRAIGHT FLUSH)

sector scanning, target tracking and target illumination in I-band (8–10 GHz). The lower parabolic acquisition and early warning antenna has two feeds: the upper for low-altitude coverage, the lower for medium–high-altitude coverage, in G/H band (7.85–8.01 GHz). The Straight Flush SSNR can engage only a single target at a time, firing up to three missiles.

With target tracking initiated, the Straight Flush SSNR can control the battery launch vehicles, and will order the launch of one to three missiles against the target. The missiles use semi-active homing consisting of a G/H band beacon transmitter to assist the SSNR in tracking them. The missile is gathered into the proper trajectory by I-band transmissions received on the missile by a reference antenna. On terminal approach, the missile homes in on continuous wave radiation from the SSNR reflected off the target. The missile has a minimum range of about 3.7km, and a minimum altitude of 50m. It has a slant range of about 24km, and a maximum altitude of 12km.

When introduced in 1967–70, the Kub system was undoubtedly the most sophisticated mobile air defence system in Soviet Army service. The fire units are more mobile than those of the Krug system, and preparation for firing is faster.

302. The Straight Flush SSNR engagement radar vehicle acquires targets for the launch vehicles and then guides the missiles to their target. This engagement radar can guide up to three missiles simultaneously against the same target. Without one of these engagement radar vehicles, the other four launch vehicles in a battery are worthless.

303. A Straight Flush SSNR engagement radar vehicle of the Indian Army with its radar antennas folded down in transit mode.

302▲ 303▼

Nevertheless, the Kub system does not have a real fire-on-the-move capability.

The first combat use of the SA-6 Gainful came in 1973 when batteries of the Egyptian Army challenged the Israeli Air Force in the 1973 Sinai campaign. These systems, combined with the static V-75 (SA-2 Guideline) and S-125 (SA-3 Goa) missile-launchers, seriously complicated Israeli efforts to conduct air-support missions near the Suez Canal. One Egyptian battery claimed ten Israeli aircraft during the fighting. The Egyptian Army eventually outran the air defence coverage offered by these systems, and the Israelis managed to countermeasure their radar fire controls to some extent. Later analyses would seem to indicate that the SA-6 Gainful did not offer a particularly good probability of hit, with some Israeli estimates claiming that only one of fifty-five missiles destroyed the target. This would indicate that the SA-6 Gainful (or at least the export version, believed to be designated Kvadrat) has dramatically lower lethality than comparable NATO systems such as the Hawk, which have demonstrated kill probabilities of more than 35 per cent in combat. Several SA-6 Gainful launchers and missiles were captured, leading to the development of electronic countermeasures. The system was used again in the 1982 fighting between Syria and Israel in the Lebanon, where it was totally ineffectual when pitted against upgraded Israeli electronic countermeasures and suppression tactics. It is difficult to determine whether Kub systems in Soviet service would be so ineffectual. The Soviets are well known for their propensity to develop special 'monkey model' derivatives of weapons for export, which usually have simplified fire-control systems and reduced electronic counter–countermeasure (ECCM) features. The SA-6 Gainful is being replaced in Category 1 divisions by the SA-6b and SA-11 Gadfly.

The SA-8 Gecko

Quite surprisingly, the PVO-Voiska fielded another divisional air defence system in 1974, the SA-8 Gecko, hardly seven years after the initial introduction of the ZRK-SD Kub. It is not at all clear whether initiation of this programme stemmed from concern over tactical shortcomings in the Kub system, or whether the PVO-Voiska simply decided to take advantage of a new air defence missile system developed by the Soviet Navy (VMF) for its surface warships. Alternatively, the new missile programme may also have been a co-operative Army/Navy effort aimed at alleviating, by splitting, the burden of high development costs. This was not without precedent. The Soviet Navy had adapted Army missiles to ships (the S-125/SA-3 Goa as the M1/SA-N-1, and the S-75/SA-2 Guideline as the M2/SA-N-2). The Navy's first independently developed air defence missile (US/NATO codename SA-N-3 Goblet) is not known to have been developed as an Army system. The Navy was the first to deploy this new system, given the NATO codename Gecko. In the late 1960s, the Soviet Navy began laying down a number of new ship classes armed with a new low–medium-altitude missile system, later designated SA-N-4, with the associated Pop Group engagement radar. The first of these to appear were the new Krivak frigates in 1970.

The primary aim of the Army programme, called ZRK-SD *Romb* (Square), was to develop a fully integrated mobile air defence system on a single vehicle. A significant shortcoming in such air defence systems as Krug and Kub is that the entire battery is dependent on a single radar fire-control vehicle. Battery rate of fire is limited by the ability of a single vehicle to control 3–4 launch vehicles. Should the SSNR fire-control

▲304 ▼305

vehicle be put out of action by a mechanical breakdown, electronic countermeasures or destruction, the remaining SPU launch vehicles are virtually useless. For example, this is believed to have occurred on a number of occasions in the 1982 Lebanon war, where Syrian air defence batteries were emasculated by Israeli anti-radiation missile-strikes against their SSNR engagement radar vehicles. The launch vehicles could then be attacked and destroyed with impunity. The PVO-Voiska sought a mobile air defence vehicle which would incorporate a surveillance, tracking and engagement radar on a single vehicle, together with missile-launch rails for greater tactical autonomy.

In lieu of an armoured, tracked vehicle, an unarmoured, wheeled vehicle was selected. The lack of armour and slight degradation in cross-country mobility may have concerned PVO-Voiska, but this chassis had its advantages. Designated Transporter 5937, it was derived from an experimental cross-country vehicle developed at the Likhachev Automobile Plant (ZiL) in Moscow, probably by V. A. Grachev's design team, and was amphibious. This would help to provide Soviet mobile columns with air defence coverage during critical river-crossing operations.

The ZRK-SD Romb system entered operational use with the regiments of the PVO-Voiska in 1974, barely four years after its naval sibling, and seven years after the ZRK-SD Kub. If NATO Intelligence had been impressed by the performance of Soviet air defence systems in the Sinai in 1973, they were even more taken aback by the design sophistication of the ZRK-SD

304. The initial series production SPU launch vehicle for the ZRK Romb (SA-8 Gecko) had a blunter nose on the vehicle than the standard production model.
305. The SA-8a Gecko had its four launch-ready missiles left exposed on the launch rails.
306. A Romb TZM transloader vehicle and a BTR-60KSh in transit on a railroad line. The transloader is based on the same ZiL chassis as the launch vehicle. The storage bay is normally covered by this large canvas tent except when actually transferring missiles.
307. Rare view of a Romb TZM transloader vehicle with its crane erected transferring missiles to a SA-8b Gecko launch vehicle of the German NVA.

306▲ 307▼

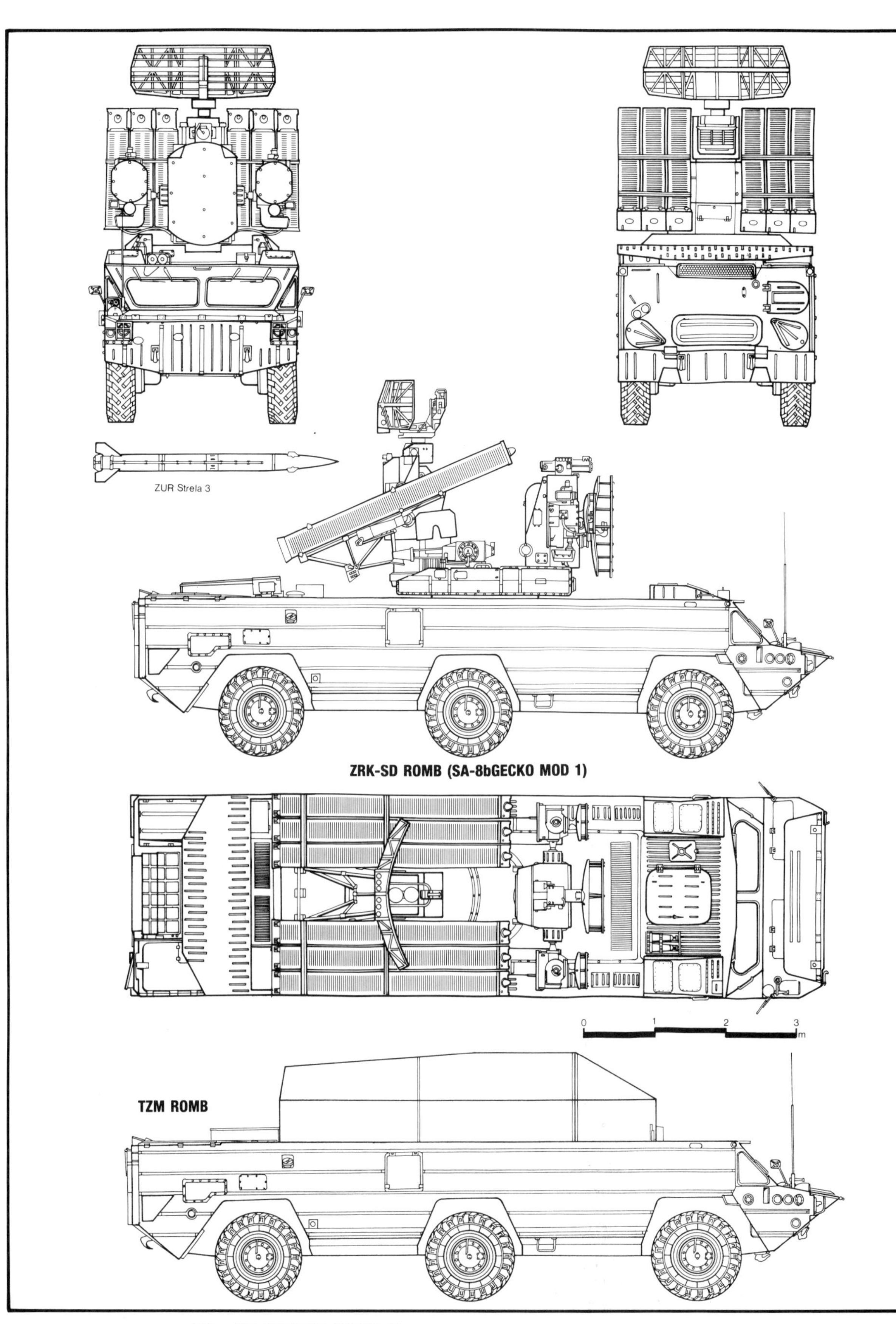
ZUR Strela 3
ZRK-SD ROMB (SA-8bGECKO MOD 1)
0
1
2
3
m
TZM ROMB

Romb. It appeared to have succeeded where the US XMIM-46 Mauler air defence system had failed and it preceded the similar Franco-German Roland system. By comparison with the ZRK-SD Kub, the Romb traded-off range and warhead size for overall system compactness and greater operational flexibility. The missile associated with the Romb had a slant range of about 12km, or half that of the Kub's ZUR 9M9. The fire-control system, derived from the naval Pop Group, was named Land Roll by NATO.

The ZRK-SD Romb was deployed in similar fashion to the ZRK-SD Kub: replacing the earlier S-60 57mm air defence gun regiments in motor rifle divisions. As in the case of the Kub, each regiment had five batteries with four SPU launch vehicles each. In NATO, launch vehicles are distinguished as TEL (Transporter-Erector-Launchers), or as TELAR (Transporter-Erector-Launchers and Radar), with the SA-8 launch vehicle being classified as a TELAR. The batteries have no SSNR engagement radar vehicles. There are two TZM transloader vehicles per battery which are supported by twenty-four ZiL-131 cargo trucks used as missile transporters at regimental level. The Romb TZM transloader is based on the same Transporter 5937 chassis as the SPU launch vehicle, but has a small crane and stowage area in lieu of the launch assembly. Each regiment also has a single radar calibration vehicle, also based on the same SPU/TZM cross-country vehicle chassis.

The initial operational test series of vehicles differed in appearance from the standard production model in a number of features, and are identifiable by their blunt, shorter bow. The initial standard production model, called SA-8a Gecko by NATO, was fitted with four exposed missiles on launch rails. In 1980, an improved version was displayed publicly for the first time, called SA-8b Gecko Mod 1 by USA/NATO. This type, shown here in the scale plan views, has six containerized missiles. Besides offering an increase in launch capability, the missiles have better environmental protection and possibly guidance improvements. The ZRK-SD Romb uses a guidance procedure similar to that of the Kub. Thin Skin, Long Track and P-15 (Flat Face) radars at regimental level provide the five launch batteries with long-range early warning. The SPU launch vehicle uses the H band (6–8 GHz) early warning and search radar at the top of the launch array for short-range target acquisition. This radar has a 30km range against most targets. Below this antenna at the front of the launcher is a large pulsed J band (14.2–14.8 GHz) tracking radar, with one, smaller parabolic antenna on each side, to transmit command guidance to the missile. The Romb system can engage one target with two missiles simultaneously in staggered launch sequence by command guidance. This is a considerable improvement in battery firing capability compared to a ZRK-SD Kub battery. The two missiles can be command-guided on different frequencies, thus thereby complicating electronic countermeasures. The Kub battery's SSNR can control only three missiles simultaneously against a single target. In contrast, the autonomous guidance offered by the Romb

308. The SA-8b Gecko has six launch-ready missiles, all in ribbed canisters. This protects the missiles and allows the vehicle to carry them in loaded position in inclement weather. (Sovfoto)

309. A ZRK Romb SPU (SA-8b Gecko) launcher vehicle of the Czechoslovak CSLA in transit configuration with the launch assembly pointed to the rear (to protect the radar antennas from rubbing against low tree branches) and the top surveillance radar antenna folded down.

system's TELAR allows a single vehicle to engage one target with two missiles, or a battery to guide up to eight missiles at any one time against four different targets.

The ZRK-SD Romb saw its first combat use in 1982 when a single SPU launch vehicle, apparently with a Soviet crew, was deployed to Lebanon alongside Syrian forces. It accounted for one of the two Israeli aircraft lost to missiles in the fighting (the other was lost when hit by several 9M32M Strela 2/SA-7b Grail missiles), but was subsequently destroyed by Israeli air-strikes. The novelty of the system may have accounted for its success, and it is not clear if the Romb is any more resistant to modern ECM tactics than its stablemate, the ZRK-SD Kub. The US Defense Intelligence Agency estimates that the Soviet Ground Forces had 625 SA-8 Gecko vehicles in service at the beginning of 1984, and more than 200 systems have been exported to the Warsaw Pact and to armies in the Middle East including Libya and Syria.

Soviet Air Defence Effectiveness

The analysis of Soviet air defence vehicles presented above has highlighted some of the tactical shortcomings of this first generation of Soviet radar-guided gun and missile systems. This should not be misconstrued to imply that Soviet air defence networks as a whole were ineffectual during this period. It is a common misconception that air defence simply involves shooting down aircraft, and that the effectiveness of an air defence network can be judged simply by counting the number of aircraft downed. But air defence is not a technological sport of aircraft skeet shooting. As the term 'air defence' implies, the primary aim of ground-based air defence networks is to *protect ground forces*. This is a subtle, but important distinction. The primary aim of ground-based air defence networks is to keep hostile aircraft from bombing and strafing other elements of the ground forces. This can be done in a variety of ways. The most obvious way is to shoot down aircraft as they attempt to attack ground units.

Yet it is often overlooked that the presence of air defence units obliges an attacking air force to divert a significant proportion of its aircraft to attack the air defences themselves. Aircraft diverted to this mission cannot be used to attack other ground forces. The Soviets consider this diversion of aircraft as *virtual attrition* since it reduces the number of aircraft actually attacking other ground units, even if the air units have not suffered *actual attrition* (that is, aircraft being shot down). For example, during the Middle East wars of 1973, the Israeli Air Force was obliged to divert between a quarter and a third of its attack sorties to air defence suppression. The presence of air defence has other less tangible, but no less real, benefits to the ground forces. Increasingly, ground attack aircraft are being encumbered with electronic countermeasure pods to jam the search and engagement radars of air defence systems. It is often forgotten that for every aircraft pylon occupied by an ECM pod, fewer bombs or other weapons can be carried.

The presence of ground-based air defence units degrades the effectiveness of aircraft attacks even when aircraft are not shot down. A stream of tracers from a ZSU-23-4 Shilka may not always down an aircraft, but it may dissuade a pilot from approaching a unit sheltered under the blasts of the Shilka, or it may force him to take evasive action which makes acquisition and attack of ground targets considerably more difficult or even impossible. Even though an anti-aircraft missile may not always strike its target, an aircraft under attack is unlikely to be as accurate in its ordnance release as it might have been; it may be forced away by missile attack, or may be forced to jettison its payload and abort its mission to avoid being hit by a missile. All these factors help to degrade the effectiveness of attacking air units, and thereby help to fulfil the primary mission of the air defence force in protecting ground units.

It is worth re-examining the effectiveness of Soviet-supplied air defence networks in the Middle East wars by these criteria. The 1973 Sinai campaign is a clear reminder of the effectiveness of the Soviet air defence network. For the first few days of the fighting, the air defence almost entirely prevented the Israeli Air Force from striking at Egyptian ground targets. Even when the air defences were finally weakened, both by Egyptian tactical mistakes and Israeli counter-actions, the Israeli Air Force was obliged to divert a considerable proportion of its aircraft to air defence suppression. Egyptian air defences in 1973, while not totally preventing Israeli air strikes against ground targets, prevented the Israeli Air Force from having the decisive impact it had in the 1967 war in the Sinai.

The 1982 war in Lebanon is frequently portrayed as indicative of Soviet shortcomings in air defence. This overlooks the fact that nearly all of the systems deployed by the Syrians in 1982 were nearly fifteen years old, had been captured by the Israelis in 1973, and therefore were relatively simple to countermeasure electronically. Despite the relative age of these systems, and their less than brilliant deployment and use, they managed to tie down a considerable number of Israeli aircraft that might otherwise have been used to engage ground targets.

Soviet air defence procurement doctrine is clearly geared towards a war of attrition *vis-à-vis* NATO aircraft, in both a *virtual* and *actual* fashion. The Soviets have demonstrated their willingness to deploy systems that would be regarded by many NATO countries, and especially the US Army, as technically immature and insufficiently effective in downing aircraft. A saying popular in the Soviet defence establishment is 'the better is the enemy of the good': the Soviets would prefer to field an adequate system today than await the possible arrival of a more sophisticated system tomorrow. A system like the Shilka, while having a lower probability of a hit than a comparable NATO system like Gepard, none the less severely constrains the use of NATO attack aircraft and helicopters by its mere presence in quantity on the battlefield. Over the past decade NATO armies and air forces have expended millions of pounds, dollars and Deutschmarks in developing a variety of ECM systems to counter it, and encumbering their aircraft with these systems.

But the problem facing NATO is not simply one system, but a host of systems: Shilka, Krug, Kub, Romb, Strela 1, and Stela 2. Each of these uses a different guidance system, a different radar, or a different guidance frequency. ECM systems that jam the radar of the Shilka do nothing to protect an aircraft from the IR seeker of a Strela 1. The Soviets have consciously fielded a wide range of systems, each with its own shortcomings and advantages. Although any one system can be overcome by NATO countermeasures, overcoming the broad spectrum of intermixed defences at one time is extremely difficult and costly. No Middle East war has seen an air force tackle an air defence network as dense and complicated as that presented by the Soviet Ground Forces PVO. The air defences made available to Egypt and Syria were technically more primitive than Soviet systems, and were not made available in the quantities available to Soviet forces.

The New Generation

Since the surge in new air defence systems in the early 1970s, the PVO has been developing a new generation of systems to replace the generation currently in the field. The first of these to appear was the SA-13 Gopher (possibly called *Strela 10* by the Soviets). The Gopher is a low-altitude system evolved from the SA-9 Gaskin. It

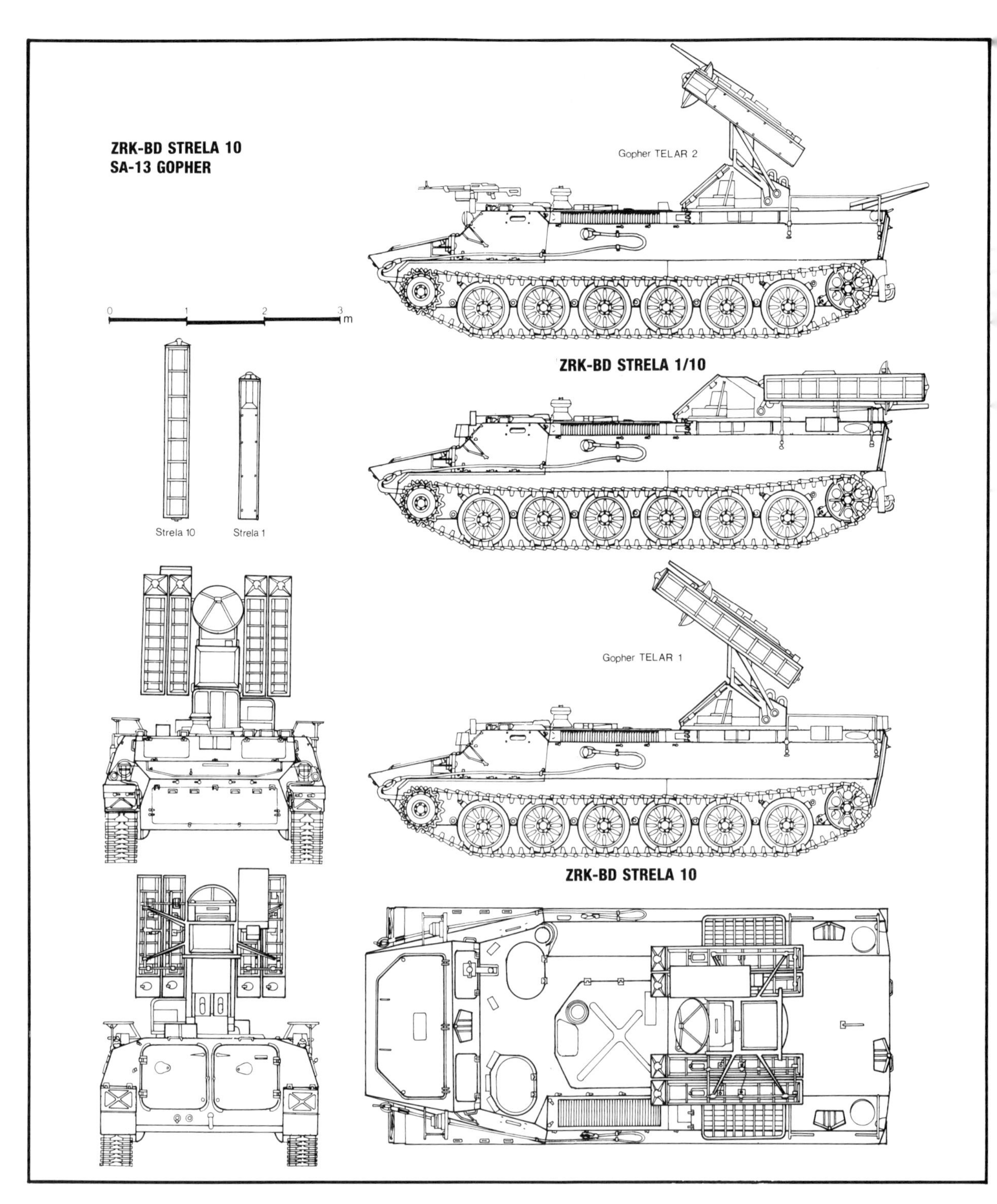

employs a new, larger missile with an improved IR seeker to allow the missile to be fired at aircraft from nearly all aspect angles, not only those where a radiant heat source (jet exhaust) is plainly visible. The SA-13 Gopher is mounted on the MT-LB tracked armoured transporter. This offers better all-terrain mobility than the SA-9 Gaskin's wheeled BRDM-2 chassis which is not very mobile in snow. The Gopher is fitted with a simple range-only radar, which allows the weapon operator to determine range before engaging. This is useful in preventing the waste of missiles against aircraft beyond their effective range. The Gopher can fire both the SA-9 missile and the improved and larger SA-13. Unlike the Gaskin, the launch vehicle probably carries four Gopher or Gaskin reloads internally. Like the Gaskin, the Gopher is seen both with and without the Hat Box passive radiation detectors; one vehicle in each platoon of four vehicles having this system. The Gopher adds a modest improvement to Soviet divisional air defence regiments where it is replacing the SA-9 Gaskin on a one-for-one basis.

The SA-6b Gainful Mod 1

In 1979, the air defence regiments began to receive the SA-6b Gainful Mod 1. Very little unclassified information about this system has been released. It is mounted on a new armoured transporter, probably based on the new MT-TB chassis. Like the familiar SA-6a, it has three missiles, but, unlike the SA-6a, the SA-6b Gainful Mod 1 TELAR launch vehicle is equipped with its own guidance radar which allows the launch vehicle to guide its missiles to target independently. The SA-6b Gainful Mod 1 was initially issued to SA-6a Gainful regiments on a scale of one per battery, replacing one of the SA-6a launchers. In this way, the battery can double the number of targets it can engage since

310. The SA-13 Gopher is intended to replace the SA-9 Gaskin. Although the launch assemblies look similar, the SA-13 Gopher assembly is larger, enabling it to load and fire either the larger Gopher missile canisters or the small Gaskin canisters. The SA-13 Gopher also has a range-only radar mounted between the two banks of canisters. The launch assembly is mounted on a modified MT-LB transporter.

310▲ 311▼

311. A SA-13 Gopher during the 1985 Moscow parade commemorating the Second World War victory of the USSR over Germany. This vehicle does not have the PK machine-gun fitted at the vehicle commander's station. (Sovfoto)

the SA-6b Gainful Mod 1 vehicle does not depend on the Straight Flush SSNR for missile guidance, but only for target identification and warning. It is not clear whether the SA-6b Gainful Mod 1 will entirely replace the older launch vehicles in Gainful regiments due to the advent of the newer SA-11 Gadfly; it appears to be an interim vehicle prior to the arrival of the Gadfly.

The SA-11 Gadfly

The Sa-11 Gadfly is another possible example of joint Soviet Army/Navy development. It first went to sea in 1981 in the new *Sovremenniy*-class destroyers and is called SA-N-7 Gadfly by US/NATO. The Soviet Army version probably entered service at about the same time. The SA-11 missile closely resembles the US Navy Standard MR RIM-66 missile in size, guidance and configuration, and may have benefited from Soviet inspection of Iranian Navy Standard missiles. The Gadfly is based on the same vehicle as the SA-6b Gainful Mod 1, but has four launch rails. Like the SA-6b Gainful Mod 1 TELAR, the SA-11 Gadfly TELAR has its own onboard engagement radar. It would appear that the SA-11 TELAR can fire either the Gainful or Gadfly missiles. The Gadfly is being deployed in a fashion similar to the Gainful. Each regiment appears to have five batteries, each with four SPU launch vehicles and one SSNR radar vehicle. The important difference is that the individual launch vehicles are not as dependent on the SSNR radar vehicle as had been the case with the SA-6a Gainful. The new Gadfly SSNR, based on the naval radar, is used mainly for early warning and target acquisition. Once the targets

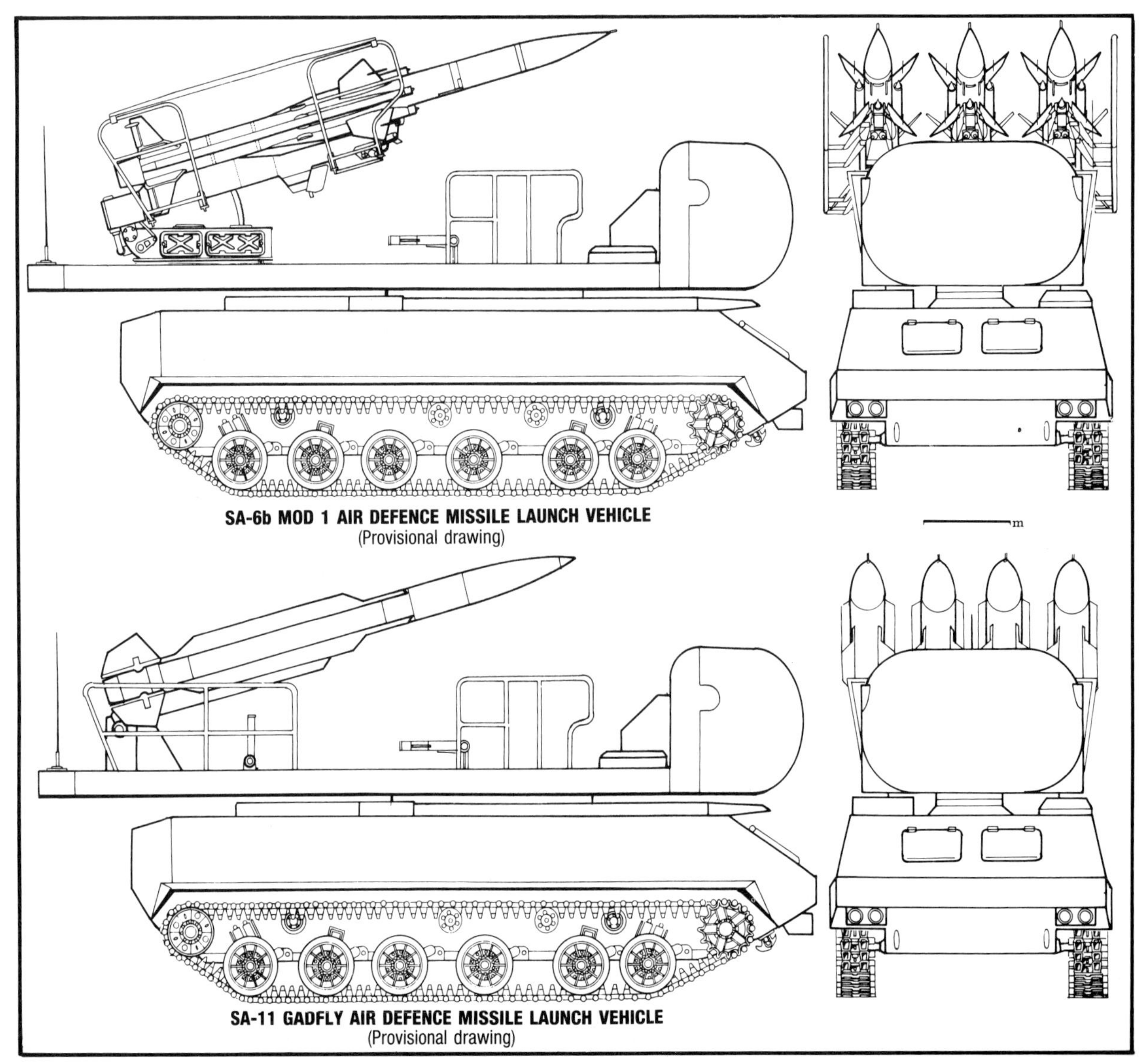

SA-6b MOD 1 AIR DEFENCE MISSILE LAUNCH VEHICLE
(Provisional drawing)

SA-11 GADFLY AIR DEFENCE MISSILE LAUNCH VEHICLE
(Provisional drawing)

are identified, they can be handed over to the SPU (TELAR) launch vehicles via a data-link for tracking and attack. This increases the number of targets a battery can engage simultaneously from one by a SA-6a Gainful battery, to two for a mixed SA-6b Gainful Mod 1 battery to four for a SA-11 Gadfly battery. The Gadfly missile is a conventional, solid rocket-powered type, and uses semi-active radar guidance.

The SA-12 Gladiator

The most sophisticated of the new Soviet Ground Forces air defence missile systems is the SA-12 Gladiator. The Gladiator is apparently being developed to supplant the SA-4 Ganef in the army and front defence role. It has greater slant range (100 v. 80–100km) and considerably more sophisticated fire controls. The system includes two entirely different missiles, a conventional one to engage aircraft and an anti-tactical ballistic missile (ATBM) for use against theatre tactical nuclear ballistic missiles such as the US Pershing II or French Pluton. The Gladiator has an effective altitude ranging from 100m to 30km, and an effective range of 100km. The associated ATBM missile is about the same size, and has demonstrated an anti-ballistic missile capability according to US sources.

The SA-12 Gladiator also appears to be the first Ground Forces' PVO missile system using phased array radars. The launch vehicle is of a new type, of significant size and possibly related to the tracked chassis of the SO-203 self-propelled gun. There are five vehicles derived from this chassis: a basic Gladiator SPU (TELAR) launch vehicle with two missile rails; a Gladiator TZM transloader carrying up to four missiles; a Gladiator KShM command and control shelter vehicle; a Gladiator SSNR engagement radar vehicle, and a Gladiator SSRTs radar search vehicle. The Gladiator SPU launch vehicle carries two missiles in cylindrical canisters, 7.5 metre long, and is fitted with a mast-mounted guidance radar, giving each vehicle a measure of firing autonomy. There are two slightly different versions of the SA-12 Gladiator TELAR: one configured for the normal SA-12 missile, the other configured for the ATBM associated with the SA-12 Gladiator system.

It would appear that, like the SA-4 Ganef, the SA-12 Gladiator is deployed in brigades at army and front level. The brigades probably consist of three battalions, each with three firing batteries. The brigade headquarters probably fields two SSRTs long-range target acquisition radar vehicles, and about three of the KShM command and control vehicles. Each battalion headquarters is likely to deploy a SSRTs long-range target acquisition radar, and a couple of KShM command and control vehicles. The nine firing batteries probably deploy three SPU (TELAR) launch vehicles each, one of the three possibly being configured for the ATBM missile. These three launch vehicles are served by a single TZM transloader vehicle, and a target acquisition/headquarters unit with an SSNR engagement radar vehicle and a single KShM command vehicle. The SSNR engagement radar can be used to control the TELAR vehicles, but more likely is used to track targets that have been handed over by battalion and brigade long-range target acquisition radars. The battery SSNR, in turn, hands over these targets when within missile range to the battery SPU (TELAR) launch vehicles. The SA-12 Gladiator entered operational service in 1984, and there have been reports that it has already been deployed in the Group of Soviet Forces Germany. According to testimony given to the US Congress in 1986, the SA-12 system has begun to be deployed in a strategic defence role alongside the new mobile SS-25 Sickle ICBM locations.

The SA-10 Grumble

The SA-10 Grumble is another example of Soviet Army/Navy missile development. It appears to be a land-launched version of the naval SA-N-6 which first appeared on the *Kirov*-class cruisers in 1980. The SA-10 is a high-speed, high-performance air defence missile believed to be capable of attacking both Cruise missiles and tactical ballistic missiles such as the Pershing 2. There is also some controversy as to whether it has any anti-ICBM (ABM) role. The relationship of the SA-10 Grumble to the Ground Forces is not yet clear. According to published accounts, the SA-10 Grumble static-emplaced version began deployment in 1983 with the National PVO. By 1985 some 60 sites had been reported as having been equipped with a total of 520 launchers (each with four missiles). This system is probably intended to replace the S-125 Pechora (SA-3 Goa) and to complement the S-200 (SA-5 Gammon) in the PVO.

The US DoD has also indicated that the Soviets are developing a mobile, truck-mounted version of the SA-10. This system is mounted on a variation of the MAZ-7910 truck and carries four launch tubes. DoD illustrations also show a related engagement radar vehicle, again, mounted on a MAZ-7910 variant, probably used for target acquisition and engagement. It is reported that the SA-10 uses an active radar seeker for guidance. If this is the case, the missile

SOVIET AIR DEFENCE MISSILE VEHICLES								
US Designation	SA-4	SA-6a	SA-8b	SA-9	SA-10	SA-11	SA-12	SA-13
NATO name	Ganef	Gainful	Gecko	Gaskin	Grumble	Gadfly	Gladiator	Gopher
Soviet Name	Krug	Kub	Romb	Strela 1				Strela 10
Missile Designation	9M8	9M9		9M23				
Related naval SAM	none	none	SA-N-4	none	SA-N-6	SA-N-7		none
LAUNCH VEHICLE (SPU) CHARACTERISTICS								
Weight (tonnes)	30	14	9	7	20	16	30	13
Crew	4	3	3	3	4	4	4	3
Length overall (m)	9.46	6.8	9.14	5.8	12.5	9.4	12.5	6.6
Width (m)	3.2	3.2	2.9	2.4	2.9	3.1	3.5	2.9
Height (m)	4.47	3.45	4.2	2.3	3.7	3.7	3.8	3.8
Related chassis	GMZ	ZSU-23-4	ZiL-5937	BRDM-2	MAZ-7910	MT-T	SO-203	MT-LB
Number of missile launchers	2	3	6	4	4	4	2	4
Number of missile reloads	0	0	0	2	0	0	0	4
Engine	D-12A	V-6R	ZiL-375	GAZ-41	D-12A			YaMZ-238V
Horsepower	525	240	175	140	525	300	525	240
Max. speed (km/h)	45	45	60	100	85	50	50	55
Max. road range (km)	450	250	500	750	650	300	300	450
Onboard guidance radar	none	none	Land Roll	none	none	yes	yes	range-only
Max. armour (mm)	15	9	none	14	none	9	9	14
MISSILE CHARACTERISTICS								
Fuselage diameter (m)	.9	.33	.21	.12	.45	.4	.5	.12
Span diameter (m)	2.6	1.24	.6	.38	1.0	1.2	1.5	.4
Length (m)	8.8	5.8	3.1	1.8	7.0	5.6	7.5	2.2
Weight (kg)	2500	580	170	30	1500	650	2000	55
Warhead weight (kg)	135	80	40	2.6	130	90	150	4
Speed (mach)	4	2.5	2	2	6	3	3	1.5
Booster propulsion	solid strap-on	solid integral	na	na				na
Sustainer propulsion	liquid ramjet	solid ramjet	solid rocket	solid rocket	solid rocket	solid rocket	solid rocket	solid rocket
Guidance	command	semi-active	command	passive IR	track-via-msl	semi-active	semi-active	passive IR
Max. altitude (km)	27	12	12	6	30	15	30	9.7
Min. altitude (m)	100	50	10	10	15	30	90	9
Max. range (km)	75-100	30	12	8	100	30	100	8
Min. range (km)	9.3	4	3	0.6	0.3	3	5.5	0.5
Slant range (km)	65	24	12	5.5	90	28	100	8
SYSTEM CHARACTERISTICS								
Associated fire control radar vehicle (SSNR)	Pat Hand	Straight Flush	none	none	none	none	yes	none
Associated surveillance radar vehicle (SSRTs)	Long Track	Long Track	Long Track	none	yes	yes	yes	none
Target tracking frequency	H band	G-H band	J band	no				no
Missile guidance frequency	H band	I band	I band	IR				IR
Max. number of missiles in flight under battery control	2	3	8	16				16
Max. number of simultaneous targets per battery	1	1	4					

would need only to be cued and locked on in co-ordination with the firing battery engagement radar vehicle, and then launched. It would be entirely autonomous and not require an engagement radar vehicle or guidance radar on the parent launch vehicle to guide it. A mobile battery is believed to consist of three TEL launch vehicles and a single engagement radar vehicle. To date, there have been no indications as to what role this system will play, if any, in the Ground Forces. It may be used to provide front air defence in place of the obsolete S-75 Volga (SA-2 Guideline) and S-125 Pechora (SA-3 Goa).

The ZSU-30-X

Not surprisingly, a replacement has been in the works for the ZSU-23-4 Shilka for some years. Apparently, it entered production in about 1983, but few reliable details have been published. It is generally credited as being a 30mm gun system, and has been referred to as the ZSU-30 or ZSU-30-X by the US Army. Although it was originally expected to be a 30mm Gatling gun system as is used on Soviet surface warships for close-in defence, recent US Army statements would seem to indicate that it is a conventional, long-barrelled gun system. A crude drawing of it, leaked in the US Press, shows what appears to be a twin 30mm gun system, possibly using the 2A42 30mm gun of the BMP-2. Such a weapon is more useful than a 30mm Gatling since it has greater range, and would offer better performance against armoured attack helicopters such as the US AH-64 Apache. Other US Army statements seem to indicate that it is mounted on an armoured chassis, possibly derived from a T-72 tank.

The SA-X-15

The SA-X-15 is a low-altitude air defence missile system, under development to replace the SA-8 Gecko. No details have been released.

312. Artist's impression of the SA-10 Grumble mobile air defence missile system. In the background to the right is the surveillance radar vehicle. There is also a fixed site version of this missile system. (US DoD)

313. Artist's impression of the many vehicles associated with the SA-12 Gladiator air defence missile system. The vehicles on side of the foreground are SPU/ TELAR launch vehicles. The vehicle in the foreground centre is a TZM/transloader vehicle which can carry up to four missile canisters. In the background are two phased array radar vehicles, one for surveillance and target acquisition and the other presumably for tracking. The vehicle in the centre rear is a KShM command vehicle. (US DoD)

312▲ 313▼

▲314

314. A Polish LWP T-34-85 fitted with the PT-54 mineclearing rollers.
315. An Egyptian PT-55 mineclearing roller clearly showing the 4 rollers per side characteristic of this type.
316. A T-55 fitted with the KMT-4 mineclearing blades, showing how they are employed.

▲315 ▼316

Combat Support Vehicles

As has been the case throughout the Soviet Army, the Soviet combat engineer force has gradually been mechanized since the end of the war. This chapter is devoted to a range of mechanized combat engineer equipment developed since the war, including mine-breaching vehicles, minelaying vehicles, armoured recovery and repair vehicles, bridging tanks, earth-moving vehicles and water-crossing vehicles. In addition, tracked utility vehicles, which are used throughout the Soviet Army in a wide variety of roles, are discussed.

Minefield Breaching Vehicles

The mine has long been an effective anti-tank weapon, since no matter what advances take place in armour technology, tracks always remain very vulnerable to emplaced mines. Manual breaching of minefields is too slow and dangerous, particularly during mobile advances. This led the Red Army to begin to explore other methods of minefield breaching during the war. A design team under P. M. Mugalev developed a mine roller system (called a trawl by the Russians), which could be fitted to the front of a tank. The tawl was heavy enough to detonate anti-tank mines, and could withstand about 8–10 AT mine detonations before it had to be replaced. During the war, the Red Army formed special engineer tank regiments equipped with the PT-34 (T-34 tank with mineroller) to support mechanized operations.

Following the war, further improvements lead to the PT-3 mine roller system which was fitted to T-34-85, T-44 and T-54 tanks. This type proved short-lived, and was replaced by the improved PT-54 mine roller system in the early 1950s. The PT-54 system used cheaper, cast rollers than the fabricated steel rollers of the PT-3. The system weighed 8.8 tonnes, and cleared two 1.3m lanes, with a 1.2m gap in the centre. The main difficulty with such systems is that they are very heavy, and readily ruin the transmission and powerplant of the tank to which they are attached. Throughout the 1950s, the main aim was to reduce the weight of the rollers, while retaining good probability of detonating and surviving anti-tank mines. In the mid-1950s, the improved PT-54M appeared which had five rollers per side, as opposed to six on the PT-54. This reduced the weight of the unit to seven tonnes, but narrowed the lane cleared to a path 0.89m wide per side. Finally, in the late 1950s, the PT-55 was introduced. This was another elaboration of the basic PT-54 design, but with only four rollers per side, and a drop in weight to 6.7 tonnes. This system could clear two lanes, each 0.83m wide, with a centre gap of 1.7m.

317▼

317. Closeup of a KMT-5 mineclearing assembly with both a mineroller and a KMT-4 mineclearing blade. (Kalevi Moilanen)

▲318

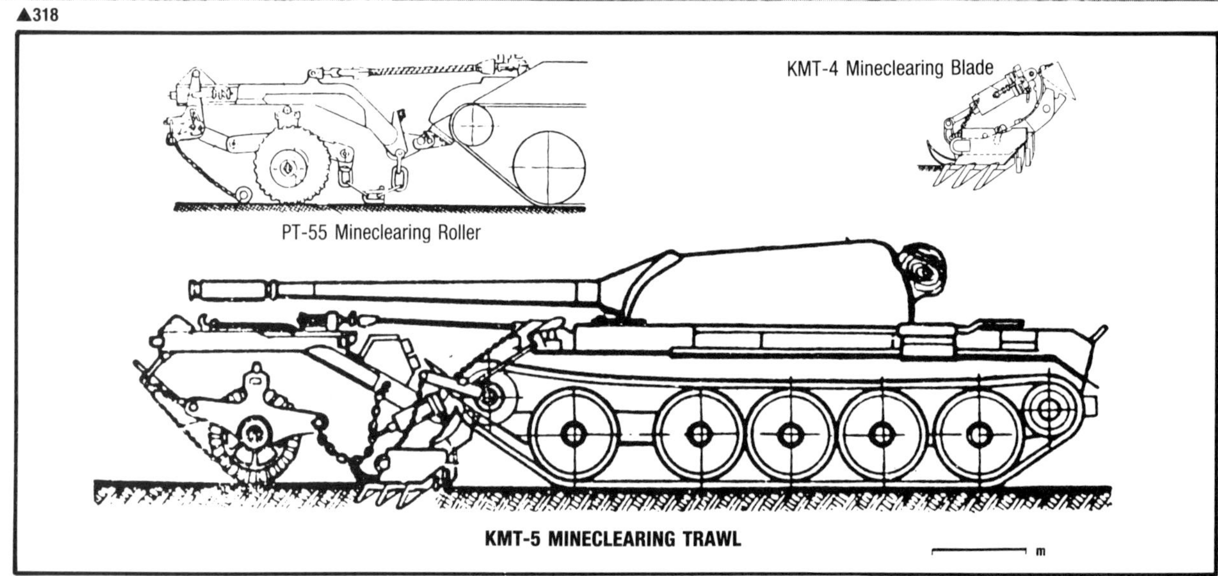

Trawls like the PT-55 greatly reduce the mobility of the tanks on which they are attached. It takes 15–20 minutes to attach the two trawl assemblies, using a crane, and this activity must take place well behind the battleline away from hostile fire. Another shortcoming of mine rollers was their inability to detonate newer NATO mines with more sophisticated fuzing. The Soviet Army desired a more mobile and less cumbersome system for fast breaching which led to the development of the KMT-4 mine plough, commonly called a mine-knife or mine-blade by the Russians. The KMT-4 was a simple device, consisting of two small plough blades each with five small tines which dug into the earth. The blade was angled outward, so that while moving forward, it disinterred the mines and pushed them aside without detonating them. A tank

318. A KMT-5 mineclearing assembly in use, showing the dog-bone dragged between the rollers to detonate tilt-fuzed mines. (K. Moilanen)
319. The Czechoslovak CSLA developed its own counterpart of the KMT-5 system.

319▲

fitted with a KMT-4 mine-clearing blade can travel at normal speeds until the blade is lowered when its speed is reduced to 12km/h. Each tank company has a normal allotment of three sets of KMT-4, although often these are held by the tank regiments' engineer company. In the late 1960s, the improved KMT-4M was introduced, which had improvements to the blade attachment system. A number of the tanks in each tank company have special mounting lugs attached to the upper and lower glacis plate to permit attachment of these devices.

The development of the KMT-4 was paralleled by the design of an improved mine-roller system, the KMT-5. (KMT: *kolesniy minniy tral*: wheeled anti-mine trawl). The KMT-5 system consisted of a KMT-4 mine-blade, and a new roller system which had been completely redesigned, although it still had a fairly similar appearance to the old PT-55. Instead of four rollers, it had three thicker rollers which could clear a path of similar width to the PT-55. The KMT-4 was added to the rig, since it could push aside newer NATO anti-tank mines with special fuzes which the roller could not detonate. Besides the blade and rollers, a weighted chain was hung between the forward roller assemblies to detonate tilt-fuzed mines which remained intact between the rollers and blades (the chain was retrofitted to the earlier systems). The entire KMT-5 system added about 7.3 tonnes to the tank, which was not significantly more than the roller assembly alone on the PT-55. The KMT-5 was fitted with an internal quick-disconnect system which enabled the driver to drop the rollers, as required, from within the vehicle. The KMT-5 became the standard Soviet mine-rolling system from the mid-1960s, supplementing the more common KMT-4. Besides the three sets of KMT-4 per tank company, each company has one set of KMT-5 components. As with the KMT-4, these components are usually retained by the tank regiment's engineer company which is better equipped to service the equipment. The KMT-5 was fitted to T-54, T-55 and T-62 tanks. In the late 1960s, the improved KMT-5M was introduced. This is an improved version of the KMT-5, but has added lane-marking equipment attached to the rear of the tank, and drops luminescent PSK marking material onto the cleared lanes to assist tanks following behind to find the cleared path. The KMT-5 takes 30–45 minutes to attach to a tank, and can be operated at 12–18km/h depending on soil conditions.

The Czechoslovak CSLA developed its own version of the KMT-5 system which is used both in the form of a separate roller, or a roller/blade combination. In the late 1960s, an improved KMT-4M blade was developed, the KMT-6, primarily for the T-64 tank. It has also been used on the T-62, and was later fitted to the T-72 as well.

Minefield breeching using mechanical systems like the KMT-4 and KMT-5 is time-consuming and dangerous. The mine-clearing tanks are a lucrative target for anti-tank teams defending the minefields, since the tank advance can be halted if the few mine-clearing vehicles are disabled. The threat of mines greatly increased in the 1970s with the advent of NATO's new mine systems which, like the US FASCAM series, can be scattered by artillery, helicopters or ground dispensers. A minefield can be sown remotely in a small fraction of the time formerly taken to sow more conventional mines. These

▲320 ▼321

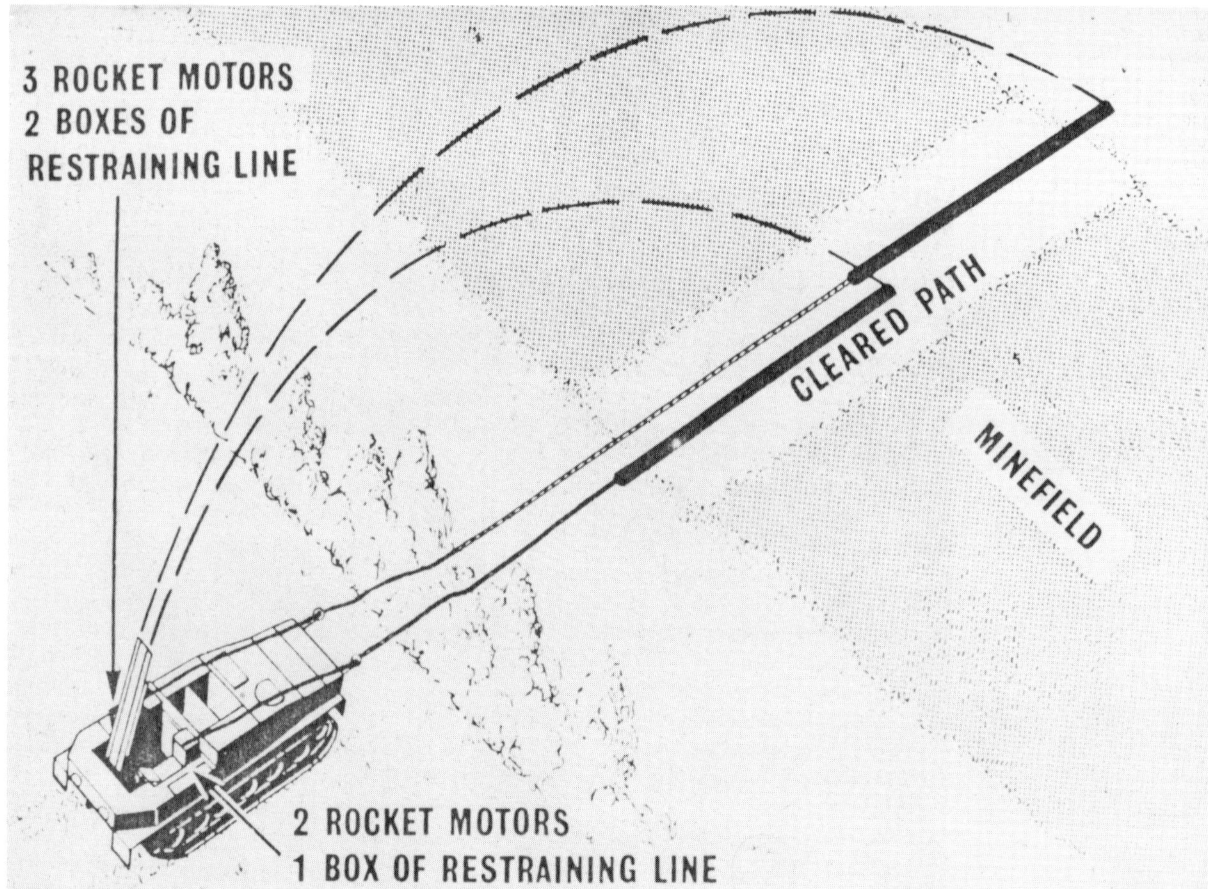
3 ROCKET MOTORS
2 BOXES OF
RESTRAINING LINE
CLEARED PATH
MINEFIELD
2 ROCKET MOTORS
1 BOX OF RESTRAINING LINE

322▲ 323▼

320. To assist more elaborate combat engineer ditching and trenching vehicles, T-54 and T-55 tank units use the BTU-55 bulldozer blade to entrench tanks in defensive positions.
321. Illustration of how the UR-67 mineclearing vehicle blasts its way through a minefield using rocket-launched line charges. (US Army)
322. A UR-67 mineclearing vehicle with a canvas tarpaulin over the rear rocket launcher.
323. A pair of the new Soviet UR-77 mineclearing vehicles in operation. These vehicles are based on the hull of the SO-122 Gvozdika mechanized howitzer.

▲324

324. This new minerolling vehicle appeared in service in Afghanistan in 1986. It is a modified T-55, fitted with a new pattern mineroller system. The raised superstructure may indicate that it is based on a rebuilt IT tank destroyer vehicle. This is the first dedicated minerolling vehicle in the Soviet Ground Forces. Behind it is an IMR combat engineer vehicle.

factors led the Soviet Army to seek a quicker minefield breaching system, and experiments with rocket-launched breaching systems began in the 1960s. These systems use a UZR-3 high-explosive line charge, in a fabric tube container which resembles a large coil of rope. A rocket is attached to one end, which carries the explosive line charge across the minefield. The line charge is then detonated, creating a cleared path. To give this system some mobility, it was fitted inside the hull of a modified BTR-50PK, with the rocket-launcher assembly on the rear deck. It is designated UR-67. Two of these vehicles are attached to each motor rifle or tank division in the engineer battalion. The Polish LWP and Czechoslovak CSLA developed their own equivalents of the UR-67. The Polish version, designated PW-LWD, is based on the T-55A tank. It is a special combat engineer tank, normally fitted with the KMT-4 mine blades and a lane-marking system. On each side of the rear deck are two large 'bathtubs' containing the rocket-launcher and explosive line charge. The bathtubs have clamshell doors which open to fire the charge, and remained shut when not in use to shelter the system. A similar bathtub launcher system is also used on unarmoured engineer vehicles. The Czechoslovak system is mounted in wheeled trailers which are generally towed behind an armoured engineer vehicle such as an OT-64 SKOT. In about 1975, the Soviet Army introduced an improved version of the UR-67, the UR-77, mounted on a turretless SO-122 (2S1) chassis. This uses a similar rocket launch system.

Minelaying Vehicles

In order to decrease the time required to lay minefields, the Soviet Ground Forces developed a number of mechanical minelaying systems. The earliest method used was to fit chutes along-side an engineer BTR-152. The mines were slid down the chutes by the crew and left exposed on the ground. This system was quick, but primitive and led to the PMR-2 which was trailer drawn, and mechanically controlled the rate at which the mines were laid. Like the chute method, the PMR-2 could only deposit mines, and could not bury them. In the 1960s, the PMR-3 trailer was introduced. This was usually towed by a specially configured BTR-152 with special racks for storing about 120 mines in the rear troop compartment. A small entrenching system on the rear buried the mines. If speed was essential the mines could be left on the surface. The East German NVA deployed the similar MLG-60 system. The main drawback to this type of system is that a wheeled engineer vehicle like the BTR-152 does not have the traction or power to entrench mines in all soil conditions, and it can be readily stopped by obstructions. This led, in the early 1960s, to the development of a dedicated minelaying vehicle the GMZ (*Gusenichniy minniy zagraditel*: tracked minelayer). The GMZ

325. The first method employed by the Warsaw Pact to lay mines rapidly was simply to slide them down a chute fitted to the side of an armoured transporter like this Polish BTR-152.
326. Later, when the PMR-3 minelaying trailer was introduced, older BTR-152V1 were reconfigured as engineer vehicles with special racks to carry 120 mines. This vehicle served in the Syrian Army until captured by Israeli forces in the 1973 war.
327. A PMR-3 minelaying trailer in use behind a Polish SKOT engineer vehicle.

325▲

326▲ 327▼

▲328

328. In the 1960s the Soviet Ground Forces began deploying the GMZ tracked minelaying vehicle. This vehicle uses an entrenching system like the PMR-3, but can carry more mines and plant them faster than the trailer methods. (US Army)

329. To assist combat engineer units, the IMR was developed. It is fitted with a large bulldozer blade at the front, but its most prominent feature is a large, hydraulically operated 'cherry-picker' which can be used to move material, or remove obstructions.

▲329 ▼330

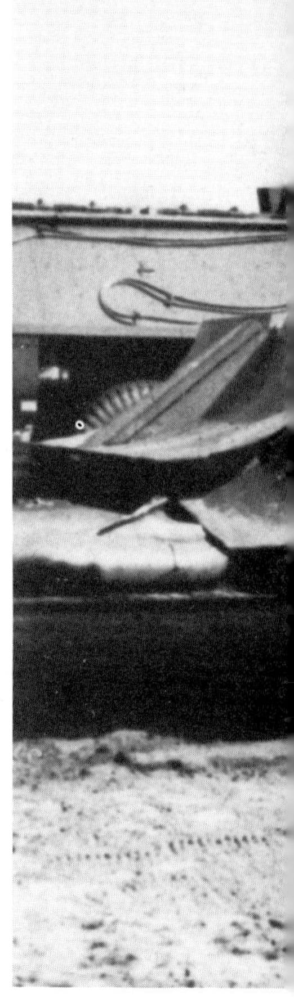

330. Many outdated armoured vehicles were converted to primitive armoured recovery vehicles like this Su-85. It has had its gun removed, and the opening plated over; little else has been added to the vehicle.
331. The IWT is the Polish equivalent of the IMR. It shares many of the same features as the IMR, but also carries a rocket-launched breaching system.

was based on the same chassis as the SA-4 Ganef (ZRK-SD Krug) air defence missile vehicles. It uses a more sophisticated entrenching system than the PMR-3, and can carry 208 anti-tank mines in its spacious armoured compartment. It has two large roof doors for reloading. The entrenching system spaces the mines 4–5.5m apart at a speed of 3km/h and a rate of four mines per minute. When laying mines on the surface, the GMZ can lay eight per minute and travels at 4–10km/h. A platoon of three GMZ is attached to the engineer battalion of each motor rifle and tank division. The GMZ is a dated system by today's standards, and it may be gradually dropped from use in favour of systems which scatter the mines as is occurring in most NATO armies.

Combat Engineer Vehicles

Unlike the US and British armies, but like the German Bundeswehr, the Soviet Ground Forces do not use combat engineer tanks. Instead the Soviet engineer force deploys an unarmed combat engineer vehicle, the IMR (*Inzhernaya mashina razgrazhdeniya*: Engineer obstacle-clearing vehicle). The IMR was introduced in the mid-1960s, based on a modified T-55 chassis. Originally it was designed to provide passage for mechanized units through areas devastated by nuclear blast which would have been littered with large debris. In place of a turret, it is fitted with a large hydraulic crane with specialized grasping tools at the end. It is also fitted with an angled bulldozer blade at the front for entrench-

▼331

332. An armoured recovery version of the T-34, typical of many converted in the 1950s. It has a heavy winch fitted over the turret opening and a tool platform added at the rear.
333. The SKP-5 was a standardized light crane introduced into Soviet tank units in the 1950s to assist in removing engines, transmissions and other heavy assemblies during repair work. It was not designed to work on the battlefield since the operator was completely exposed.
334. In the 1960s, the Polish LWP converted many of its old SU-85 and SU-100 into specialized armoured recovery vehicles, which were referred to generically as WPT-34 even though they differed somewhat in detail.

▲332

▲333 ▼334

ing, or for pushing aside obstacles. The crew has full nuclear and chemical filtration, and so can operate in contaminated environments. The IMR can be used in the building of field fortifications, or to clear enemy obstructions. Two IMR are attached to the engineer battalion of each tank and motor rifle division. A new version of the IMR (IMR-2?) has recently appeared, based on the T-72 chassis. The Polish LWP developed its own combat engineer vehicle, loosely based on the IMR, and designated IWT (*inzynieryjny woz torujacy*). It has a supplementary role in mineclearing and serves in place of both the Soviet IMR and UR-67. It is fitted with two bathtub mine-clearing line charge systems, like those used on the PW-LWD tank, and has a dozer blade with supplementary mine-clearing features.

Armoured Recovery Vehicles

During the early years of the war, Soviet tank losses were very high because of the lack of tank recovery tactics and equipment. Damaged tanks had to be written off because there was no way to recover them in battle. In contrast, the German Wehrmacht had specialized tank recovery vehicles which were able to retrieve many damaged vehicles even in the last year of the war. The Red Army began to experiment with armoured recovery vehicles in the final year of the war. These were usually tanks, especially T-34, with their turrets removed. They seldom had any specialized equipment such as winches or cranes. After the war, little serious attention was paid to recovery requirements. The only standardized recovery vehicle to appear was the T-34-T which was simply a T-34-85 hull with the turret opening plated over and a cupola added for the vehicle commander. There was a fair amount of improvisation, with civilian winches and cranes being fitted on old tank hulls. The first serious attempts at armoured recovery development took place in Czechoslovakia. The Czechoslovak Army sponsored the development of a recovery vehicle on the locally produced T-34-85 chassis. This vehicle, the VT-34, followed the lines of the German wartime Bergepather recovery vehicle. It was fitted with a powerful winch inside a new, boxy superstructure, and at the rear of the vehicle was an entrenching spade to anchor the VT-34 while its winch was being used to pull a tank out of a ditch or other obstruction. The Polish LWP purchased the VT-34, and modified it with other features as the CW-34 and later, the WPT-34. Both the Polish and Czechoslovak armies developed a heavy crane version of the T-34, but only the Czech version entered production. The Soviet Army also fielded a crane vehicle on the T-34 chassis, the SPK-5 (*strelovoi kran gusenichniy*: tracked jib crane), but it was considerably less sophisticated than the Czech vehicle.

In the 1950s, the Soviet Army finally began to examine its requirements for armoured recovery vehicles. A new vehicle, the BTS-1, was simply a

335. The VT-34 developed in Czechoslovakia was the most sophisticated of the T-34-derived armoured recovery vehicles. It was based on experience with the wartime German Bergepanther. In Polish service it was called the CW-34.

▲336 ▼337

336. This WPT-34 was clearly based on an SU-85, and has a small machine-gun cupola.
337. The Poles converted old ISU-122 and ISU-152 to heavy armoured recovery vehicles, and these differed in features, though not concept, from the Soviet types. These were called CW-ISU.
338. For heavy repair work, the Czechoslovak CSLA developed a heavy crane vehicle to assist the VT-34.
339. Many old IS-2 tanks had their turrets removed and were employed as recovery vehicles. They were called CW-IS in Polish service or IS-T in Soviet service.
340. The Soviet ISU-T heavy recovery vehicles fell into two main families. This vehicle, captured by the Israelis from the Egyptians, was the simpler type having had a winch and entrenching spade added along with a tool platform over the rear engine deck.

338▲

339▲ 340▼

turretless T-54A with few features, but it was followed by the BTS-2 (*bronetankoviy tyagach sredniy*: medium armoured tractor) in the late 1950s, based on the T-54 chassis. The BTS-2 was also based on the Bergepanther recovery vehicle and had a nearly identical configuration. In lieu of the turret, a winch was fitted in the hull, and above this was a small open container for tools and repair equipment. A small tripod jib crane was also carried, and at the rear of the vehicle was a large entrenching spade for use in combination with the winch. The vehicle was also built in a modified form in Czechoslovakia and Poland (as the WZT-1). The East German NVA purchased a number of them from Czechoslovakia and Poland, but carried out extensive modifications in their own workshops. A heavy lift crane vehicle was also developed in the USSR for rear area repair work, the SPK-12G. The crane on this vehicle was heavy enough to remove the turret from a T-55 for repair.

Besides these newly manufactured vehicles, the heavy ISU assault guns began to be withdrawn from service in the late 1950s and early 1960s and they provided an excellent basis for a heavy recovery vehicle to assist T-10 heavy tank units. The earliest versions of the ISU-T simply had their guns removed, but most of the vehicles were heavily rebuilt in two configurations. The basic version had winches added in the front hull, rear entrenching spades like those on the BTS-2, and stowage boxes added over the rear engine deck. The more elaborate version had a large crane added to the hull front. There was some variation in these vehicles, some having additional features added later such as OPVT deep wading snorkels and push bars. A similar programme was undertaken in Poland, though the details differed. Even as late as the 1960s, the Soviet Army was still improvising armoured recovery vehicles from unarmed tanks and assault guns such as the SU-100, IS-2 and SU-85.

The 1960s saw the first development of more sophisticated armoured recovery vehicles with cranes and other technical aids. An armoured heavy crane counterpart of the SPK-12G was developed, which was probably designated BTS-3. This had the large 20-tonne capacity hydraulic crane mounted on the left front of the hull. The Polish LWP developed a similar vehicle, the WPT-2. These heavy crane vehicles could lift the turret from a T-55, or lift out engines and other large components. A light crane vehicle was also developed, the BTS-4. This was, in many respects, a more sophisticated version of the BTS-2, and had many of the same features. Its main advantage was the addition of a 1.5-tonne crane on the right rear of the vehicle to lift smaller components, such as transmissions. It would appear that the BTS-4 was manufactured in the USSR and in Czechoslovakia.

To support the expanding number of light armoured vehicles, a number of technical support derivatives of existing light armoured vehicles were designed. The MTP (*mashina tekhnicheskoi pomoshi*: technical assistance

341. The more elaborate ISU-T also had a heavy-duty jib crane added to the front of the hull superstructure. (US Army)

▼341

342. The BTS-3 heavy crane vehicle is fitted with a winch, heavy hydraulic crane, and BTU-55 bulldozing blade.
343. The BTS-4 light crane vehicle fulfills many of the same functions as the basic BTS-2, but has a light hydraulic crane on the right rear corner of the hull for lifting engines, transmissions or other assemblies.
344. The SPG-12 is another T-54 heavy crane vehicle, but it is designed for use in military construction, not battlefield repair as the operator is completely unprotected.

342▲

343▲ 344▼

vehicle) was a BTR-50PK with a raised roof, enclosing a small workshop which housed welding and machine tools to carry out field repairs on light armoured vehicles. In the 1970s, this was supplemented by the MTP-LB, a similar light repair vehicle based on the MT-LB. This too is fitted with a light crane to remove engines and transmissions, and is fitted with a winch and entrenching spade. The MTO-SG (*masterskaya tekhnicheskogo obsluzhivania*: technical workshop support) was a GT-T light transporter configured with a workshop box body in the rear. To recover light armoured vehicles, the GET-S (*gusenichniy evakyuatsionniy tyagach sredniy*: medium tracked recovery tractor) was developed by mating an ATS-59G tractor with a winch and other technical assistance features.

The Polish LWP developed repair versions of both the OT-64 and OT-62 as the WPT-SKOT and WPT-TOPAS. These were fitted with light repair equipment to support OT-62 and OT-64 units in the field. In the early 1980s, the Czechoslovak CSLA began fielding a repair

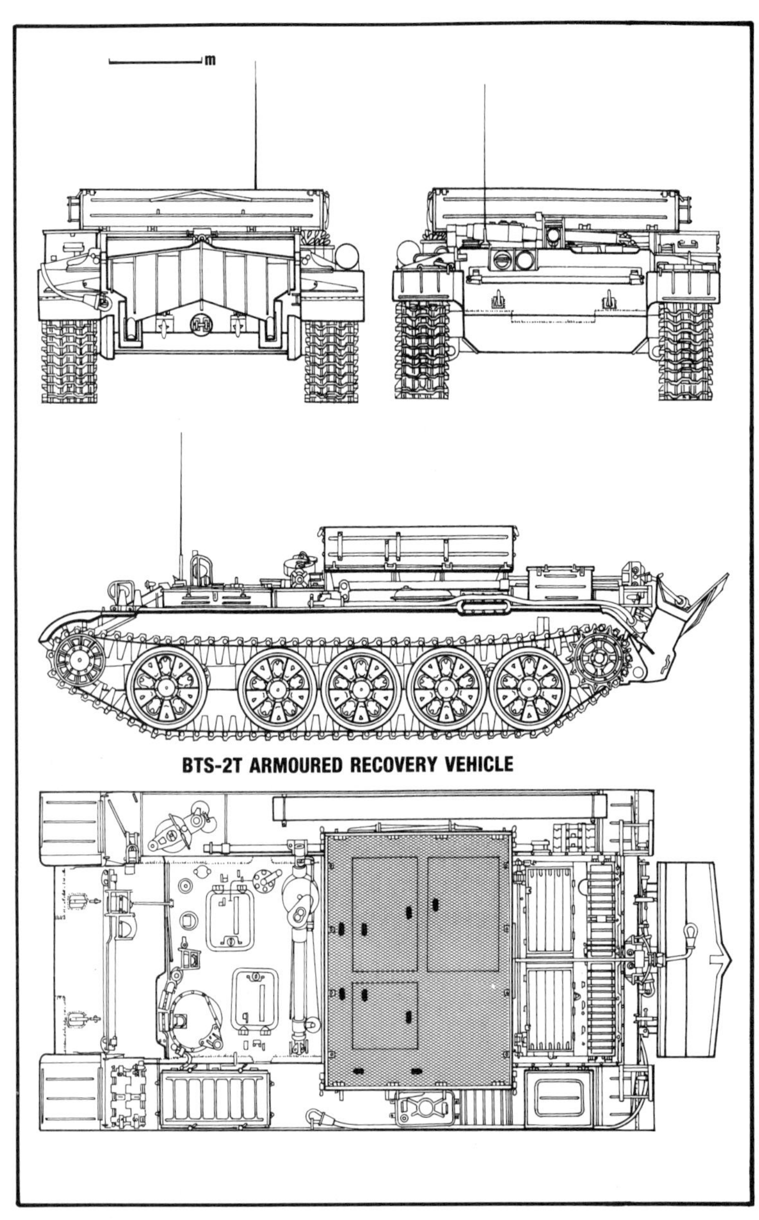

▲345 ▼346

345. A German NVA BTS-3 in operation, lifting a disabled BRDM-2.
346. The Finnish Army developed its own crane version of the T-55 to supplement the BTS-2 and it is designated the KAM-1.

version of the BVP-1 (BMP) with a light crane on the rear, to service BMP units.

To support the new T-72 tank, the BREM-1 (*bronirovannaya remontno-evakuatsionnaya mashina*: armoured repair-recovery vehicle) was first fielded in the late 1970s. The BREM-1 is based on a T-72 chassis, and is a counterpart of the BTS-4. It is fitted with a 12-tonne capacity hydraulic crane on the left front corner of the hull, which can be powered off the engine, or with an auxiliary electric motor. On the centre of the vehicle is a platform for storing tools and equipment. An electrical welding system is installed. Unlike the BTS-2, the BREM-1 uses a forward-pulling winch system. A conventional bulldozer blade, in lieu of a dedicated entrenching spade, is fitted at the front of the vehicle. The winch is rated at 25 to 100 tonnes force depending on the configuration, and uses a 200m cable. It seems likely that the BREM will serve in lieu of the BTS-2 and BTS-4 in T-72 units. Currently, Soviet tank regiments have five armoured recovery vehicles in their maintenance company.

347▲

348▲ 349▼

347. The latest Soviet armoured recovery vehicle is the BREM-1 based on the T-72 chassis.
348. To serve as a mobile workshop, the Soviet Ground Forces adopted the MTP, based on the BTR-50P chassis. This vehicle contains welding equipment and machine tools to carry out battlefield repair of light armoured vehicles.
349. The Poles built a local derivative of the BTS-2 as the WZT-1, and developed their own equivalent of the Soviet BTS-4 crane vehicles as the WZT-2.

▲350

350. The Polish equivalent of the MTP is the WPT-TOPAS, based on the OT-62 TOPAS.
351. The MTP was superseded by the MTP-LB in the 1970s, based on the MT-LB chassis. The new MTP-LB has more features than the MTP, including a small, bow-mounted, jib crane.

▼351

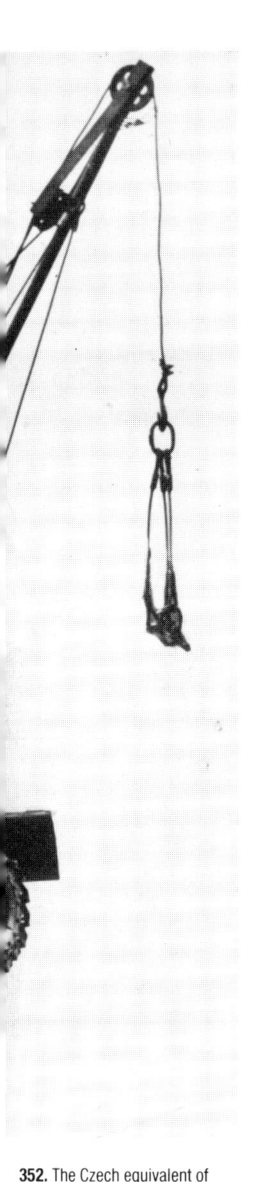

352▲ 353▼

352. The Czech equivalent of the MTP-LB is this light recovery vehicle based on the locally produced BVP-1.
353. The GETS-M is an older recovery vehicle based on the unarmoured ATS-59G chassis which is fitted with a winch to tow trucks and light armoured vehicles.

Bridging Tanks

During the war, the Soviet Army made some experimental use of bridging tanks to cross rivers and other natural obstructions. In view of the enormous cost in lives and equipment in the many river-crossing operations during the last two years of the war, the Soviet Army has paid special attention to modernizing its technical means of crossing rivers. Bridging tanks were a fairly minor aspect of this effort, being seldom long enough to cross anything other than fairly narrow streams. Bridging tanks were developed for a wider range of applications, especially the crossing of dry gaps such as anti-tank trenches, ravines and ditches. In 1957, the Soviet Army began receiving small numbers of a T-34 bridging tank, but this was followed in 1958 by the MTU-1 (*Mostoykladchik tankoviy ustroystvo*: tank launched bridge) based on the T-54A chassis. The MTU-1 launched a 12.3m bridge using a chain-drive system powered off the vehicle's engine. It was a fairly simple design, the bridge being carried unfolded, and was the standard Soviet bridging tank during the late 1950s and early 1960s. In 1960, the Czechoslovak Army began receiving a scissors bridge tank, based on the old T-34-85 hull, the MT-34. The advantage of this approach compared to the Soviet bridging tank is that the bridge was considerably

▲354

▼355

354. One of the earliest attempts in the Warsaw Pact at developing an armoured tactical gap-crossing system was the Polish tracked bridge which was pushed into place by a tank.

355. The MTU, also known as the MTU-1, was the first post-war Soviet tactical bridging tank.

356. The MTU-20, also called MTU-2, was a longer and more effective successor to the MTU-1 and used a unique front and rear folding system rather than the more common scissors bridge approach. (Kalevi Moilanen)

357. Interesting view of the MTU-20 bridge during launching, showing the elaborate launching frame assembly. (Kalevi Moilanen)

356▲ 357▼

▲358 ▼359

358. The Poles and East Germans jointly developed the BLG-60 and BLG-60M bridges in lieu of the Soviet MTU-20, feeling that the quicker launch time was tactically desirable. The Czechoslovak CSLA developed a similar system, the MT-55.

359. The GPT, better known as the K-61, is a tracked amphibian designed to assist combat engineer units in river-crossing operations. Here, a GPT is being followed by TMM ribbon bridge trucks. (Sovfoto)

360. The GPT was succeeded by the larger PTS-M, seen here in Bulgarian service carrying a 100mm anti-tank gun in the rear compartment.

360▲

more compact before launching, and the vehicle was not so unwieldy on roads. The MT-34 also served with other armies of the Warsaw Pact.

The shortcomings of the MTU-1 led, in 1967, to the MTU-20 which used an unusual approach to reduce the size of the bridge before launch. Instead of a complicated scissors bridge arrangement, the front and rear treadway sections of the 20m aluminium bridge fold, reducing its length to 11.3m. This enables the vehicle to use a simple chain-drive launch system in lieu of the more complicated hydraulic systems of the scissors-type bridge. The MTU-20 became the standard Soviet bridging tank, with one deployed in each motor rifle regiment, and three in each tank regiment.

The Warsaw Pact countries were not as enamoured of this approach as the Soviet Ground Forces. The MTU takes about five minutes to launch, compared to about 1.5 minutes for electro-hydraulically launched scissors bridges. This can be critical when bridging anti-tank ditches, which are likely to be protected by anti-tank weapons. East Germany and Poland jointly developed a scissors bridge design, the BLG-60. This is a 21.6m bridge, launched from a modified T-55 chassis, and with a capacity of 50 tons. It is very similar in appearance to the MT-55, developed in Czechoslovakia in 1970, with an 18m scissors bridge. In the 1970s, the Soviet Army introduced its first modern scissors bridge design, the MTU-3, based on the T-55 chassis. An improved version of the German/Polish BLG-60 appeared in the late 1970s as the BLG-60M.

River-Crossing Vehicles

The heavy losses incurred in the river-crossing operations of 1944-45 convinced the Soviet Army of the need for modernized equipment. Conventional bridging equipment is vulnerable

361▼

361. The GSP tracked ferry hardly looks like a tracked vehicle when in use like this – ferrying a T-54A ashore.

▲362 ▼363

362. The left half of a GSP tracked ferry in Egyptian service in 1973. In operation, the pontoon carried on the roof of the vehicle is folded down into the water by hydraulic cylinders inside the vehicle.
363. Side view of a Bulgarian GSP showing the considerable size of the vehicle.
364. The PTS-2 is a successor to the PTS-M, and is based on MT-T components rather than ATS-59 components.

364▲

to interdiction by air or artillery strikes. As a result, in the 1950s, the Soviet Army attempted to circumvent the need for bridging equipment in the first phases of the river-crossing operation. Light armoured vehicles, such as the BTR-60 infantry vehicle, and BRDM scout vehicle were designed to be amphibious. Tanks of the period were fitted with OPVT snorkel equipment to permit them to use 'deep wading' tactics to cross rivers. Certain vehicles, such as air defence guns, air defence missile launch vehicles and other critical equipment could not be designed with amphibious features, and in some cases, tanks would be unable to cross rivers even with OPVT equipment. A method of ferrying heavy armoured vehicles rapidly across rivers was required, and this led to the development of the GSP (*gusenichniy samokhodniy parom*: Mechanized ferry) in 1959. The GSP is peculiar in that two vehicles are required to form the ferry. The two vehicles are mirror-images of each other; the pontoons unfolding outwards on the left side of one vehicle and the right side of the other. The two matched vehicles are driven into the water, where they are mated up, and then fold down their pontoons and treadways. The pontoons are filled with a plastic foam to prevent them from filling with water if damaged in combat. The GSP uses a tracked suspension derived from the PT-76 tank, but is powered by the 8D6 engine. The assembled ferry can carry up to 50 tonnes of vehicles or equipment. It takes about 3 to 5 minutes to assemble in the water, and can travel at about 8km/h in the water with a full load. Each tank division has twelve half-ferry GSP, and each motor rifle division has six half-ferries. In the late 1970s, the Soviet engineer brigades began to receive a new wheeled ferry, apparently based on the BAZ-135 truck.

During the war the Red Army used Lend-Lease Ford 5cwt GPA and 2.5ton DUKW-353 amphibious trucks to support river-crossing operations, and after the war developed derivative vehicles such as the GAZ-46 and BAV. Neither of these was large enough to transport a truck or an artillery piece, which led to a requirement for a larger amphibious transporter. This resulted in the K-61 GPT (*Gusenichniy plavaushiy transporter*: Tracked amphibious transporter) in 1950. The K-61 used a suspension derived from the T-70/SU-76M family of light armoured vehicles, but was not itself armoured. It could carry 50 troops or up to 5 tonnes of equipment in the water. It was usually used to carry an artillery piece or a truck. In 1966, it began to be replaced by the PTS-M (*Plavayushiy transporter sredniy*: Medium amphibious transporter). The PTS-M is larger than the K-61 and was designed with an associated PKP amphibious trailer. It can carry up to 15 tonnes in the water and 7.5 tonnes on land. A single PTS-M with its PKP trailer could ferry an artillery piece and its associated towing truck. It uses a more powerful A-712P engine which gives it better speed in water, and more power on land. The basic chassis was derived from the ATS-59 artillery tractor. In the late 1970s, a heavily modernized version of the PTS-M entered service, the PTS-2, with a new suspension derived from the MT-T artillery tractor. Each division has twelve PTS-M or PTS-2 in the divisional assault river-crossing company, and one more in the divisional maintenance battalion.

365. The ATP-M was developed at the close of the Second World War to replace the pre-war T-20 Komsomolyets light artillery tractor.
366. The ATP-M was used mainly to tow anti-tank guns. Its role was subsequently taken over by a combination of vehicles including trucks and light armoured vehicles such as the MT-LB. (George Balin)
367. The AT-LM was the light artillery tractor in the post-war artillery tractor trio.

▲365

▲366 ▼367

Tracked Support Vehicles

In 1941, the Soviet artillery force made extensive use of unarmoured, tracked vehicles to tow heavy and specialized artillery. Most of these tracked vehicles were destroyed in 1941, and were replaced by expedient towing vehicles, especially agricultural tractors. In 1943, the Ya-12 was adopted as a medium artillery tractor, and was based on components from the T-60 and T-70 light tanks. In 1944, design work began on four new artillery tractors: a light armoured tractor for anti-tank guns, a light tractor for smaller field pieces like the 122mm howitzer, a medium tractor for larger artillery such as the 152mm gun, and a heavy tractor for heavy artillery. Tracked vehicles were popular in these roles since the trucks of the period had very poor cross-country performance when towing heavy loads.

The light tractor was developed on the basis of suspension elements from the SU-76M and T-70 light tanks and was intended to replace the pre-war T-20 Komsomolyets light armoured artillery tractor. It entered service in about 1947 as the ATP-M (*Artilleriskiy tyagach-polubronirovanniy*: lightly armoured artillery tractor). It was most commonly used to tow 85mm and 100mm anti-tank guns, but was also used with the 122mm howitzers and towed mortars. In a slightly modified form, it was used as an armoured command post for artillery units and its chassis served as the basis for the ASU-57 airborne assault gun. It gradually faded from use in the 1960s, its role being largely taken over by trucks. Its role as an anti-tank gun tractor was taken over by the MT-LB in the 1970s.

The light tractor requirement was satisfied by the AT-L (*artilleriskiy tyagach-legkiy*: light artillery tractor) which first appeared in 1953. The initial version, with small road wheels and return rollers, was unsuccessful, and was soon replaced by the AT-LM with larger road wheels. The AT-L was used mainly to tow large divisional mortars such as the M-160 160mm and M-240 240mm mortars. A variety of special communications and surveillance versions were also built, including the SNAR-2 (Pork Trough) battlefield surveillance radar vehicle. The AT-L had begun to disappear by the mid-1960s, with many of its roles being taken over by improved trucks such as the Ural-375 family. The Hungarian Army adopted a locally produced light artillery tractor, the Csepel K-800 in lieu of the AT-L.

The medium requirement was satisfied by the AT-S (ATS-712 *artilleriskiy tyagach sredniy*: medium artillery transporter) which appeared in 1953. The AT-S was used to tow larger field pieces including the 130mm field gun, 152mm gun-howitzer and KS-19 100mm anti-aircraft gun. Besides the basic tractor version, the AT-S

368▼

368. The Poles built the D-350 Mazur for their own use in lieu of the similar Soviet ATS-712.

▲369

▲370 ▼371

369. The ATS-712 medium artillery tractor was used to tow medium artillery and also served as the basis for the BM-24T multiple rocket launcher.
370. The ATS-712 was replaced in the 1960s by the ATS-59. This vehicle served with Egyptian forces in 1973.
371. An ATS-59 of the Romanian Army.

372. In 1965, the improved ATS-59G was introduced, which had a larger, reconfigured cab.
373. The AT-T heavy artillery tractor was used in the 1950s for heavy towing, but is better known for its use as the basis for a variety of combat engineer vehicles.

372▲ 373▼

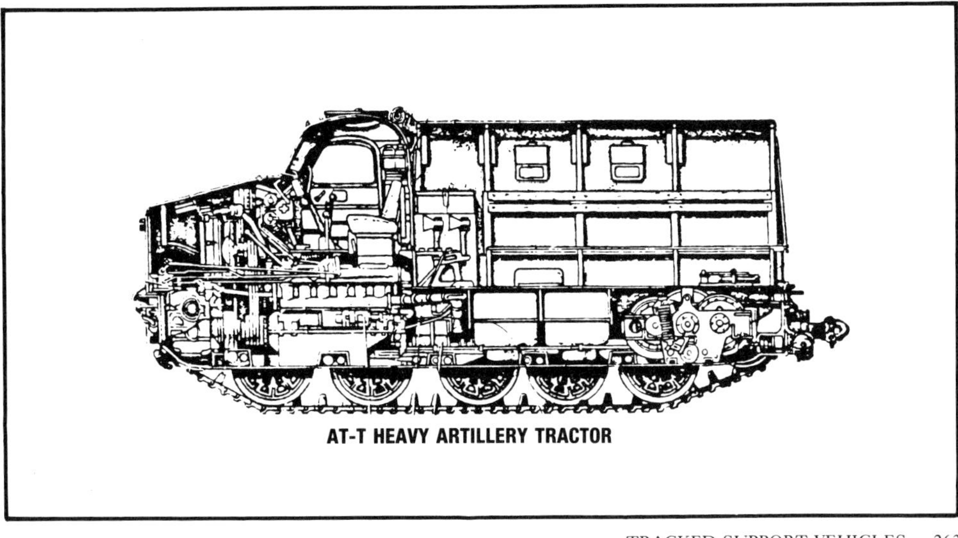

AT-T HEAVY ARTILLERY TRACTOR

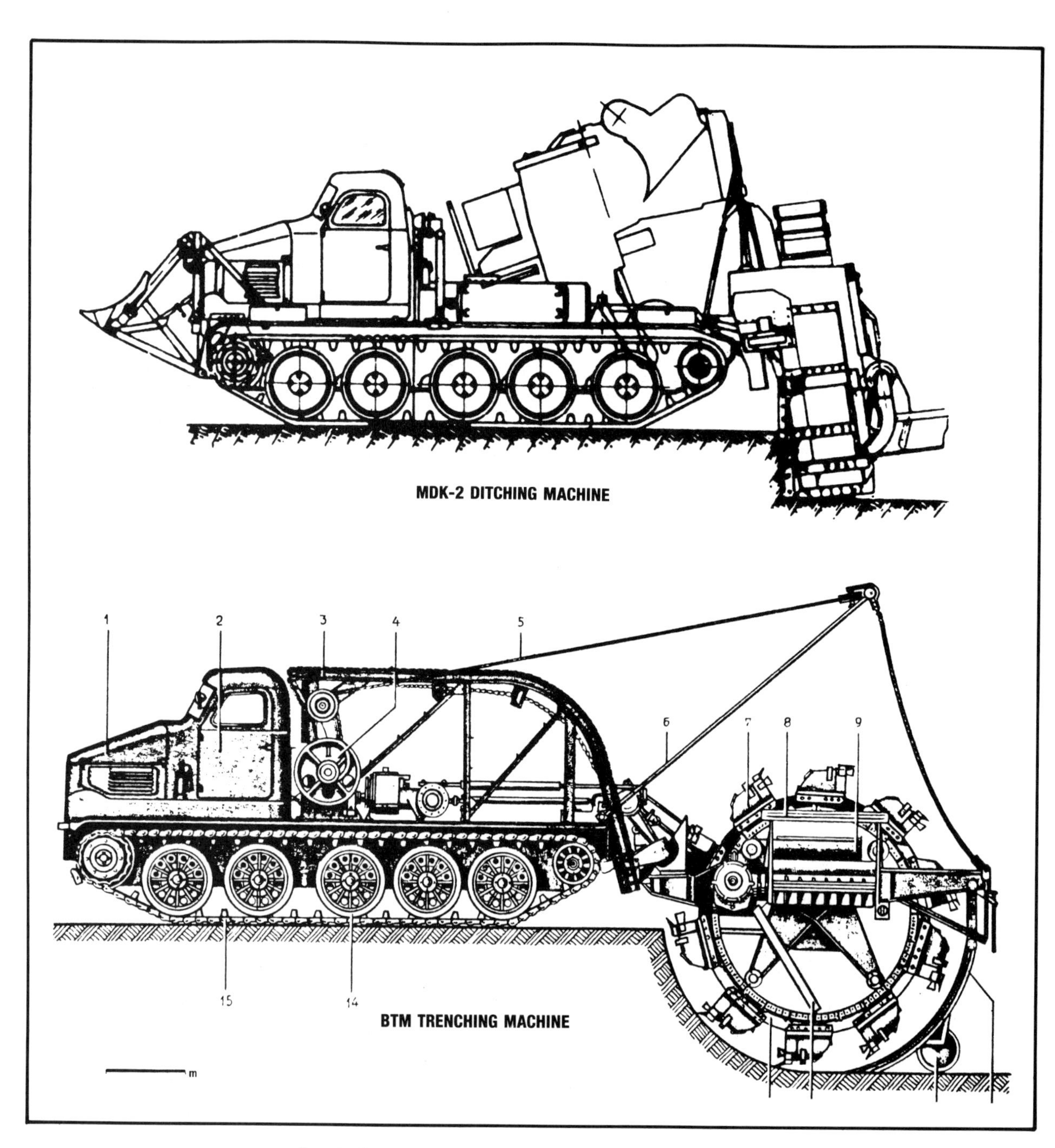

was used with the BM-24T Katyusha multiple rocket-launcher. The Polish LWP developed a local equivalent of the AT-S, the Mazur D-350 ACS (*Artileryjski ciagnik sredni*: medium artillery tractor). It would appear that the AT-S was not entirely successful, as it was replaced from 1959 by the entirely new ATS-59. The ATS-59 was used in the same roles as the AT-S, and it was also produced in Poland in lieu of the D-350 Mazur. The ATS-59 used an improved version of the V-54 diesel engine, but was fitted with a suspension of wholly new design. In about 1965 it was redesigned as the ATS-59G which used a cab-over-engine configuration to give a larger rear stowage area.

The most successful and long-lived of this post-war family of artillery transporters was the AT-T (*Artilleriiskiy tygach tyazheliy*: heavy artillery tractor) which appeared in 1950, but its longevity was probably due more to its utility in roles other than as an artillery transporter. It was based on automotive elements of the T-54 tank and was originally designed to tow large artillery pieces such as the 203mm gun-howitzer. Its role as an artillery tractor, however, was largely taken over by vehicles such as the ATS-59. In the

374. The BTM-3M is used to dig communication trenches or defence trenches, and is capable of digging in frozen ground.
375. The MDK-2 is used as a ditching machine for preparing emplacements for tanks or artillery. It can move earth faster than the BTM-3, and so is more commonly seen.

374▲ 375▼

meantime, a number of combat engineer and electronics version had been developed. It was used as the basis for the ARSOM-1 artillery surveillance radar vehicle, and a lengthened version was developed for use with the Long Track surveillance radar used with air defence missile systems. Its most common role was with combat engineer earth-moving equipment.

The BTM (*Bystrokhodnaya trasheihaya mashina*: high-speed trench-digging vehicle) was introduced in 1958 to assist engineer units in digging trenches. The BTM was based on the AT-T tractor, and used a civil-type bucket excavator. In typical soil conditions the excavator could dig a 1.5m deep trench at a rate of 230–810m an hour. In 1968, an improved type, the BTM-3, was introduced. This uses reinforced buckets, and there are usually only 8–10 compared to the 10–12 on the initial BTM. The BTM-3 was designed to permit operation in frozen ground, and can operate at speeds of up to 100m an hour in these conditions. The BTM's stablemate in the engineer battalions is the MDK-2M (*Mashina dorozhnaya kopatelnaya*: excavation vehicle) which was introduced in 1965. This is used to dig larger entrenchments

▲376

376. An MDK-2 crossing a bridge laid by an MTU-1 bridgelaying tank. (Sovfoto)
377. An MDK-2 in action beginning an emplacement.
378. An MDK-2 digging a tank emplacement.
379. The BAT-M is used as a general engineer utility vehicle and is fitted with a bulldozer blade and a light crane.

▼377

378▲ 379▼

380. The GT-S (GAZ-47) was designed primarily as a light transporter for construction troops and workers in the Arctic regions of the Soviet Union. It was also widely used by the Soviet Ground Forces in northern regions as a general-purpose utility vehicle.
381. The GT-SM was a modernized version of the GT-S with its cab over the engine to provide more rear cargo room. This particular vehicle is configured as a tracked ambulance.

▲380 ▼381

such as anti-tank ditches, gun-pits or armoured vehicle trenches. It can excavate 120–300 square metres per hour depending on soil conditions. Usually, one is assigned to each motor rifle and tank regiment, and each divisional engineer battalion has a further four. The most common of the AT-T-derived engineer vehicles are the BAT, and the improved BAT-M, with hydraulic operation features and a light crane. The BAT is used as a bulldozer to plough up protective earthworks, but is not fitted with a light crane. There is a single BAT-M in each tank and motor rifle regiment, and each divisional engineer battalion has eight more. In the late 1970s, a new family of combat engineer earth-moving equipment was introduced, based on the new MT-T chassis. Very few details are known of these systems, but they probably duplicate the functions of the BAT-M, MDK-2M and BTM-3.

Tracked Transporters

Besides the unarmoured tracked vehicles developed for the Soviet Army's artillery and combat engineer units, a separate category of vehicles was developed for general utility tasks. These vehicles were designed for the civil as well as military sectors, and are widely used in Arctic regions of the USSR. The smallest of these vehicles, the GT-S (*gusenichniy tyagach sredniy*: medium tracked tractor), or GAZ-47, was designed as a light utility vehicle for operations in snow. In its military role, it is used to tow light field pieces. In the late 1960s, it was redesigned as the GT-SM (GAZ-71) which reconfigured it to cab-over-engine style to increase the rear stowage area. It is commonly used by the military as a tracked ambulance. The GT-T (*gusenichniy tyagach tyazheliy*: heavy tracked tractor) is used to

382. The GT-T was intended for Ground Force units in the Arctic in lieu of the BTR-152. It was built with a wide variety of rear bodies, including this mobile bakery version!
383. The MT-L light tractor is the unarmoured version of the MT-LB. It does not appear to have been adopted in any significant numbers.

382▲ 383▼

tow medium artillery in units stationed in the northern USSR. The basic chassis has also been configured with a variety of different rear features, including use as a towing vehicle for S-75 (SA-2 missile) loading trailers, as a portable bakery and as a mobile ambulance.

In the late 1960s, development of a new family of light tracked utility vehicles began to replace the AT-PM and GT-T. These vehicles were designed in both an unarmoured, and a lightly armoured version. The first of these to appear were the MT-L and MT-LB. The MT-LB entered service in about 1966. As mentioned in Chapter 4, the MT-LB has been used as an infantry transporter in some Soviet divisions in Arctic regions. However, its main role is that of an artillery tractor for towed anti-tank guns. It also serves as a general-purpose armoured utility vehicle, and a large number of vehicles have been based on it including the MTP-LV mobile repair vehicle, SA-13 Gopher air defence missile vehicle, SNAR-10 artillery radar surveillance vehicle and others. Automotively, the MT-LB is related to the longer SO-122 (2S1) self-propelled howitzer and its derivative vehicles. The unarmoured MT-L does not appear to be in widespread military use.

In the same vein, a heavy transporter family was developed sometime after the MT-L family, designated MT-T. The first pictures of these appeared in 1985, and they show that the MT-T has been used as the basis for a new generation of combat engineer vehicles including replacements for the MDK-2M (MDK-3), BAT-M, and PTS-M (PTS-2). It may also serve as the basis for the launch vehicle of the SA-11 Gadfly missile system. It is likely that it will also be the basis for a new generation of electronics vehicles.

▲384

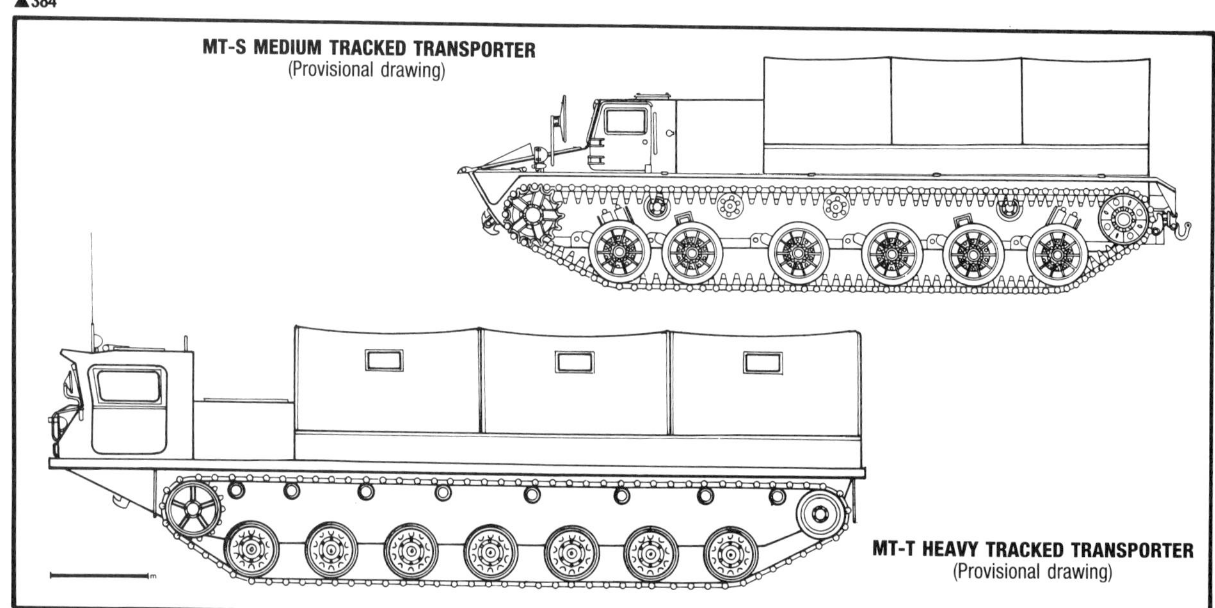
MT-S MEDIUM TRACKED TRANSPORTER
(Provisional drawing)
MT-T HEAVY TRACKED TRANSPORTER
(Provisional drawing)

▼385

386▲

384. The engineer version of the MT-LB showing its rear spade fitted in place. (Mike Green)
385. The MT-LB is a general-purpose armoured utility vehicle, and is commonly used as an artillery tractor to tow weapons like the T-12 100mm anti-tank gun. This particular MT-LB is in Bulgarian service.
386. Another view of the MT-LB engineer version, this time with its spade stowed on the hull side.
387. The MT-T is a new heavy tractor which appears to have been based on T-64 tank components.
388. A new vehicle, based on the MT-T entered service in the 1970s, presumably to replace the BAT-M.

387▲ 388▼

▲389

▲390 ▼391

389. A column of new combat engineer vehicles based on the new MT-T chassis. The vehicle in the foreground is intended to replace the BAT-M, while the second vehicle will replace the MDK-2.

390. Rear view of the new MT-T derived ditching machine.

391. The East German Army converted some of its outdated ZSU-57-2 hulls to FAP-200U training tanks, thereby extending their useful life and cutting down on the wear and tear to operational tanks.

Glossary*

*Foreign terms are in Russian unless otherwise noted.

ACRV: Armoured Command and Reconnaissance Vehicle.
Akatsiya: (Acacia), name of Soviet SO-152 (2S3) 152mm self-propelled howitzer.
AP: *Avtomobilnoi promyshlennosti* (automotive industry), industrial agency responsible for Soviet wheeled armoured vehicle production.
APFSDS: Armour-piercing, fin-stabilized, discarding sabot; a type of anti-tank projectile relying on kinetic energy for penetration.
ASR: *Armata Socialiste Romania*, Army of Socialist Romania.
ASU: *Aviadesantnaya samokhodnaya ustanovka* (airborne mechanized gun), such as ASU-57, ASU-85.
AT-L: *Artilleriskiy tyagach legkiy* (light artillery tractor).
AT-P: *Artilleriskiy tyagach polubronirovanniy* (lightly armoured artillery tractor).
ATS: *Artilleriskiy tyagach sredniy* (medium artillery tractor).
AT-T: *Artilleriskiy tyagach tyazheliy* (heavy artillery tractor).
BM: *Boyevaya mashina* (combat vehicle), cover name for multiple rocket-launchers.
BMD: *Boyevaya Mashina Desantnaya* (air assault vehicle).
BMP: *Boyevaya Mashina Pyekhota* (infantry fighting vehicle).
BNA: *Bulgarska Narodna Armiya* (Bulgarian People's Army).
BRDM: *Bronirovannaya razvedivatelnaya dozornaya mashina* (armoured scout patrol vehicle).
BREM: *Bronirovannaya remontno-evakuatsionnaya mashina* (armoured repair and recovery vehicle).
BRM: *Bronirovannaya razvedivatelnaya mashina* (armoured reconnaissance vehicle).
BTM: *Bystrokhodnaya trashenaya mashina* (high-speed trench-digging vehicle).
BTR: *Bronetransporter* (armoured transporter).
BTS: *Bronetankoviy tyagach sredniy* (armoured medium tractor), Russian term for armoured recovery vehicle.
BVP: *Bojove vozidlo pechoty* (infantry fighting vehicle); Czech for BMP.
BWP: *Bojowy woz piechoty* (infantry fighting vehicle); Polish for BMP.
CEP: Circular error probability.
COMECON: Council of Mutual Economic Assistance; economic administration of the Warsaw Pact countries.
CSLA: *Ceskoslovenska lidova armada* (Czechoslovak People's Army).
DIA: *Defense Intelligence Agency*, US combined services Intelligence organization.
Fagot: (Bassoon), Russian name for AT-4 Spigot anti-tank missile.
Falanga: (Phalanx), Russian name for the AT-2 Swatter anti-tank missile.
FLIR: Forward Looking Infra-Red, term for a thermal imaging night vision system.
FROG: Free Rocket Over Ground, NATO term for the Soviet Luna family of unguided ballistic rockets.
GAKB: *Glavnoye artilleriskoye konstruktorskoye biuro* (Main Artillery Design Bureau), located in Kalinigrad, outside Moscow.
GAU: *Glavnoye artilleriskoye upravleniye* (Main Artillery Administration), currently GRAU.
GAZ: *Gorkovskiy Avtomobilniy Zavod* (Gorkiy Automobile Factory).
GMZ: *Gusenichniy minniy zagraditel* (tracked minelayer).
GPT: *Gusenichniy plavaushniy transporter* (tracked amphibious transporter).
Grad: (Hail), Russian term for BM-21 multiple rocket-launcher and related systems.
GRAU: *Glavnoye rakietnoye i artilleriskoye upravleniye* (Main Missile and Artillery Administration).
GSP: *Gusenichniy samokhodniy parom* (mechanized ferry).
GT-S: *Gusenichniy tyagach sredniy* (medium tractor).
GT-T: *Gusenichniy tyagach tyazheliy* (heavy tractor).
Gvozdika: (Carnation), Soviet name for SO-122 (2S1) 122mm self-propelled howitzer.
HEAT: High-explosive anti-tank; a type of artillery or tank gun projectile with a shaped charge, high-explosive warhead.
HVAPDS: High-velocity, armour-piercing, discarding sabot; a type of tank gun projectile relying on kinetic energy for penetration. Unlike the later APFSDS projectile, the HVAPDS subcalibre penetrator is not finned.
IMR: *Inzhernaya mashina razgrazhdeniya* (engi-

neer obstacle-clearing vehicle).

IPR: *Inzherniy plavaushniy razvednik* (amphibious engineer scout).

IR: Infra-red.

IS: *Iosef Stalin*, Soviet heavy tank series named after the Soviet leader.

ISU: Russian term for an SU (mechanized gun) based on an IS heavy tank chassis.

IT: *Istrebitel tankov* (tank destroyer).

IWT: *Inzynieryjny woz torujacy* (engineer clearing vehicle), Polish equivalent of Soviet IMR.

KB: *Konstruktorskoye biuro* (design bureau), also OKB, TsKB, GKB.

KMT: *Kolesniy minniy tral* (wheeled mine trawl).

Kobra: (Cobra), Russian name for AT-8 anti-tank missile.

Korshun: (Kite), Russian name for BMP variant.

KPVT: *Krupnokaliberniy pulemet Vladimirova tankoviy* (Vladimirov heavy tank machine-gun).

Krug: (Circle), Russian name for SA-4 Ganef air defence missile system.

KShM: *Komandno-shtabnaya mashina* (command-staff vehicle).

Kub: (Cube), Russian name for SA-6 Gainful air defence missile system.

Kvadrat: (Rectangle), Russian name, possibly for export model of *Kub*.

Luna: (Moon), Russian name for FROG ballistic rocket series, also name for infra-red searchlights on Soviet tanks.

LWP: *Ludowe Wojsko Polskie* (Polish People's Army).

Malyutka: (Little One), Russian name for AT-3 Sagger anti-tank missile.

MCLOS: Manual, Command-to-Line-of-Sight; refers to first generation of anti-tank guided missile guidance systems.

MDK: *Mashina dorozhnaya kopatelnaya* (excavating vehicle).

MN: *Magyar Nepkoztarsasag* (Hungarian Army).

MT-LB: *Mnogotselevoi tyagach legko bronirovanniy* (multi-purpose, lightly armoured tractor).

MT-LBV: *Mnogotselvoi tyagach legko bronirovanniy viezdiekkhod* (all-terrain, multi-purpose, lightly armoured tractor).

MTP: *Mashina tekhnicheskoi pomoshi* (technical assistance vehicle).

MTU: *Mostoykladchik tankoviy ustroystvo* (tank bridge-layer).

NII: *Nauchno ispytatielniy institut* (Research Institute).

NIIBT: *Nauchno ispytatelniy institut bronetankovoy tekniki* (Armoured Technology Research Institute), located at the proving grounds in Kubinka.

NKTMP: *Narodniy Komissariat Transportnogo Mashinoststroeniia Promyshlennosti* (National Commissariat for the Transport Machine-Building Industry); organization responsible for administration of the tank industry immediately after the end of Second World War.

NKTP: *Narodniy Komissariat Tankovoi Promyshlennosti* (National Tank Industry Commissariat); organization which controlled Soviet wartime tank production.

NSVT: *Nikitin, Sokolov, Volkov-tankoviy*; 12.7mm machine-gun named after its three designers, Nikitin, Sokolov, and Volkov, adapted for tank use.

NVA: *Nationale Volksarmee* (National People's Army); army of East Germany.

OBIEKT: (Project), Russian term often used for armoured vehicle prototype, followed by a number, such as Obiekt 137A (T-54A tank project). The term *zavodskoye izdeliye* also used in the same fashion or as a substitute for *obiekt*.

OKB: *Opitnoye konstruktorskoye biuro* (Experimental Design Bureau); also KB, TsKB.

OPVT: *Oborudovanie dla podvodnogo vodzhenya* (deep wading equipment).

PAZ: *Protivo-atomnaya zashita* (nuclear defence system).

PRP: *Podvizhni razvedivatelniy punkt* (mobile reconnaissance post).

PT: *Plavaushniy tank* (amphibious tank).

PT: *Protivo-minniy tral* (anti-mine trawl).

PVO: *Protivozdushnoy Oborony* (Air Defence Force), the Russian term for the branch of the armed forces controlling national air defence, formerly (up to 1982) called *PVO-Strany*. The air defence elements of the Ground Forces are called *PVO-Voiska* or *PVO-SV*.

PU: *Punkt upravleniya* (command post); commonly used as a suffix on a vehicle designation, such as BTR-60PU, to indicate a command vehicle.

PUAZO: *Pribor upravleniya artilleriskim zenitnim ognem* (anti-aircraft fire control director).

RGK: *Reserv Glavnogo komandovaniya* (High Command Reserve).

RKhM: *Razvedivatelnaya khimicheskaya mashina* (chemical scout vehicle).

Romb: (Square), Russian name for SA-8 Gecko air defence missile system.

RSVN: *Raketniye Voiska Strategicheskovo Naznacheniya* (Strategic Missile Force), the branch of the Soviet armed forces which controls land-based strategic missiles, split off in 1959–60 from the artillery branch of the Ground Forces. Also sometimes called Strategic Rocket Force.

SACLOS: Semi-Automatic, Command-to-Line-of-Sight; second generation guidance method for anti-tank missiles.

Shchuka: (Pike), name for two Soviet heavy tanks, IS-3 and VL-1.

Shilka: (Awl), Russian name for ZSU-23-4 air

defence gun vehicle.

Shmel: (Bumblebee), Russian name for AT-1 Snapper anti-tank missile.

SKOT: *Stredni kolovy obrneny transporter* (Czech) or *Sredni kolowy opancerzony transporter* (Polish) for OT-64 (medium armoured wheeled transporter).

SNAR: *Stanitsiya nazemnoi artilleriy radiolokatsionaya* (artillery reconnaissance radar).

SO: *Samokhodnoye oruzhiye* (mobile gun).

SPK: *Spetsialniy podemniy kran* (special crane).

SPU: *Samokhodnaya puskovaya ustanovka* (mobile launcher unit); usually the launch vehicle of an air defence missile system.

SSNR: *Samokhodnaya stanitsiya navedeniya raket* (mobile missile guidance station); usually the tracking and engagement radar vehicle associated with a mobile air defence missile system.

SSRTs: *Samokhodnaya stanitsiya razvedki i tselyukazaniya* (mobile detection and designation radar station); a mobile surveillance and long-range warning radar system.

SU: *Samokhodnaya ustanovka*, literally 'mobile unit', usually used as designation for self-propelled artillery. Also SO and SAU.

SV: *Sukhoputniye Voiska* (Ground Forces), the official Russian term for the branch of the armed services normally called the Army in the West.

TDA: *Termicheskaya dimovaya apparatura* (thermal smoke device); integral smoke-laying system on Soviet armoured vehicles.

TEL: Transporter-Erector-Launcher; refers to vehicle which independently carries, erects and launches a missile.

TELAR: Transporter-Erector-Launcher-And-Radar; refers to an air defence missile vehicle which carries a radar.

TiSMP: *Traktornogo i selskokhoziaistvennogo mashinostroeniia promyshlennosti* (Tractor and Agricultural Machine Building Industry), organization responsible for the production of light tracked and all-terrain vehicles for the Soviet Army.

TiTMP: *Tiazhelogo i transportnogo mashinostroeniia promyshlennosti* (Transport and Heavy Machine Building Industry), current ministry responsible for the production of tanks and self-propelled guns.

Tochka: (Point), Russian name for the SS-21 Scarab tactical missile system.

TO&E: Tables of Organization and Equipment, the formal listing of the men and equipment of military units.

TOPAS: *Transporter Obrneny Pasovy* (Czech: tracked armoured transporter).

TsKB: *Tsentralnoye konstruktornoye biuro* (Central Design Bureau), also OKB, KB.

TTZ: *Taktiko-tekhnichesoye zadaniye*, or TTT, *taktiko-tekhnicheskoye trebovaniye* (Tactical-Technical Assignment/Requirement).

TZM: *Transportna zaryyazyushcha mashina* (transporter-loader vehicle); vehicle for carrying and loading missiles, called a transloader in the USA.

VDV: *Vozdushno Desantnaya Voiska* (Air Assault Force), the semi-autonomous branch of the Soviet Army responsible for the mobile strategic forces such as air assault divisions.

VPK: *Voenniy Promyshlennostniy Komitet* (Military Industrial Committee), Soviet military-industrial agency for co-ordinating military production plans between military and civil ministries.

VVS: *Voyenno Vozdushniye Sily* (Air Force); term for the Soviet Air Force.

WZT: *Woz zabezpieczny techniczny* (technical recovery vehicle); Polish equivalent of Soviet BTS or BREM.

Yubileyniy: (Jubilee), Russian name for T-62 tank.

Zavodskoye izdeliye: (factory product); code name for a new weapon system, usually followed by a number such as *zavodskoye izdeliye 40.* Sometimes used interchangeably with the expression *Obiekt.*

ZiL: *Zavod imeni Likhacheva* (factory named after Likhachev); Moscow automotive plant, formerly called AMO, then ZiS, becoming ZiL in 1954.

ZRK: *Zenitniy raketniy kompleks* (anti-aircraft missile system). Sometimes also called ZRK-SD (*srednoye deistvie*: medium range).

Bibliography

This bibliography lists books, studies and government reports used in the preparation of this book. Due to space limitations, a list of articles used is not included, but a list of periodicals consulted is appended at the end. All books and reports cited are unclassified in the USA. Reports which originally appeared in a classified, secret or top secret form and were subsequently declassified have their initial publication date noted, followed by the 'declassification to unclassified level' date appended, with the letter 'd' suffix.

Alexander, A. J. *Armor Development in the Soviet Union and the United States*. Rand Corporation, Santa Monica, CA, 1976

— *Decision Making in Soviet Weapons Procurement, Adelphi Paper 147/148*. IISS, London, 1979

Anashkin, I. N., and Belokur, M. N. *Spravochnik serzhanta artillerii (Handbook for Artillery Sergeants)*. Voenizdat, Moscow, 1981

Andersen, Yu. A., et al. *Protivovozdushnaya oborona sukhoputnikh voisk (Anti-aircraft Defence of the Ground Forces)*. Voenizdat, Moscow, 1979

Andrionikov, I. G., et al. *Bronietankovie i mekhanisierovanie voiska sovietskoi armiy (Tank and Mechanized Forces of the Soviet Army)*. Voenizdat, Moscow, 1958

Antonov, A. S., et al. *Tank*. Voenizdat, Moscow, 1954

Aristov, A. D., et al. *Sluzhi sovetskomu soyuzu (Serving the Soviet Union)*. Voenizdat, Moscow, 1978

Arkin, W. M., and Fieldhouse, R. W. *Nuclear Battlefields: Global Links in the Arms Race*. Ballinger Publishing, Cambridge, MA, 1985

Avidar, Y. *The Party and the Army in the Soviet Union*. Pennsylvania State University Press, University Park, PA, 1983

Ayliffe-Jones, N. *World Tanks and Reconnaissance Vehicles Since 1945*. Ian Allen, London, 1984

Babadzhanyan, A. Kh. *Tanki i tankovie voiska (Tanks and Tank Forces)*. Voenizdat, Moscow, 1980

Balcerzak, J., et al. *Technika Wojskowa LWP:XXX lat rozwoju 1943–73 (Military Technology of the Polish People's Army: 30 Years of Development 1943–73)*. WMON, Warsaw, 1973

Ball, N., and Leitenberg, M. *Structure of the Defence Industry*. Croom Helm, London, 1983

Baxter, William P. *Soviet Air Land Battle Tactics*. Presdiio Press, Novato, CA, 1986

Bellamy, Chris. *Red God of War: Soviet Artillery and Rocket Forces*. Brassey's Defence Publishers, London, 1986

Bogatskiy, A. P., et al. (eds.). *Slovar raketnikh i artilleriyskikh terminov (Dictionary of Missile and Artillery Terms)*. Voenizdat, Moscow, 1968

Bolotin, D. N. *Sovetskoe strelkovoe oruzhie (Soviet Small Arms)*. Voenizdat, Moscow, 1983

Bonds, E. (ed.). *Russian Military Power*. Salamander Books, London, 1980

— *The Soviet War Machine*. Salamander Books, London, 1976

— *Weapons of the Modern Soviet Ground Forces*. Salamander Books, London, 1981

Brereton, J. M. *Russian Tanks: Evolution and Development 1915–1968*. Feist Publications, Berkeley, CA, 1970

Brudny, S., and Cebulski, J. *Wspolczesne pojazdy terenowe (Contemporary All-terrain Vehicles)*. WMON, Warsaw, 1975

Burakowski, T., and Sala, A. *Rakiety bojowe (Military Missiles)*. WMON, Warsaw, 1973

— *Wyrzutnia rakietowa katiusza (Katyusha Rocket Launchers)*. WMON, Warsaw, 1971

Castner, J. M. *An Annotated Dictionary of Soviet Military Equipment Designators*. US Army Russian Institute, Garmisch, FRG, 1981

Chaban, D. V. *Kratkiy spravochnik po otechestvennym avtomobilyam i pritsepam (Concise Handbook of Domestic Vehicles and Trailers)*. Voenizdat, Moscow, 1971

Chalmaev, V. *Malyshev*. Molodaya Gvardiya, Moscow, 1978

Checinski, M. *The Armament Administration of Soviet Bloc States: Organization and Function*. Sonderveroffentlichung des Bundesinstituts fur ostwissenschaftliche und internationale Studien, Bonn, FRG, 1979

— *A Comparison of the Polish and Soviet Armaments Decision-making Systems*. Rad Corporation, Santa Monica, CA, 1981

— *The Costs of Armament Production and the Profitability of Armament Exports in COMECON Countries*. Hebrew University, Jerusalem, 1974

Central Intelligence Agency. *Directory of USSR*

Ministry of Defense and Armed Forces Officials. CIA, Langley, VA, 1978
— *Soviet and US Defense Activities 1971–80: A Dollar Cost Comparison.* CIA, Langley, VA, 1981
— *A Summary of Soviet Guided Missile Intelligence.* CIA, Langley, VA, 1953/1978d
— *The Tank and Assault Gun Industry of the USSR.* CIA, Langley, VA, 1953/1979d
— *USSR: Ministry of Defense Officials.* CIA, Langley, VA, 1985
Cockburn, A. *The Threat: Inside the Soviet Military Machine.* Random House, NY, 1983
Cocks, P. M. *Science Policy: USA/USSR; Vol. II, Science Policy in the Soviet Union.* National Science Foundation, Washington, DC, 1980
Collins, J. M. *American and Soviet Military Trends Since the Cuban Missile Crisis.* CSIS, Washington, DC, 1978
— *US-Soviet Military Balance: Concepts and Capabilities, 1960–1980.* McGraw Hill, New York, 1980
— *US-Soviet Military Balance: Statistical Trends, 1970–1980.* Congressional Research Service, Washington, DC, 1981
— *US/Soviet Military Balance: Statistical Trends 1970–1982.* Congressional Research Service, Washington, DC, 1983
— *US-Soviet Military Balance 1980–1985.* Congressional Research Service, Washington, DC, 1985
Congress of the USA. *Allocation of Resources in the Soviet Union and China – 1981.* Joint Economic Committee, Congress of the USA, 1981
— *Allocation of Resources in the Soviet Union and China – 1983.* Joint Economic Committee, Congress of the USA, 1983
— *Economic Performance and the Military Burden in the Soviet Union.* Joint Economic Committee, Congress of the USA, 1970
— *Soviet Military Economic Relations.* Joint Economic Committee, Congress of the USA, 1983
Congressional Budget Office. *Assessing the NATO/Warsaw Pact Military Balance.* CBO, Washington, DC, 1977
Crommelin, Q., and Sullivan, D. S. *Soviet Military Supremacy.* University of Southern California, 1985
Currie, K. M., and Varhall, G. (eds.). *The Soviet Union: What Lies Ahead? – Military Political Affairs in the 1980s.* USAF, Washington, DC, 1985
Czuchrowski, F., and Mikrut, M. *Zolnierska powinnosc (Soldier's Duty).* WMON, Warsaw, 1983
Defense Intelligence Agency. *Handbook on the Non-Soviet Warsaw Pact Armies.* DIA, Washington, DC, 1972
— *Handbook on the Soviet Armed Forces.* DIA, Washington, DC, 1978
— *Handbook of Soviet Armed Forces Military Symbols.* DIA, Washington, DC, 1978
— *Soviet Ground Forces Night Operations.* DIA, Washington, DC, 1976
— *The Soviet Motorized Rifle Battalion.* DIA, Washington, DC, 1978
— *The Soviet Motorized Rifle Company.* DIA, Washington, DC, 1976
— *Soviet Divisional Organization Guide.* DIA, Washington, DC, 1982
— *Soviet Ground Force Logistics.* DIA, Washington, DC, 1972/1984d
— *Soviet and NSWP Amphibious Warfare.* DIA, Washington, DC, 1984
— *Soviet Tactical Trends Since the October 1973 War.* DIA, Washington, DC, 1977/1985d
— *Soviet Tank Regiment Tactics.* DIA, Washington, DC, 1979
— *Soviet and Warsaw Pact River Crossing: Doctrine and Capabilities.* DIA, Washington, DC, 1977
— *Warsaw Pact Ground Forces Equipment Identification Guide: Armored Fighting Vehicles DDB-1100-255-80.* DIA, Washington, DC, 1980
— *Warsaw Pact Ground Forces Equipment Identification Guide: Artillery, Rockets and Missiles DDB-1100-313-82.* DIA, Washington, DC, 1982
— *Warsaw Pact Ground Forces Equipment Handbook: Armored Fighting Vehicles.* DIA, Washington, DC, 1980
Defense Nuclear Agency. *Soviet Army Echelonment & Objectives.* US DNA, Washington, DC, 1978
Douglass, J. D. *The Soviet Theater Nuclear Offensive.* USAF, 1982

Douglass, J. D., Hoeber, A. M., et al. (eds.). *Selected Readings from Military Thought 1963–73*. USAF, Washington, DC, 1982

Drobisz, T., and Paprocki, R. *Przeciwpancerny pocisk kierowany 3M6 (The 3M6 Guided Anti-tank Missile)*. WMON, Warsaw, 1976

Dunskaya, Irina. *Security Practices at Soviet Scientific Research Facilities*. Delphic Associates, Falls Church, VA, 1983

Dupouy, A. *Les Tracteurs et Engines Spéciaux Chenilles Soviétiques, Tomes 1 et 2 (Soviet Tractors and Special Tracked Vehicles)*. Privately published, Grenoble, 1986

Dupouy, A., and Sanseu, N. *Musées de l'Armée de RDA: Dresde-Potsdam (Museums of the Army of the German Democratic Republic at Dresden and Potsdam)*. A. Dupouy, Grenoble, 1983

English, J. A., et al. *The Mechanized Battlefield: A Tactical Analysis*. Pergammon-Brassey, New York, NY, 1985

Erickson, J., and Hansen, L. *Soviet Combined Arms: Past & Present*. Center for Strategic Technology, College Station, TX, 1981

Erickson, J., Hansen, L., and Schneider, W. *Soviet Ground Forces: An Operational Assessment*. Westview Press, Boulder, CO, 1986

Erickson, J., and Feuchtwanger, E. J. (eds.). *Soviet Military Power and Performance*. Macmillan Press, London, 1979

Eshel, D. *Soviet APCs*. Eshel-Dramit, Tel Aviv, 1981

Eustace, H. F. *The International Countermeasures Handbook*. EW Communications, Palo Alto, CA, 1977, 1978, 1979, 1980, 1981, 1982, 1983, 1984, 1985

Evans, T. C. *Current Objectives and Deficiencies in the Training of the Soviet Tanker*. US Army Institute for Advanced Russian and East European Studies, Garmisch, FRG, 1975

Firdman, Henry. *Decision Making in the Soviet Microelectronics Industry*. Delphic Associates, Falls Church, VA, 1985

Forster, T. M. *The East German Army*. George Allen & Unwin, London, 1980

Foss, C. F. *Jane's Armour and Artillery*. Jane's Publishing, London, 1980, 1981, 1982, 1983, 1984, 1985

Foss, C. F., and Gander, T. J. *Jane's Military Vehicles and Ground Support Equipment*. Jane's Publishing, London, 1980, 1981, 1982, 1983, 1984, 1985

Gabriel, R. A. (ed.). *Fighting Armies: NATO and the Warsaw Pact, A Combat Assessment*. Greenwood Press, Westport, CT, 1983

Gajkowski, E. *Na Poligonie i na Defiladzie (On the Proving Grounds and on Parade)*. Wyd. Horyzonty, Warsaw, 1975

Gardner, M. *A History of the Soviet Army*. Praeger, New York, NY, 1966

Glantz, D. M. *The Soviet Airborne Experience*. US Army Command and General Staff College, Ft. Leavenworth, KS, 1984

Gogolev, L. *Avtomobili v boevom stroyu (Vehicles in Military Employment)*. Molodaya Gvardiya, Moscow, 1981

Grabovoi, I. D., and Kadyuk, V. K. *Zazhgatelnoe oruzhie i zashchita ot nego (Incendiary Weapons and Defence From Them)*. Voenizdat, Moscow, 1983

Greenberg, Karl. *The Central Materials Research Institute of the Soviet Ministry of the Defense Industry (TsNIIM)*. Delphic Associates, Falls Church, VA, 1986

Govorov, V. L., et al. (eds.). *Voennie paradi na krasnoi ploshadi (Military Parades on Red Square)*. Voenizdat, Moscow, 1980

Grimmett, R. F. *Trends in Conventional Arms Transfers to the Third World by Major Suppliers, 1976–1983*. Congressional Research Service, Washington, DC, 1984

HERO; *A Historical Analysis of the Effectiveness of Tactical Air Operations against and in Support of Armored Forces*. HERO, Dunn Loring, VA, 1980

Holloway, D. *The Soviet Union and the Arms Race*. Yale University Press, New Haven, CT, 1983

Holloway, D., and Sharp, J. M. O. *The Warsaw Pact: Alliance in Transition?* Cornell University Press, Ithaca, NY, 1984

Holub, O. *Ceskoslovenske tanky a tankiste (Czechoslovak Tanks and Tankers)*. Nase Vojsko, Prague, 1980

House, J. M. *Toward Combined Arms Warfare, A Survey of 20th Century Tactics, Doctrine and Organization*. US Army Command and General Staff College, Ft. Leavenworth, KS, 1984

Isby, D. *Weapons and Tactics of the Soviet Army*. Jane's Publishing, London, 1980

Ivanov, D. A., et al. *Osnovi upravleniya voiskami v boyu (Fundamentals of Military Command in Combat)*. Voenizdat, Moscow, 1977; published by USAF in English translation as *Fundamentals of Tactical Command and Control, The Soviet View*. 1977

Jessup, John. *The Development of Soviet Air Defense Doctrine and Practice*. Sandia Laboratories, Sandia, NM, 1981

Johnson, A. R., Dean, R. W., and Alexiev, A. *East European Military Establishments: The Warsaw Pact Northern Tier*. Crane Russak, New York, NY, 1982

Joint Technical Language Service; *Russian-English Military Dictionary*. HMSO, London, 1983

Jones, David R. *Soviet Armed Forces Review*

Annual, vols. 1–9. Academic International Press, 1975–85

Kamoff-Nicolsky, G. *Soviet and East European Arms Deliveries to Lesser Developed Countries, 1955–1980: An Interpretation of Trends*. Department of National Defence, Ottawa, 1980

Kaplan, S. S. *Diplomacy of Power: Soviet Armed Forces as a Political Instrument*. The Brookings Institution, Washington, DC, 1981

Karlicky, V. *Ceskoslovenske delostrelecke zbrane (Czechoslovak Artillery Weapons)*. Nase Vojsko, Prague, 1975

Katunskiy, A. M. *Vozhdenie tankov (Driving Tanks)*. Voenizdat, Moscow, 1976

Kazakov, K. P. *Artilleria i rakiety (Artillery and Missiles)*. Voenizdat, Moscow, 1968

Keegan, J. (ed.). *World Armies*. Macmillan, London, 1979, 1983

Koenig, W., and Scofield, P. *Soviet Military Power*. Bison Books, Greenwich, CT, 1983

Kolibernov, E. S. et al. *Inzhenernoe obespechenie boya (Engineer Combat Support)*. Voenizdat, Moscow, 1984

Komorova, F. I. (ed.). *Voenno-meditsinskaya podgotovka (Military Medical Preparations)*. Izd. Meditsina, Moscow, 1983

Konrad, F. *So Stark ist Russland (So Strong is Russia)*. Podzun-Pallas, Freidberg, 1982

Kozlov, M. M. *Velikaya Otechestvennaya Voina 1941–1945: Entsiklopediya (The Great Patriotic War 1941–45: Encyclopedia)*. Sovetskaya Entsiklopediya, Moscow, 1985

Krauze, M., and Nowak, I. *Wspolczesne wojska chemiczne (Contemporary Chemical Forces)*. WMON, Warsaw, 1983

Kuth, R. A. *Soviet Airborne Anti-Armor Tactics*. US Army Russian Institute, Garmisch, FRG, 1981

Kuusela, K., and Muikku, E. *Puolustusvoimien panssarikalusto 1918–1981 (Armoured Vehicles of the Finnish Defence Force 1918–1981)*. Panssarikilta, Parola, Finland, 1982

Kuznetsov, M. I. et al. *Tankovie navigatsionnie sistemi (Tank navigation systems)*. Voenizdat, Moscow, 1978

Lapshin, V. I. et al. (eds.). *Kratkiy avtomobili spravochnik (Concise Automotive Handbook)*. Izd. Transport, Moscow, 1984

Latukhin, A. N. (ed.). *Bog Voini (The God of War)*. Molodaya Gvardiya, Moscow, 1979

— *Boyevaya tekhnika armii i flota (Military Technology of the Army and Fleet)*. DOSAAF, Moscow, 1981

Lee, William, and Starr, Richard. *Soviet Military Policy since World War II*. Hoover Institute Press, Stanford, 1986

Lewis, W. J. *The Warsaw Pact: Arms, Doctrine and Strategy*. McGraw-Hill, New York, NY, 1982

Lisov, I. I. *Desantniki-Vozdushniye desanty (Paratroopers-Airborne Assault)*. Voenizdat, Moscow, 1968

Listrovoi, V., and Slobodin, K. *Konstruktor Morozov (Designer Morozov)*. Politizdat, Moscow, 1983

Lobanov, M. M. *Razvitie sovetskoi radiolokatsionnoi tekhniki (The Development of Soviet Radar Technology)*. Voenizdat, Moscow, 1982

Luttwak, E. N. *The Grand Strategy of the Soviet Union*. St. Martin's Press, New York, NY, 1983

Mackintosh, M. *Juggernaut: The Russian Forces, 1918–1966*. Macmillan, New York, NY, 1967

Magnuski, J. *Ciezki dzialo samobiezne ISU (ISU Heavy Assault Guns)*. WMON, Warsaw, 1980

— *Czolg ciezki IS (IS Heavy Tank)*. WMON, Warsaw, 1974

— *Czolg plywajacy PT-76 (PT-76 Amphibious Tank)*. WMON, Warsaw, 1971

— *Czolg sredni T-54 (T-54 Medium Tank)*. WMON, Warsaw, 1972

— *Radzieckie dziala samobiezne (Soviet Self-Propelled Guns)*. WMON, Warsaw, 1975

— *Transporter opancerzony SKOT (SKOT Armoured Transporter)*. WMON, Warsaw, 1971

— *Transporter opancerzony TOPAS (TOPAS Armoured Transporter)*. WMON, Warsaw, 1978

— *Wozy bojowe LWP 1943–1983 (Combat Vehicles of the Polish People's Army 1943–83)*. WMON, Warsaw, 1985

Medvedkov, V. I., Komarov, Yu. N., and Lobzin, A. F. *Ustroistvo i ekspluyatatsiya bronetransporterov BTR-60PB, BTR-70 i avtomobilei ZiL-130, ZiL-131 (Design and Employment of the BTR-60PB and BTR-70 Armoured Transporters and the ZiL-130 and ZiL-131 Vehicles)*. DOSAAF, Moscow, 1984

Mikhailov, V. P., and Nazarov, G. A. *Razvitie tekhniki puska raket (The Development of Missiles)*. Voenizdat, Moscow, 1976

Milsom, J. *Russian Tanks 1900–1970*. Arms & Armour Press, London, 1970

Meyer, S. M. *Soviet Theatre Nuclear Forces*. IISS, London, 1983–4

Monks, A. L. *Soviet Military Doctrine: 1960 to the Present*. Irvington Publishers, New York, NY, 1984

Murray, D. J., and Viotti, P. R. (eds.). *The Defense Policies of Nations: A Comparative Study*. Johns Hopkins University Press, Baltimore, MD, 1982

Modrzewski, J. et al. (eds.). *Encyclopedia techniki wojskowej (Encyclopedia of Military Technology)*. WMON, Warsaw, 1978

Mullady, B. P. *Soviet Air Defenses against Attack Helicopters*. US Army Russian Institute,

Garmisch, FRG, 1980
Musienko, V. A., and Pechenezhckiy, K. S. *Tankoviy vzvod v boyu (The Tank Platoon in Combat)*. Voenizdat, Moscow, 1967
NATO. *NATO and the Warsaw Pact: Force Comparisons*. NATO, Brussels, 1984
Nelson, D. N. *Soviet Allies: The Warsaw Pact and the Issue of Reliability*. Westview Press, Boulder, CO, 1984
Nelyubin, L. L. *Illustrovanniy voenno-tekhnicheskiy slovar (Illustrated Military-Technical Dictionary)*. Voenizdat, Moscow, 1968
Ness, L. *World Armored Vehicle Forecast*. DMS, Greenwich, CT, 1982, 1983, 1984, 1985, 1986
Nimitz, Nancy. *The Structure of Soviet Outlays on R&D in 1960 and 1968*. Rand Corporation, Santa Monica, 1974
Oakes, D. *Soviet Military Sales: Why Are They So Cheap?*. USAF Air War College, Maxwell AFB, AL, 1985
O'Ballance, E. *The Red Army*. Faber & Faber, London, 1964
Ogarkov, N. V. (ed.). *Voenniy entsiklopedicheskiy slovar (Military Encyclopedic Dictionary)*. Voenizdat, Moscow, 1983
Oswald, W. *Kraftfahrzeuge der DDR: Zivil-und Militärfahrzeuge 1945 bis heute (Vehicles of the German Democratic Republic: Civil and Military Vehicles 1945 to Today)*. Motorbuch Verlag, Stuttgart, 1975
Owen, J. I. H. *Warsaw Pact Infantry and its Weapons*. Brassey's, London, 1976
Pafi, B. *L'armata Rossa dal 1946 al 1974 (The Russian Army from 1946 to 1974)*. Intergest, Milan, 1974
Pavlovskiy, I. G. *Sukhoputnie Voiska SSSR: zarozhdenie, razvitie, sovremennost (The Ground Forces of the USSR: Genesis, Development, Contemporary Situation)*. Voenizdat, Moscow, 1985
Peredelskiy, G. E. *Artilleriiskiy divizion v boyu (Artillery Battalion in Combat)*. Voenizdat, Moscow, 1984
Poor, I. et al. (eds.). *Harckocsik es pancelozott jarmuvek tipuskonyve (Tanks and Armoured Vehicles)*. Zrinyi, Budapest, 1983
Prados, J. *The Soviet Estimate: US Intelligence Analysis and Russian Military Strength*. Dial Press, New York, NY, 1982
Przyluski, Z. (ed.). *Nasze Ludowe (Our People's Army)*. WMON, Warsaw, 1963
Radzievskiy, A. I. *Dictionary of Basic Military Terms*. USAF, Washington, DC, 1976
Regenstreif, P. *Munitions Soviétiques et des Pays de l'Est (Soviet and Eastern Bloc Ammunition)*. Crepin-Leblond, Paris, 1983
Rice, C. *The Soviet Union and the Czechoslovak Army, 1948–1983: Uncertain Allegiance*. Princeton University Press, Princeton, NJ, 1984
Rogov, I. V., and Bolshev, B. N. *Metodika izucheniya materialnoi chasti tankovogo vooruzheniya (Study Methods of Tank Armament Components)*. Voenizdat, Moscow, 1968
Rosefielde, S. *False Science: Underestimating the Soviet Arms Buildup, An Appraisal of the CIA's Direct Costing Effort, 1960–80*. Transaction Books, New Brunswick, NJ, 1982
Ruszkiewicz, I. *Braterstwo Broni (Brotherhood of Arms)*. WMON, Warsaw, 1977
Ryabov, V. S. (ed.). *Dvina, voiskovie manevri provedennie na territorii belorussii v marte 1970 goda (Dvina, The Military Manoeuvres Conducted in Belorussia in March, 1970)*. Voenizdat, Moscow, 1970
Rybecky, V. *Bratrstvi a tradice armad Varsavske smouvy (Fraternity and Traditions of the Armies of the Warsaw Pact)*. Nase Vojsko, Prague, 1983
Schaffer, M. B. et al. *NATO and Warsaw Pact Tank and Anti-tank Systems*. Office of the Assistant Secretary of Defense (Int.), Washington, DC, 1974/1982d
Scott, H. F., and Scott, W. F. *The Armed Forces of the USSR*. Westview Press, Boulder, CO, 1979, 1981, 1984
— *The Soviet Control Structure: Capabilities for Wartime Survival*. Crane Russak, New York, NY, 1983
Scott, H. F., and Scott, W. F. (eds.). *The Soviet Art of War: Doctrine, Strategy and Tactics*. Westview Press, Boulder, CO, 1982
Sejna, J. *We Will Bury You*. Sidgwick & Jackson, London, 1982
Shabad, T. *Basic Industrial Resources of the USSR*. Columbia University Press, New York, NY, 1969
Shamshurov, V. K. *Inzhenernoe obespechenie boya v osobikh usloviyakh (Engineer Support Combat in Basic Conditions)*. Voenizdat, Moscow, 1985
Shmelev, I. *Tanki v boyu (Tanks in Combat)*. Molodaya Gvardiya, Moscow, 1984
Shugurov, L. M., and Shirshov, V. P. *Avtomobili strani sovetov (Vehicles of the Soviet Nation)*. DOSAAF, Moscow, 1980, 1983
Sibilev, M. U. *Armiya strani sovetov (Army of the Soviet Nation)*. Voenizdat, Moscow, 1985
Simon, J. *Warsaw Pact Forces: Problems of Command and Control*. Westview Press, Boulder, CO, 1985
Simpkin, R. *Red Armour: An Examination of the Soviet Mobile Force Concept*. Brassey, London, 1984
Sloan, C. E. E. *Mine Warfare on Land*. Brassey's Defence Publishers, London, 1986

Smith, M. J. *The Soviet Army: A Guide to Sources in English*. ABC-Clio, Santa Barbara, CA, 1983
Sokolovskiy, V. D. *Soviet Military Strategy*. Prentice-Hall, Englewood Cliffs, NJ, 1963
Soviet Armed Forces and Their Equipment: IDR Special Series No 16. Interavia, Geneva, 1982
Soviet and East European Aid And Arms Deliveries to Developing Countries. Government Business Worldwide Reports, Washington, DC, 1984
The Soviet Land Forces. R&F, Sleaford, UK, 1983
Steinhaus, Alexander. *The Beginnings of Soviet Military Electronics 1948–61*. Delphic Associates, Falls Church, VA, 1986
Sukhodolskiy, V. *Soldati rodini moei (Soldiers of My Homeland)*. DOSAAF, Moscow, 1982
Surikov, B. T. *Boyevoye primenenie raket sukhoputnikh voisk (Military Applications of Missiles in the Ground Forces)*. Voenizdat, Moscow, 1979
Sutton, Anthony. *National Suicide: Military Aid to the Soviet Union*. Arlington House, New Rochelle, NY, 1974
Suvorov, V. *Inside the Soviet Army*. Hamish Hamilton, London, 1982
— *The Liberators*. Hamish Hamilton, London, 1981
— *Soviet Military Intelligence*. Hamish Hamilton, London, 1984
Szatarski, M. R. *Radary (Radars)*. WMON, Warsaw, 1981
Szkoda, Z., Dubrawski, J. *et al. Wojsko (Army)*. WMON, Warsaw, 1968
Torecki, S. *Bron i amunicja strzelecka LWP (Small Arms and Ammunition of the Polish People's Army)*. WMON, Warsaw, 1985
Tsigankov, I. S., and Sosulin, E. A. *Orudiye, minomet, boyevaya mashina (Gun, Mortar and Combat Vehicle)*. Voenizdat, Moscow, 1980
Tyushkevich, S. A. *Sovetskie vooruzhennie sili: istoriya stroitelstva (The Soviet Armed Forces: A History of their Organizational Development)*. Voenizdat, Moscow, 1978; English trans., USAF, Washington, DC, 1985
Urban, M. *Soviet Land Power*. Ian Allen, London, 1984
Urbanowicz, J. et al. (eds.). *Mala Encyclopedia Wojskowa (Small Military Encyclopedia)*. WMON, Warsaw, 1971
US Arms Control and Disarmament Agency. *World Military Expenditures and Arms Transfers* (1967–1985: eight editions). Department of State, Washington, DC, 1978–85
US Army. *The BMP: Capabilities and Limitations*. US Army TRADOC, Ft. Monroe, VA, 1977
— *A Comparison of Selected NATO and Warsaw Pact Engineer Organizations and Equipment*. US Army TRADOC, Ft. Monroe, VA, 1977
— *Consolidated Technical Intelligence Bulletins*. 203rd MI Bn, Aberdeen Proving Ground, MD, 1985
— *Glossary of Soviet Military and Related Abbreviations TM 30–546*. US Army, DA, Washington, DC, 1957
— *Handbook on Aggressor Military Forces FM 30–102*. US Army, Washington, DC, 1959, 1960, 1973
— *Handbook on the Soviet Armed Forces*. US Army, Washington, DC, 1969
— *Handbook on the Soviet Army DA Pam No 30–50–1*. US Army, Washington, DC, 1958
— *Handbook on Soviet Ground Forces FM 30–40*. US Army, HQ–DA, 1975
— *Handbook on the Soviet and Satellite Armies, Part 1. The Soviet Army*. US Army, Washington, DC, 1953
— *Identification Guide, Soviet Box-Bodied Vehicles (USAREUR Pam No 30–60–7)*. US Army, HQ USAEUR, 1971
— *Identification Guide (Ordnance Equipment), Warsaw Pact Countries, Pts. 1, 2*. US Army-Europe, 1968
— *Identification Guide (Engineer Equipment, Warsaw Pact Countries*. US Army-Europe, 1970
— *Identification Guide USAREUR No. 30–60–1 (Part 1) Vol. 1: Tractors and Trucks, Amphibious Vehicles, Snow and Swamp Vehicles; Vol. 2: Artillery; Vol. 3: Armored Vehicles, Tanks and Self-Propelled Artillery; Vol. 4: Armored Vehicles: Scout Cars, APCs and Tank Recovery Vehicles; (Part 3) Vol. 1: Bridging and Stream-Crossing Equipment; Vol. 2: Mine Warfare and Demolition Equipment; General Ammunition and Small Arms; Chemical, Biological and Radiological Equipment*. HQ, US Army-Europe and 7th Army, 1973, 1975, multiple editions
— *Instruction Manual for the Components and Operation of the T-54 Tank*. 507th Ordnance Det./TACOM, Warren, MI, 1961/1976d
— *Military Intelligence: Key Weapons and Equipment Guide, Warsaw Pact Armies Pamphlet No. 30–60–11, January 1974*. US Army, HQ 7th Army-Europe, 1974
— *The Motorized Rifle Regiment TC 30–4*. US Army, Washington, DC, 1975
— *The Motorized Rifle Company TC 30–102*. US Army, Washington, DC, 1975
— *Operator's Manual: BTR-50 Armored Carrier*. 519th MI Bn, Aberdeen Proving Ground, MD, 1978
— *Operator's Manual: BTR-152 Armored Carrier*. 519th MI Bn, Aberdeen Proving Ground, MD, 1978
— *Operator's Manual: OT-62 Armored Carrier*. 519th MI Bn, Aberdeen Proving Ground, MD, 1978

— *Operator's Manual: Soviet Communications Devices*. 203rd MI Bn, Aberdeen Proving Ground, MD, 1983
— *Operator's Manual: T-62 Medium Tank*. 519th MI Bn, Aberdeen Proving Ground, MD, 1978
— *Opposing Forces: Europe FM 30–102*. US Army, Washington, DC, 1977
— *Organization and Equipment of the Soviet Army HB 550–2*. Threats Division, CACDA, Ft. Leavenworth, KS, 1976
— *Range and Lethality of US and Soviet Anti-Armor Weapons*. US Army TRADOC, Ft. Monroe, VA, 1975
— *Selected Soviet Weapons and Equipment, Vol. 1 ST 30–40–1*. US Army Armor School, Ft. Knox, KY, 1976
— *The Soviet Army DA Pam No 30–2*. US Army, Washington, DC, 1949
— *The Soviet Army: Operations and Tactics FM 100–2–1*. HQ, DA, Washington, DC, 1984
— *The Soviet Army: Specialized Warfare and Rear Area Support FM 100–2–2*. HQ, DA, Washington, DC, 1984
— *The Soviet Army: Troops, Organization and Equipment FM 100–2–3*. HQ, DA, Washington, DC, 1984
— *Soviet Army Operations IAG–13–U–78*. US Army, Washington, DC, 1979
— *Soviet Projectile Identification Guide TM 30–240*. US Army, Washington, DC, 1953, 1961/1981d
— *Soviet RPG-7 Anti-tank Grenade Launcher*. US Army TRADOC, Ft. Monroe, VA, 1976
— *Soviet and United States Division Comparison Handbook IAG–35–U–78*. US Army Intelligence & Security Command, Arlington, VA, 1978
— *Surface Transport Equipment: Eurasian Communist Countries' Vehicles. (FOMCAT Vol. 22A)*. HQ, US Army, Washington, DC, 1979
— *Understanding Soviet Military Developments*. Office of the Chief of Staff for Intelligence, Washington, DC, 1977
US Department of Defense. *Soviet Military Power*. Office of the Secretary of Defense, 1982, 1983, 1984, 1985
US Department of State. *Conventional Arms Transfers in the Third World, 1972–81*. Department of State, Washington, DC, 1982
Valenta, J., and Potter, W. (eds.). *Soviet Decision-making for National Security*. Allen & Unwin, London, 1984
Vanderveen, B. H. *The Observer's Military Vehicles Directory From 1945*. Frederick Warne, London, 1972
Vasilev, B. A. *Dalnyaya, raketnosnaya (Long-Range, Missile-Equipped)*. DOSAAF, Moscow, 1972; English trans. USAF, Washington, DC, 1979
Verbitskiy, A. D. et al. *Armii stran Varshavskogo Dogovozo (Armies of the Warsaw Pact Countries)*. Voenizdat, Moscow, 1985
Senger und Etterlin, F. M. von. *Der sowjetische mittlere Kampfpanzer der Baureihe T-34 bis T-62 (The Soviet Medium Tanks from the T-34 to the T-62)*. J. F. Lehmanns Verlag, Munich, 1970
— *Taschenbuch der Panzer 1976 (Tank Handbook 1976)*. J. F. Lehmanns Verlag, Munich, 1976
Wiener, F. *Die Armeen der Ostblock-Staaten (The Armies of the East Block States)*. J. F. Lehmanns Verlag, Munich, 1967
— *The Armies of the Warsaw Pact Nations*. Carl Ueberreuter, Vienna, 1981
— *Die Armeen der Warschauer-Pakt-Staaten (The Armies of the Warsaw Pact States)*. J. F. Lehmanns Verlag, Munich, 1974
— *Soldaten im Ostblock (Soldiers of the Eastern Bloc)*. J. F. Lehmanns Verlag, Munich, 1972
Wiener, F., and Lewis, W. J. *The Warsaw Pact Armies*. Carl Ueberreuter, Vienna, 1977
Woff, R. *Soviet Missile Troops and Artillery-Command Changes 1977–78*. Center for Strategic Technology, College Station, TX, 1983
Wright, Barton. *World Weapons Database, Vol. 1: Soviet Missiles*. Lexington Books, Lexington, MA, 1986
Zakharov, M. V. *50 let vooruzhennikh sil SSSR (50 Years of the Soviet Armed Forces)*. Voenizdat, Moscow, 1968
Zaloga, S. *Modern Soviet Armour, Combat Vehicles of the USSR and Warsaw Pact Today*. Arms & Armour Press, London, 1979
— *Modern Soviet Combat Tanks*. Osprey Publishing, London, 1984
— *Tanks Illustrated: Soviet Tanks Today*. Arms & Armour Press, London, 1983
— and Grandsen, J. *Soviet Tanks and Combat Vehicles of World War Two*. Arms & Armour Press, London, 1984
— and Loop, J. *Elite Forces of the Soviet Bloc*. Osprey Publishing, London, 1985

Periodicals

AFV-G2 (USA)
AFV News (Canada)
Air Defense Artillery (USA)
Air Force Magazine (USA)
Amphibious Warfare Review (USA)
Armada (Switzerland)
Armed Forces (UK)
Armed Forces Journal (USA)
Armee Rundschau (DDR)
Armenytt (Sweden)

Armor (USA)
Army (USA)
Army Times (USA)
Asian Defense Journal (Singapore)
ATOM (Czechoslovakia)
Aviation Week and Space Technology (USA)
British Army Review (UK)
Comparative Strategy (USA)
Conmilit (Hong Kong)
Current Threat Articles (USA)
Defence (UK)
Defence Attaché (UK)
Defence International Bulletin (Switzerland)
Defense Update (Israel)
Défense Afrique (France)
Defense Electronics (USA)
Field Artillery Journal (USA)
Front (Yugoslavia)
Herkenning (The Netherlands)
Infantry (USA)
International Defense Review (Switzerland)
International Security (USA)
Jane's Defence Review (UK)
Jane's Defence Weekly (UK)
Journal of Electronic Defense (USA)
Krasnaya Zvezda (USSR)
Marine Corps Gazette (USA)
Military Review (USA)
Military Technology (FRG)
Miltartechnik (DDR)
Modelist Konstruktor (USSR)
National Defense (USA)
NATO Review (Belgium)
NATO's Sixteen Nations (FRG)
Osterreichische Militärische Zeitschrift (Austria)
Pacific Defence Reporter (Australia)
Panzer (Japan)
Problems of Communism (USA)
Red Thrust (USA)
Review of the Soviet Ground Forces (USA)
RUSI Journal (UK)
Soldat und Technik (FRG)
Sovetskiy Voin (USSR)
Soviet Military Review (USSR)
Tank (Japan)
Tankette (UK)
Tekhnika i Vooruzhenie (USSR)
Tekhnika Molodezhi (USSR)
Truppendienst (Austria)
Voenny Vestnik (USSR)
Wehrtechnik (FRG)
Wojskowy Przeglad Techniczny (Poland)
Zapisnik (Czechoslovakia)
Znamenosets (USSR)

Index

392. The T-54A introduced gun stabilization to the T-54 series. This T-54A is fitted with a small muzzle counterweight rather than the later fume-extractor.

455